Quantitative Conservation of Vertebrates

An electronic companion to the book is available in two formats: hypertext on CD, and a webpage maintained at the University of Georgia, accessible through

www.blackwellpublishing.com/conroy

See p. x for further details.

Quantitative Conservation of Vertebrates

Michael J. Conroy and John P. Carroll
University of Georgia

WILEY-BLACKWELL
A John Wiley & Sons, Ltd., Publication

This edition first published 2009

Blackwell Publishing was acquired by John Wiley & Sons in February 2007. Blackwell's publishing program has been merged with Wiley's global Scientific, Technical and Medical business to form Wiley-Blackwell.

Registered office
John Wiley & Sons Ltd, The Atrium, Southern Gate, Chichester, West Sussex, PO19 8SQ, UK

Editorial offices
9600 Garsington Road, Oxford, OX4 2DQ, UK
The Atrium, Southern Gate, Chichester, West Sussex, PO19 8SQ, UK
111 River Street, Hoboken, NJ 07030-5774, USA

For details of our global editorial offices, for customer services and for information about how to apply for permission to reuse the copyright material in this book please see our website at www.wiley.com/wiley-blackwell.

Library of Congress Cataloguing-in-Publication Data
Conroy, Michael J. (Michael James), 1952-
Quantitative conservation of vertebrates / Michael J. Conroy and John P. Carroll.
p. cm.
Includes bibliographical references.
ISBN: 978-1-4051-9098-5 (hardback : alk. paper)
ISBN: 978-1-4051-8228-7 (paperback : alk. paper)
1. Vertebrate populations–Mathematical models. 2. Conservation biology–Mathematical models. I. Carroll, John P. II. Title.
QL607.6.C66 2009
639.901′5118–dc22

2008029041

A catalogue record for this book is available from the British Library.

Set in 10.5/13 pt Minion by Newgen Imaging Systems (P) Ltd, Chennai, India
Printed and bound in Malaysia by Vivar Printing Sdn Bhd
1 2009

Contents

Preface

This book is intended for use by field biologists and others, including future field biologists who might be in a university course, engaged in the day-to-day study and conservation of vertebrate animals. Our goal is that conservation biologists use this book as a (with apologies to our colleague Evan Cooch) "gentle introduction" to the field of quantitative ecology. We hope to convince readers that the methods and approaches within are *not* the domain of mathematicians, statisticians, and computer programers, but in fact are essential tools to doing the job of conservation in the twenty-first century.

We intend this book to be used. Read it, mark it up, and take it into the field. Consult it *before* collecting field data, to motivate and design your monitoring and research programs (Part I), and afterwards to properly analyze and interpret the data that (hopefully) have now been properly gathered (Part II). Especially in Part II we hope that this introduction gives field biologists the basic tools and confidence to tackle the specialized books covering many of the field techniques that we cite in this book.

We draw particular attention to Part III of the book, which deals with structured decision making and adaptive management. We would actually encourage readers to skip ahead to this section and get to grips with the essential ideas of applying models to conservation decisions. Then return to Parts I and II for the details of how to build models and collect and analyze field data. This will help keep the focus where we want it – on the practical application of these methods to solving real conservation problems.

As noted on page ii, we have provided a website for the book and an accompanying CD. The website will be updated (and corrected) periodically as new developments occur and as (inevitably) mistakes are found. The CD contains all the material on the website but cannot, of course, be kept up to date as easily as the website. Both provide ready access to all the worked examples in the boxes in the book, with much more detail than allowed for in the printed book. To that end, we have provided links to software and other resources, most of it freely available on the internet. The website and CD are essential resources for the book, so we strongly encourage readers to use them to repeat for themselves the analyses performed in the book, and as a template for performing analyses of their own data.

Finally, this book is not intended as a substitute for other, more comprehensive books, notably Williams *et al.* (2002). To keep this book to a reasonable length, and in order to remain accessible to a less mathematically oriented audience, we chose not to cover all the methods available, and have not provided the sort of depth that more advanced references such as Williams *et al.* (2002) provide. So, for example, we have only briefly described such important approaches as the Pradel temporal symmetry model, Barker/Burnham joint recapture–recover models, and multi-state models (Chapter 12), but have instead provided a context in which readers might assess whether these models could be useful in their applications, and have pointed the reader to the appropriate in-depth background and relevant software. Likewise, we have given only a "barebones" treatment of the Robust Design (Chapter 12), but we have provided an example that should give readers a good idea of just how powerful an approach this is. We have, rather, emphasized practical applications and examples – which is why we again exhort readers to use the CD and website to full advantage.

Acknowledgements

This book was made possible by the support and help of many people. M.J.C. thanks Liz, Mary, and Laura for putting up with another book project; his current and past graduate students for keeping him relatively honest; and colleagues and occasional partners in crime including Richard Barker, Bob Cooper, Chris Fonnesbeck, Clint Moore, Jim Nichols, Bill Palmer, Jim Peterson, Jon Runge, Juan Carlos Senar, Jeff Thompson, Ken Williams, and of course his coauthor John Carroll, to name a few. J.P.C. thanks Eileen, Caitlin, and Sean for their patience and understanding especially during periods of frustration and chaos. Also, to his partner in this venture, Mike Conroy, who provided lots of interesting times during our tenure teaching Applied Population Dynamics together and then the Galliformes Shortcourse. J.P.C. particularly thanks the 'UGA Gamebird Posse,' especially Brant Faircloth, Theron Terhune, and Jeff Thompson. We all upgraded our quantitative skills together, although J.P.C. now lags well behind the rest. It was 5 or 6 years of APD students who put the authors on the course for writing this book and they deserve our thanks. As a student once wrote in a course evaluation, 'Dr. Conroy needs to learn how to dumb down and Dr. Carroll needs to get on Ritalin.' This pretty much sums up our working relationship. Cheers!

Companion website and CD-ROM

We have provided an electronic companion to the book in two formats: hypertext on CD, and a webpage maintained at the University of Georgia available via **www.blackwellpublishing.com/conroy**

The companion contains the details of all the Box examples in the book, including data input and program output where specialty programs (such as MARK or DISTANCE) are used, or in many simpler cases, spreadsheets in Microsoft Excel format.

All software (except Microsoft and other standard proprietary products) referenced herein can be obtained, usually free of charge, via the internet.

We have provided links to these programs, as well as to other modeling and statistical software that, while not directly referenced, may be useful to readers. Readers should always obtain the most up-to-date versions of these programs.

Finally, we have provided links to advanced undergraduate and graduate courses that we and colleagues have taught at the University of Georgia, as well as to short courses and workshops on topics covered in the book.

We encourage readers to periodically consult the webpage and check for updates to this material, as well as to report to us any errors that they may find.

We trust that readers will find this material useful, and suggest that it is mainly by applying the concepts in the book to real examples that readers will most benefit from this material.

1
Introduction: the role of science in conservation

The impetus for this book began as the result of a rather fortunate convergence of the careers of the authors at the University of Georgia. Although we were educated in traditional **wildlife management** programs during the 1970s and 1980s, we both developed an interest in what is now better defined as **conservation biology**. Interestingly, we underwent an evolution in our thinking, leading to similar ideas relative to what we perceived as weaknesses in our own profession and to how the creation of conservation biology as a profession, while addressing some of these weaknesses, fell short in many areas. We have also become increasingly involved in international issues in wildlife conservation, leading to further career intersections with other collaborators. Indeed, we have discovered that our interest in mixing conservation and science transcends political boundaries and sub-disciplines.

Evolution of conservation science

The integration of science and conservation of wildlife has quite a long history and is found in many forms. **Game management** in Europe and North America is based on the fundamentals of agricultural management and animal husbandry. This form of conservation biology is essentially the treatment of stocks of wild animals as domestic livestock and has evolved over hundreds of years. In both North America and Europe, wildlife management as a profession developed over much of the twentieth century following a somewhat parallel course that focused on particular species or groups of species and their management. The resulting body of literature and understanding of the population dynamics of those species and their management is enormous and some of the best information is available on vertebrates.

A second development occurred during the latter part of the twentieth century as interest and concern for the diversity of wildlife in mainly tropical parts of the world moved to the forefront. Scientists who worked predominantly in the area of ecology theory began several attempts to integrate ecology as a science with biological conservation. Driven in large part by North American and Australian scientists and coming to fruition by the late 1980s, we see the wholesale movement of scientists who traditionally dealt with empirical questions in ecology adopt an additional strategy concerned with the conservation of biological diversity.

Quantitative Conservation of Vertebrates, 1st edition. By M.J. Conroy and J.P. Carroll. Published 2009 by Blackwell Publishing, ISBN 978-1-4051-8228-7 (pb) and 978-1-4051-9098-5 (hb).

The above developments resulted in several scientific disciplines, each with different strengths, converging to form scientific conservation biology. We believe that each discipline brings different strengths to conservation science. For example, wildlife management in North America has an excellent track record of applying scientific research to management and policy making. By contrast, the discipline of conservation biology has generally excelled at integrating ecological principles and conservation. The third important component here is the popularization of conservation among the general public which has resulted in an enormous influence of popular culture and activism on conservation and biodiversity management.

These developments then leave us with two scientific disciplines – wildlife (and/or game) management and its sister profession conservation biology. These disciplines can aptly be described by the general heading **applied ecology**, and are driven in part by non-scientific goals. This creates an interesting and sometimes complex series of relationships that can affect the ability of professional "applied ecologists" to strive toward their scientific objectives of obtaining reliable knowledge. We encounter several issues that are critically important at this juncture. First, as with any applied or endpoint-driven research, we must be particularly careful that our research does not simply become a series of self-fulfilling prophecies. Just as in theoretical–ecological research, our preconceptions about how systems operate must not cloud our ability to undertake objective research. In many ways the goal objectivity is easier to attain in theoretical research, because the results of theoretical[1] research might only involve individual egos and career development, rather than ecological systems and biodiversity that we as individuals and conservation biologists hold dear to us. Over the course of history in scientific endeavors someone who develops some "new" theory would be under some pressure to defend the theory and other scientists might strive to find evidence to falsify it. These traditional scientific tensions are also important in applied research; however, there are now the added pressures created by outside forces from those having a stake in the outcome of research. This is because conservation scientists operate within a socio-economic-political "real world" that includes other values and tradeoffs. Even with a sympathetic public, conservation scientists and managers must act responsibly to allow policy makers to make the best decisions possible, often with limited resources and competing demands.

Conservation advocacy versus science

We distinguish between conservation advocacy – where conservationists become directly involved in promoting policies relative to biological diversity – and conservation science – which uses science to help society make more informed decisions. The latter is the target of this book. We believe that by adopting a scientific approach, not only is science better served, but also in the long-term conservation will be better served. The task is to simultaneously increase our understanding of systems in a dynamic world

[1] Interestingly, theoretical biologists now find that outside influences are very much invading their realm, including recent debates involving religious organizations in the USA and other countries over evolutionary theory and natural selection.

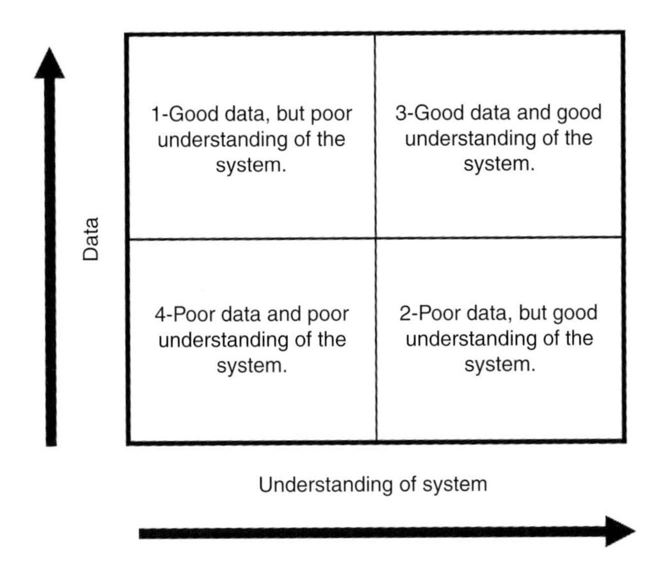

Fig. 1.1 **Classification of the relationship between data collection and understanding of systems. In theory we would like all of our conservation questions and issues to move into Box 3, where we have good data and good understanding of the system. Box 1 represents poor use of conservation effort and money. Boxes 2 and 4 represent the place where conservation biologists are starting their research on a particular issue.**

and to provide decision makers with the necessary information. This is why we believe that **modeling** approaches and **adaptive management** are critical components of the conservation research "system."

In this book we will often use **models** to summarize how we think a particular population or other resource behaves and might respond to various factors, including management. Our models will involve a combination of (i) our understanding of basic biological processes, and (ii) data available to support the various model components (Figure 1.1, from Williams *et al.* 2002, p. 112). Typically we will need to increase each of these two factors, as represented by the x and y axes of the graph (Figure 1.1). On the x axis, we wish to move to the right, which represents increasing understanding of the mechanisms driving a particular system. On the y axis, we move vertically as we increase the amount of data available on the system or parts of it. The box itself represents general areas of data quantity and system understanding. Ideally we should be in Box 3, where we have good amounts of empirical data and also good understanding of how particular systems operate. This is why we can use our understanding of gravity, material properties, and other components of physics to build bridges – which generally do not fail. Although this works well in many of the physical sciences, the complexity of combining biological and social/political issues makes this a difficult direction to move in for conservation questions or issues. More likely we are working in Boxes 2 or 4, where we lack data, knowledge, or both. In fact, in dealing with some conservation questions and species outside of the charismatic megafauna or well-studied game species, we are often starting in Box 4 with the proverbial "blank slate." Making matters worse is the fact that biologists are often in the position where policy and/or management recommendations are expected after a single inadequately funded study. Although never ideal, this is political reality. Beginning in Box 2 is slightly better because we can use our base knowledge of similar systems to hopefully give us a stronger starting point. In both of these scenarios (Boxes 2 and 4) modeling approaches combined with good data collection will be useful. In wildlife conservation and tradition game or wildlife management in North America and Europe we may also be operating in Box 1. We may have high-quality and long-term biological data, but in many cases our understanding of the mechanisms driving systems for issues we are interested in tackling is still lacking. The integration of science in conservation management will ultimately provide the foundation for more informed conservation decisions and management.

Good science is cost effective

One of the common issues in conservation biology is the problem of inadequate funding. Outside of a few areas of conservation that can garner large amounts of money, most conservation biologists are faced with enormous questions and tasks, but limited time and financial resources. Even in programs that are relatively well funded, such as game management in North America and Europe, the scale at which many biological questions should be addressed and the resources that are available often are quite disparate. Conservation research competes for limited funding with conservation implementation ("management"). This means that if funding for research increases then funding for management decreases and *vice versa.* The only way to "win" at this zero-sum game is to improve efficiency. As we will argue in a number of places in this book, *bad* research is almost worse than *no* research. It can lead to wrong conclusions and wrong management.

In this book we argue that poorly designed conservation research projects also steal resources from conservation. That is, spending money on bad science not only wastes that money, but also takes money from good science and good management. Thus good science combined with improved efficiency will yield better conservation.

Conservation under fire

More and more frequently we are faced with skeptical and even hostile groups, who demand that conservationists "prove" claims of adverse impacts of desired development, ecological benefits of restrictions of forest logging or other resource consumption, proposed reserve systems, or declaring a species endangered, to name a few. While it can never be possible to "prove" (in the logical sense) such assertions, it is possible to collect and analyze data in such a way that the evidence so provided is repeatable *and defensible.* Conversely, data collected or analyzed in an unscientific way lead to conclusions that, while perhaps intuitively reasonable, are not repeatable, and will not stand up to scientific scrutiny. Increasingly the opponents of conservation projects are technically informed, and will eagerly reveal conclusions made by the conservation community that are based on flawed approaches. Here we emphasize that ethical, scientific conservation includes the honest reporting of study and data flaws, so that results may be appropriately interpreted. Improper reporting of results, especially to exaggerate certitude of estimates or effects, is both unethical and, in the long term, counter-productive, because when (inevitably) discovered the resulting loss of credibility can be devastating (Beier *et al.* 2006; Conroy *et al.* 2006).

Structure of the book

We envision this book as a practical and hands-on resource for field biologists. This book should be analogous to the field identification guides. It is the book you take with you and use all the time, but is not the one where you go to obtain the in-depth theory or mathematical derivations. We hope it complements some recent volumes, such as Williams *et al.* (2002), in assisting practitioners and students. We also envision the book being used in short courses for field conservationists. In fact, the impetus for this book came as a result of the participation of J.P.C. and M.J.C. in development of a week-long short course following the main conference in each of the last three International Galliformes Symposia.

Part I covers mainly the background we believe all biologists should review when presented with a conservation problem or question and asked to develop a research program. Chapter 2 provides some basic concepts in **modeling**. This is not "ugly" and complex modeling that most field biologists fear, but practical modeling that assists us in problem solving. Chapter 3 is a review and application of some basic population models. Chapter 4 deals with the issues of applying models to conservation questions. Chapter 5 provides a basic review of study design. Again, this part of the book is setting the stage for couching conservation questions in a way that makes our research more scientifically sound, economically efficient, and defendable.

Part II moves on to those topics of most importance to field biologists in collecting appropriate data in answering conservation questions. In Chapter 6, we begin with the general principles of estimation. Chapter 7 is a basic overview of occupancy studies. We believe that occupancy research is underutilized, but will eventually be viewed as one of the most important techniques in conservation. Chapter 8 covers the estimation of abundance from sample counts, and introduced the importance issue of incomplete detection, a recurrent theme through the book. Chapters 9 covers the basic principles of distance sampling, including line transect and point counts (the latter are also now called point transects). Chapter 10 provides background on mark-recapture (re-sighting) and mark-removal sampling in abundance estimation. Chapter 11 focuses on the estimation of demographic rates using data from radio-telemetry, nesting success, and age distributions. Chapter 12 expands on the issues of demographic parameters by incorporating some aspects of Chapters 10 and 11. Chapter 13 deals with the issue of habitat use and selection. Finally, in Chapter 14 we touch on some sampling and estimation issues for wildlife communities.

In Part III we begin to apply modeling and estimation tools to conservation decision making. In Chapter 15 we describe how conservation goals can be combined with predictive models and used as tools for decision making. In Chapter 16 we deal with issues of uncertainty in research and conservation decision making. We remind readers that in the real world we are faced with profound uncertainties, in part because nature cannot be controlled, but also because of our incomplete understanding of how ecological systems work. This leads on to Chapter 17, in which we show how monitoring information can be integrated into decision making, leading to adaptive management. In Chapter 18 we illustrate many of the principles of the book via an example of conservation of grassland birds in North America. Chapter 19 provides a short summary of the book.

We also provide several appendices that we hope readers will find useful. Because many readers will be familiar with some but not all the terminology we use, in the Glossary we provide a comprehensive list of terms. See p. ii of this book for numerical examples in electronic form with a detailed accompanying narrative. In Appendices A and B we provide links to sites where software and other resources can be obtained, much of it at no cost. In Appendix C we provide a comprehensive explanation and cross-referencing for modeling and statistical notation. Finally, in Appendix D we provide a dichotomous key for abundance and parameter estimation that can be used to assist in identifying appropriate estimation techniques, in much the same way that taxonomic keys are used to aid in animal or plant identification.

We especially hope that the chapters in this book give field conservationists the courage to tackle some new ways of viewing conservation problems. This is where we believe this book is most useful – in taking the fear out of quantitative and modeling approaches to conservation, and making field conservationists realize they are not "black boxes" that are to be relegated to "systems ecologists" locked away in an office somewhere.

Part I

Basic concepts in scientific investigations for conservation

2
Using models in conservation biology

The word "model" tends to strike fear in the hearts of conservation biologists, who think of models as devices that can only be constructed (and understood) by quantitative specialists – and definitely not by field biologists. In fact, we will now argue that models are part of everyday life, and are used (consciously or not) by virtually everyone to make daily decisions. This is a critical starting point – we all use models all the time, so why are we so afraid of them when applied to conservation issues?

In this chapter, we first endeavor to de-mystify models, with some very simple examples, in which modeling is stripped to its essential elements. We then apply simple graphical and numerical models – most of which can be built using spreadsheets – to investigate population growth (exponential and logistic). More complicated models incorporating age structure and random variability are also considered. We apply simple models to two of the most important problems in conservation, namely that of harvesting (and "overharvest") and conservation of "small" populations. We extend modeling to populations with spatial structure, critical to the important concepts of source–sink dynamics, habitat fragmentation, and population isolation, and to simple competition and predator–prey models.

We later spend some time discussing the use of "canned" models for investigating population dynamics, particularly **population viability analysis (PVA)**. At this point we strongly warn readers about the dangers of naïve use of these packages, which often rely on numerous (and often not testable) assumptions. These warnings also apply to all statistical packages – generally no matter what you put in the front end of the program it will generate an "answer." In addition, "canned" models are often designed to fit a wide range of systems – therefore many of these might not be appropriate for specific applications, creating additional problems. We are proponents of simpler, but more transparent, models that will be more informative about the system, and will be easier to evaluate with data. We provide several real examples of population modeling, both with user-developed models and "canned" approaches, to illustrate these ideas.

Types of models

What is a model? Quite simply, a **model** is an **abstraction** of something real. Even though models are mysterious and frightening to many, in fact we use them in everyday

---

Quantitative Conservation of Vertebrates, 1st edition. By M.J. Conroy and J.P. Carroll. Published 2009 by Blackwell Publishing, ISBN 978-1-4051-8228-7 (pb) and 978-1-4051-9098-5 (hb).

life. A map is a model – basically a scaled-down, two-dimensional drawing of a part of the Earth's surface. It is not the Earth itself, nor is it even necessarily very realistic – it simply needs to get us from point A to point B and may do so in a rather artificial way. A very simple sketch of roads from your house to a friend's house can be crude but extremely useful in meeting your objective of getting to your friend's house safely. This just emphasizes that there are many kinds of models, and they don't all live in computers or in lists of complicated equations.

The following is a range of models that the reader should recognize and use, some on a daily basis:

1. ***Conceptual models*** are really just ideas about how a system looks, works, or interacts with other systems. Such a model may reside completely in the brain of the person thinking about it – the "conceptualizer," be represented in flow diagrams, or be formalized mathematically.
2. ***Physical models*** are physical representations of a system that work in some way that is analogous to how the system of interest works. For example, Pearson (1960) developed a sort of pinball machine (for those younger than the authors, these are old-fashioned mechanical video games) as an analogy for how birth and death processes work in populations: new balls released represented births, and balls dropping through holes deaths.
3. ***Graphical models*** are represented by anything we might show in graph form. For example, plots of average temperature versus rainfall might be very useful in predicting regions of drought.
4. ***Analytical models*** turn our ideas into a series of mathematical equations which may then be converted into computer code.
5. ***Numerical models*** report the quantitative outcome, often of a number of pieced-together predictions calculated by hand, in a spreadsheet, or in a computer program.
6. ***Empirical*** or ***statistical models*** use data in order to estimate parameters, and then test predictions and other hypotheses, using sample data. It is this type of model and the previous two that often scare and excite conservation biologists and comprise the heart of many useful conservation programs.

It should be clear to the astute reader that the above classification of models is artificial, and that there is much overlap among the categories. At the very least, it is easy to see how development of one type of model can easily lead to another. For example, one might have a purely theoretical idea of a relationship between a biological response and an environmental predictor (conceptual model), which might then be plotted (graphical model). One might even wish to make up some values for the coefficients of the model and generate some predictions (numerical model), or explore the general behavior of the model under a wide range of possible parameter values (analytical model). As good field biologists, however, we should not be happy until we have collected some data, estimated parameters, and tested some predictions of alternative models (statistical models). Closing the loop, the statistical models may reinforce

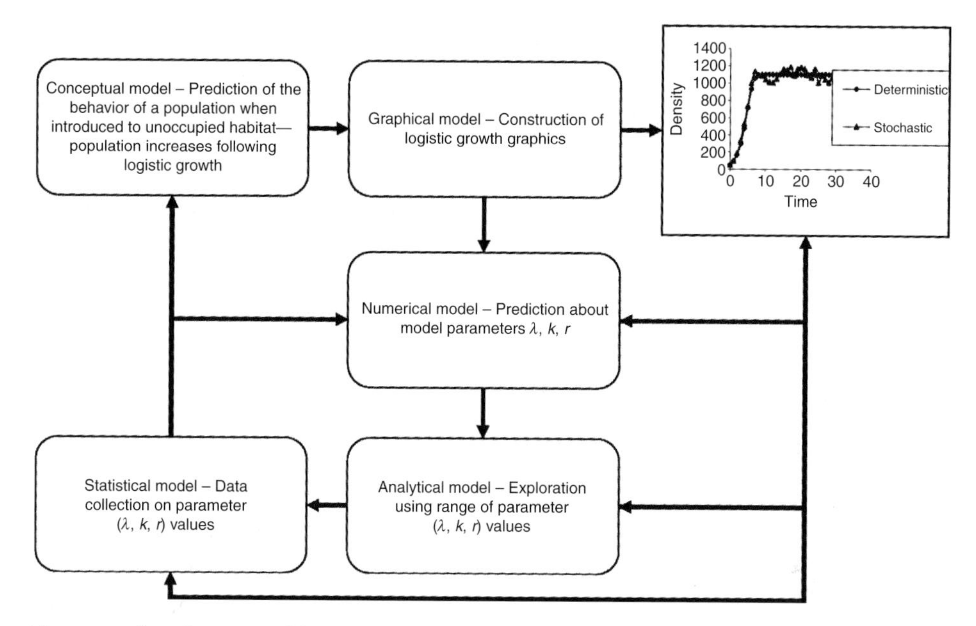

Fig. 2.1 **Flow diagram of feedbacks on various types of models that might be used to better understand problems in conservation biology.**

the original conceptual model, or they may challenge it, leading to a revised conceptual model, more graphing, analysis, and prediction, and so on (Figure 2.1).

Basic principles of modeling

Perhaps the second biggest mistake conservation biologists make about modeling – next to fearing and avoiding the topic – is embarking on a modeling exercise in a haphazard and arbitrary way. Modeling can be very useful, but only if done so methodically, with a purpose in mind, and remembering George Box's admonition that "all models are wrong, but some may still be useful" (Box 1979).

Defining the objective

As with any approach, it is important to keep the objective of modeling firmly in mind. This will determine such things as the scale or detail of the modeling; what sort of system features need to be included and which do not; and whether the model is purely a "thinking exercise" versus an actual predictive tool. For example, if our objective is to manage a population for sustainable harvest, we should be mainly interested in modeling aspects of population dynamics as they relate to the impacts of harvest. Inclusion of details about individual animal behavior, resource selection, and other features, while interesting, are probably not germane to the issue of sustainable harvest, and should not be included. In fact, these latter components might serve to make understanding the dynamics of harvest much more difficult to tease out of the system, by creating large amounts of noise in our model. Conversely, genetic composition of a population may be critical to a decision we are about to make about conservation. In this case, modeling focused only on abundance and other population-level parameters will be insufficiently detailed for our needs.

Defining parameters, variables, and functional relationships

Most models will involve a variety of inputs, outputs, and functional relationships that specify the biological features we are trying to mimic. Features like population size, age structure, and habitat condition that tend to vary over time and space are typically referred to as **state variables** (or simply "variables"). Constants that control the rate of change, or otherwise express relationships between variables, are **parameters.** Examples of parameters include survival and birth rates. Two simple examples illustrate these terms, and the idea of simple model building. First, suppose that we wish to translate the prediction "as amount of habitat increases the abundance of our species of interest increases linearly." In this example, abundance and habitat are state variables, which we might label as Y (abundance) and X(amount of habitat), respectively. The hypothetical increase in abundance with increasing habitat occurs at a rate b, so our model is simply:

$$Y = bX$$

(Something to think about – we could have included a Y-intercept term, rather than the assumed value of "0" in our equation, but any positive value would have resulted in a prediction for positive abundance in the absence of any habitat! Some more observant readers might catch us here and point out that there could be a negative Y intercept. This suggests that there is some level of habitat (X intercept) for which the population drops to "0".) The actual value of b could be chosen by us arbitrarily; such as a value approximately based on first principles of biology, or estimated statistically (e.g., using linear regression methods).

To take another example, suppose we wish to predict population change over time. Our state variable, abundance, now should be indexed to time (t); we will represent abundance at time t as $N(t)$. A simple model of population growth (which we will explore further in the next section) supposes that birth (b) and death rates (d) are constant over time, leading (in the absence of immigration or emigration) to constant growth $r = b - d$. These are the model parameters (in this case r alone suffices). Our basic dynamic model is

$$N(t + 1) = N(t)(1 + r)$$

simply, that next year's abundance $[N(t + 1)]$ is equal to this year's abundance times a growth multiplier. Actually, we need one more feature to complete our model: a place for the population to start. This **initial condition** is the population's abundance at some initial time $t = 0$, $N(0)$. Given this value, and a value for r, we have a working model.

For example, if we take $r = 0.05$ and $N(0) = 100$ we have:

$$N(1) = 1000(1 + 0.05) = 1050$$
$$N(2) = 1050(1 + 0.05) = 1103$$

and so on. The result is that a small amount of information about a population can allow us to create a simple and possibly useful model in describing the abundance of some species.

Discrete or continuous models: stochastic or deterministic

There are many mathematical ways to construct models, and the above simple examples represent two types of choices for model construction. If our models are dynamic (meaning that the population or other state changes over time), then we must decide whether to represent time in **discrete** terms as above, or in **continuous** form. For most of the modeling in this book we favor discrete-time models, because many of the animals we deal with reproduce seasonally, so discrete time seems appropriate. Also, many population surveys are conducted annually at specific dates, making it easier to think about population change as occurring over intervals $[t, t+1]$ rather than instantaneously. Finally, the mathematics of continuous-time models can be more difficult, involving differential calculus; discrete-time models are represented by **difference equations**, somewhat easier to grasp, and also easier to translate into spreadsheets or other computer code. However, continuous-time models are important in much of ecology, so advanced readers are encouraged to study them further in references such as Williams *et al.* (2002).

Conservation modelers must also decide whether to build models that are **deterministic** – that is, contain no random elements – or **stochastic**, containing random elements (and thus predictions that vary from one run to the next). There are advantages and disadvantages of each type of model. It is often a good idea to start with deterministic models and focus on the mathematical behavior of the model, such as **equilibrium** and **sensitivity analysis**, without the added distraction of random effects. For example, the relative impact of one parameter versus another on the outcome from your modeling will be much clearer without random variation included. Once the mathematics of the model are well understood then random effects are often added to create additional model realism (since real populations are subject to many different types of random influences!) In the next section we build both deterministic and stochastic population models.

Verification and validation

Hopefully, any model we create is at least a plausible, if not necessarily correct, version of reality. However, it is very important to perform "reality checks" on models that we have built. Model **verification** is essentially a check to see that the model produces results similar to what we intended and (if data are involved) matches well the data used to build the model. At this step, we may discover that the model produces results that are nonsensical or biologically counterintuitive (e.g., negative population values, or survival rates >1.0) or that otherwise make no sense. This is the time to discover why these aberrant results are occurring – and to fix them. Of course, just because the model produces results that look right does not mean that they *are* right. This is where model **validation** comes in. True validation involves the comparison of model predictions to data collected independently of the model construction (the data were not used to build the model). This is a very strong test of the model, and one that is unfortunately rarely done. We will return to model validation and ways to improve models through time later in this chapter.

Model behavior and sensitivity analysis

It is often very important to have an idea of how models behave over ranges of parameter values, or (for dynamic models) how they perform over time. Model behavior is especially relevant to conservation issues such as sustainable harvest and viability analysis, since we are usually interested in how real populations will behave over long time horizons, or in response to management actions. For dynamic models, it is especially important to determine whether the system will reach **equilibrium**, and, if so, where it (or they) exists. An equilibrium is simply a state at which the system no longer changes over time; for abundance that is where $N(t+1) = N(t)$. For many models, it is also important to determine model **stability**, essentially the tendency of a model to return to an equilibrium following a perturbation.

It is also important to evaluate the model's **sensitivity** to variations in parameter values, for a number of reasons. First, some parameters may be controllable by management, and therefore knowledge of how these parameters influence the system (e.g., equilibrium abundance) can be very important to conservation and/or management. Second, most parameters will not be known with certainty, and a knowledge of how much it matters that parameter values are possibly varying from true values can focus priorities on improving these values.

In this chapter we should have accomplished two important things about models. First, and most importantly, we should have shown the reader that models are not to be feared and should be fairly useful to those of us doing conservation science. The second goal is to provide the lead-in for Chapter 3 where we expand our understanding of models to some practical examples.

3
Models of population dynamics

In this chapter, we apply the general ideas of modeling developed in Chapter 2 to the specific problem of modeling population dynamics. Here, our important state variables will usually be summary statistics of some kind, typically **abundance** of the population at a particular time and location. By dynamics, we simply mean how abundance, age structure, distribution, or other state variables change through time. Our model **parameters** will then describe the rates at which these state variables change through time, and will include such quantities as birth, death, and movement rates.

Balance equation of population growth

Essentially, dynamic models of population growth start from a very simple idea that comes from accounting: the balance sheet, or in even simpler terms, the act of balancing your personal checking account at the bank. We can view the population size at any given time as our "net balance" which changes through time via credits (additions to the account) and debits (subtractions). With population growth, the "credits" are births and immigrants entering the population, and the "debits" are deaths and emigrants leaving the population. Suppose we know abundance N in a particular year (t) and we wish to account for change until the next year ($t + 1$). We do so by applying our principles of accounting, namely, adding credits and subtracting debits:

$$N(t+1) = N(t) + B(t) + I(t) - D(t) - E(t) \tag{3.1}$$

In this expression, $N(t)$ is the population size (abundance) that we started with, $B(t)$ and $I(t)$ are additions from birth and immigration, and $D(t)$ and $E(t)$ are subtractions from death and emigration. This basic balance equation, called the "BIDE" (birth–death–immigration–emigration) model, sets the stage for all of the following population models, which are really either special cases or elaborations of this general model.

The BIDE model easily leads into some of our more general and useful models. Although the BIDE model is often expressed in terms of raw numbers of animals, for our purpose it is often more useful to re-express change in terms of **per capita rates.** It is also convenient for now to ignore immigration and emigration (essentially we are assuming that the population's area is so big that these do not matter – they functionally cancel each other out). These modifications are accomplished by changing

Quantitative Conservation of Vertebrates, 1st edition. By M.J. Conroy and J.P. Carroll. Published 2009 by Blackwell Publishing, ISBN 978-1-4051-8228-7 (pb) and 978-1-4051-9098-5 (hb).

Equation (3.1) to eliminate $I(t)$ and $E(t)$, and then dividing both sides of the equation by $N(t)$. When we do this we obtain:

$$\frac{N(t+1)}{N(t)} = 1 + \frac{B(t)}{N(t)} - \frac{D(t)}{N(t)}$$

or

$$\lambda(t) = 1 + b(t) - d(t) = 1 + r(t) \tag{3.2}$$

where $b(t)$ and $d(t)$ are now per-capita rates for birth and death, and $\lambda(t) = 1 + r(t)$ is the per-capita rate of population change, also called the **finite rate of increase**. This equation gets across the idea that per-capita population growth rates can change over time, and that they do so (in the absence of immigration and emigration) as a function of birth rates and death rates. With this simplification, we can rewrite the basic growth equation as

$$N(t+1) = N(t) + N(t)r(t) \tag{3.3}$$

Density-independent (geometric) population growth

Our first "formal" population model is actually a simplification of the model in Equations (3.2) and (3.3). Suppose that birth rates and death rates remain constant over time, so that $b(t) = b$ and $d(t) = d$. Then, we have $r(t) = r = b - d$, and our population will grow according to

$$N(t+1) = N(t) + N(t)r = N(t)(1+r) \tag{3.4}$$

that is, the per-capita growth rate remains constant – irrespective of environmental conditions, density, or other factors. Notice that if we start at some arbitrary initial time $t = 0$ with an initial abundance $N(0)$, Equation (3.4) produces:

$$N(1) = N(0)(1+r)$$

After two time steps, the equation produces:

$$N(2) = N(1)(1+r) = N(0)(1+r)^2$$

and so on. This leads to a general equation for population size after t time steps of

$$N(t) = N(0)(1+r)^t \tag{3.5}$$

Notice too that if $r = 0.0$ (i.e., $\lambda = 1.0$) the population remains unchanged; if $r < 0.0$ ($\lambda < 1.0$) the population declines exponentially until extinction; and if $r > 0.0$ ($\lambda > 1.0$) the population increases exponentially without limit (Figure 3.1). Because of these features, equilibrium [again, $N(t+1) = N(t)$] only occurs when $r = 0.0$ [so the population stays at $N(0)$] or when $N(t) = 0$ (where it stays stuck!)

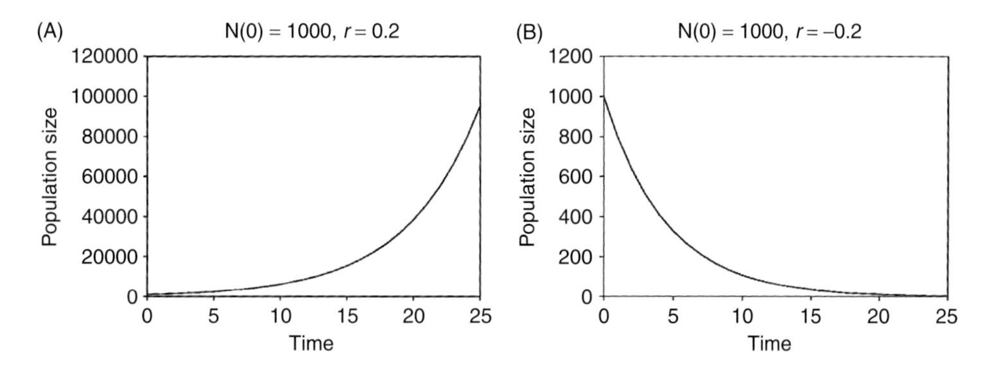

Fig. 3.1 **Density-independent (exponential) population growth. (A) $N(0) = 1000$, $r = 0.2$. (B) $N(0) = 1000$, $r = -0.2$.**

Note that the equivalent, continuous-time model based on differential calculus is

$$N(t) = N(0)e^{r't} \tag{3.6}$$

where r' in Equation (3.6) is an **instantaneous growth rate** (see Williams *et al.* 2002, Chapter 8, for more details), and is approximately related to $\lambda = r + 1$ by

$$r' \approx \log_e \lambda$$

The type of population growth given by Equations (3.4) and (3.5) is sometimes called "geometric" or "exponential" growth. It is also aptly described as **density-independent** growth because the rate r of growth never depends on population size or density (Figure 3.1, Box 3.1). In the next section we will relax this idea and allow for density to influence population growth.

Density-dependent population growth

Many if not most populations seem to be regulated by some type of density feedback, where the population growth rate is influenced by the size or density of the population. The idea is that at low numbers, there are plenty of resources for animals and little to inhibit population growth. At these low numbers, the population grows at its fastest per capita rate, which we will denote as r_{max}. As the population increase, competition, predation, disease, and other factors act to suppress birth rates (b) or increase death rates (d), so that these no longer are fixed, but vary in relation to abundance. Growth rates decrease until an upper limit K (often called the **carrying capacity**) is reached; at this level of abundance the population is at equilibrium [$r(t) = 0.0$]. Above this level, the population growth rate is negative ($r(t) < 0.0$). These ideas are captured by a modification of Equation (3.4) allowing for density effects:

$$N(t+1) = N(t) + N(t)r_{max}\left[1 - \frac{N(t)}{K}\right] \tag{3.7}$$

Box 3.1 Exponential population growth.

To see that Equations (3.4) and (3.5) produce the same result, let us take a case where initial abundance (N) is 1000 and $r = 0.10$. This is easy to do in a spreadsheet, for example using a simple spreadsheet program. Enter the values "0" and "1000" under columns labeled "t" and "N." Continue entering values "$t = 1, 2, \ldots, 10$" in the "t" column (or compute these values in the spreadsheet). Now compute the value of $N(1)$ by multiplying $(1 + 0.10)$ times the value of $N(0)$; this is easier to do, for instance, if a spreadsheet cell equation looks something like:

$$B2 = B1 * (1 + 0.10)$$

Then copy this cell down the page till you get to year 10. You should get something that looks like this (here we have rounded calculations to the nearest individual):

t	N
0	1000
1	1100
2	1210
3	1331
4	1464
5	1611
6	1772
7	1949
8	2144
9	2358
10	2594

Now try computing these values again, this time using Equation (3.5). In a spreadsheet, for $t = 10$ this might look like:

$$B10 = 1000 * (1 + 0.10)^\wedge 10$$

This should give you the identical result as in the table for year 10.

Using Equation (3.4), you have to build up each year from the previous year, so this requires 10 calculations. With Equation (3.5) you can get the same result with a single equation, no matter how many years have elapsed.

The complete spreadsheet example can be found in the electronic companion to the book (see enclosed CD and website address on p. ii).

Notice that Equation (3.7) is obtained from Equation (3.4) by adjusting r_{max} by an additional term $[1 - (N(t)/K)]$, which expresses the "braking" effect of population size on future population growth. This is often called "**environmental resistance.**" If you look at the two factors that can change in this term, you see as $N(t)$ increases from

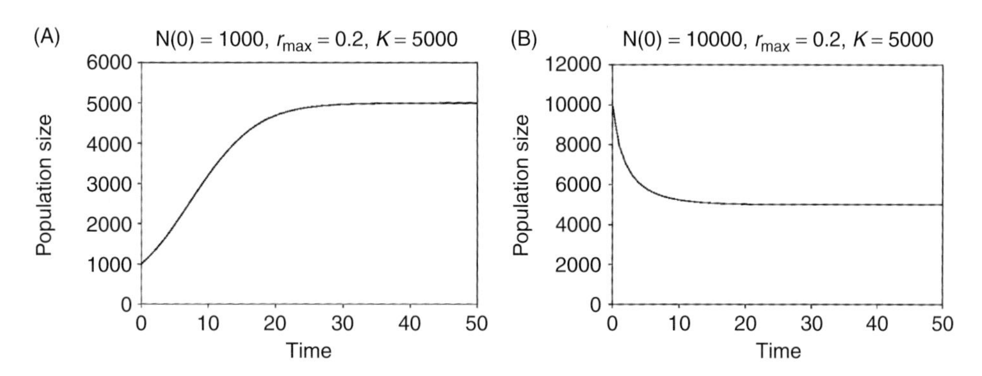

Fig. 3.2 **Density-dependent (logistic) population growth. (A) $N(0) = 1000$, $r_{max} = 0.2$, $K = 5000$. (B) $N(0) = 10000$, $r_{max} = 0.2$, $K = 5000$.**

a very small number to being very close to K that the ratio goes from being a very small number to being equal to 1.0. When you subtract that from 1.0 then you see the value of the result is equal to 0.0. When you multiply this by any value of growth rate (r_{max}) you always get zero growth. This means we have "braked" to a complete stop.

This model results in populations that follow the familiar sigmoid ("S") pattern of growth exhibited in Figure 3.2, in which populations approach K (from below or above) and remain there unless conditions change (e.g., there is an environmental disturbance of some kind). That is, the K represents a **stable equilibrium** in the logistic model.

The above discussion deals with the situation where increasing population density negatively influences population growth rates. In some instances, we can have a situation where the reverse occurs: at extremely low population numbers population growth rates also decrease. This phenomenon, known as the **Allee effect** (Allee *et al.* 1949), may occur, for instance, when an area becomes so thinly populated that individual animals have a difficult time finding mates, thus reducing per-capita birth rates. In some "small population" problems it will be important to consider Allee effects, but in most larger population problems (for instance, sustainable harvest) these effects can be safely ignored.

Finally, we point out that, as useful as the logistic model is for capturing the idea of density dependence, its utility can be limited by the fact that r_{max} and K are to some extent theoretical values that are difficult to observe in nature. We will discuss some of these points again in Chapter 4, when we apply the logistic and other models to conservation problems (see Box 3.2).

Populations: age-structured growth

Both of the above models assume that either the population is growing at a constant rate or population size is limiting growth uniformly for all individuals. However, many animal populations exhibit age structure, which also influences how the population grows. Typically this happens because birth rates, death rates, or both tend to be different among different age classes. Now also remember that the number of age classes can be

Box 3.2 Logistic population growth.

You can generate the logistic curve yourself in a spreadsheet with just a slight modification of the example in Box 3.1. As in that example, enter the starting values "0" and "1000" under columns labeled "t" and "N." We will need to create about 50 years worth of data, so continue entering values "$t = 1, 2, \ldots, 50$" in the "t" column. Better yet, use the spreadsheet to compute these values; for example, if cell A1 contains 0 (for $t = 0$) then enter the formula:

$$A2 = A1 + 1$$

in cell A; copy this formula up to $t = 50$. We "grow" the population given the initial value of 1000 by creating a spreadsheet formula for Equation (3.7). If cell B1 contains 1000 [for $N(0) = 1000$] then enter the formula:

$$= B1 + 0.2 * B1 * (1 - B1/5000)$$

to generate logistic growth for $r_{max} = 0.2$ and $K = 5000$. Your results to $t = 50$ should look like this:

t	N	t	N
0	1000	26	4914
1	1160	27	4931
2	1338	28	4944
3	1534	29	4955
4	1747	30	4964
5	1974	31	4971
6	2213	32	4977
7	2460	33	4982
8	2710	34	4985
9	2958	35	4988
10	3200	36	4991
11	3430	37	4992
12	3645	38	4994
13	3843	39	4995
14	4021	40	4996
15	4178	41	4997
16	4316	42	4998
17	4434	43	4998
18	4534	44	4998
19	4619	45	4999
20	4689	46	4999
21	4747	47	4999
22	4795	48	4999
23	4835	49	4999
24	4867	50	5000
25	4893		

Box 3.2 Continued.

You can make your model more flexible by setting the values for r_{max} and K as variables in spreadsheet cells, and then referring to these in your equation; Excel lets you easily do this by assigning names to the cells where the values for r_{max} and K are stored. Then you can use a command like:

$$= \mathrm{B1} + r_{max} * (1 - \mathrm{B1}/K)$$

to create your model.

The complete spreadsheet example can be found in the electronic companion to the book (see enclosed CD and website address on p. ii).

quite different depending on the species. For example, for a very short-lived species, such as a northern bobwhite (*Colinus virginianus*), it might be simply divided into juveniles or adults. For species that survive a number of years, such as some deer (*Odocoileus* spp., *Cervus* spp.), the population might be divided into year classes. In very long-lived species, such as African elephants (*Loxodonta africana*) or whales (Cetacea) – or humans, individuals might be assigned to multiple year age classes.

We can illustrate age stratification by returning to the density-dependent model [Equation (3.4)], but in this case separating the model into age strata (in this example we will use two age classes): a "birth year" class that survives at the rate S_j each year (equivalently, has mortality $1 - S_j$), but does not reproduce, and an "adult" class that survives at the rate S_a. In this simple model, we will assume that adults (if they do not die) stay adults, but juveniles all become adults after one year. We now need two equations to describe growth. For adults, population size at $t + 1$ is simply the total number of adults and juveniles surviving from the previous year:

$$N_a(t+1) = N_a(t)S_a + N_j(t)S_j$$

We will assume that we're counting animals immediately after reproduction occurs; therefore the number of juveniles produced this year is calculated by the number of surviving adults and juveniles (now adults) that are now reproducing at the per-capita rate b. This gives us

$$N_j(t+1) = [N_a(t)S_a + N_j(t)S_j]b$$

With a little algebra we can see that the growth rates for adults and juveniles actually are not constant over time, even though the survival and birth rates are constant:

$$\lambda_a(t) = \frac{N_a(t+1)}{N_a(t)} = S_a + S_j\frac{N_j(t)}{N_a(t)}$$

$$\lambda_j(t) = \frac{N_j(t+1)}{N_j(t)} = \left(S_a\frac{N_a(t)}{N_j(t)} + S_j\right)b$$

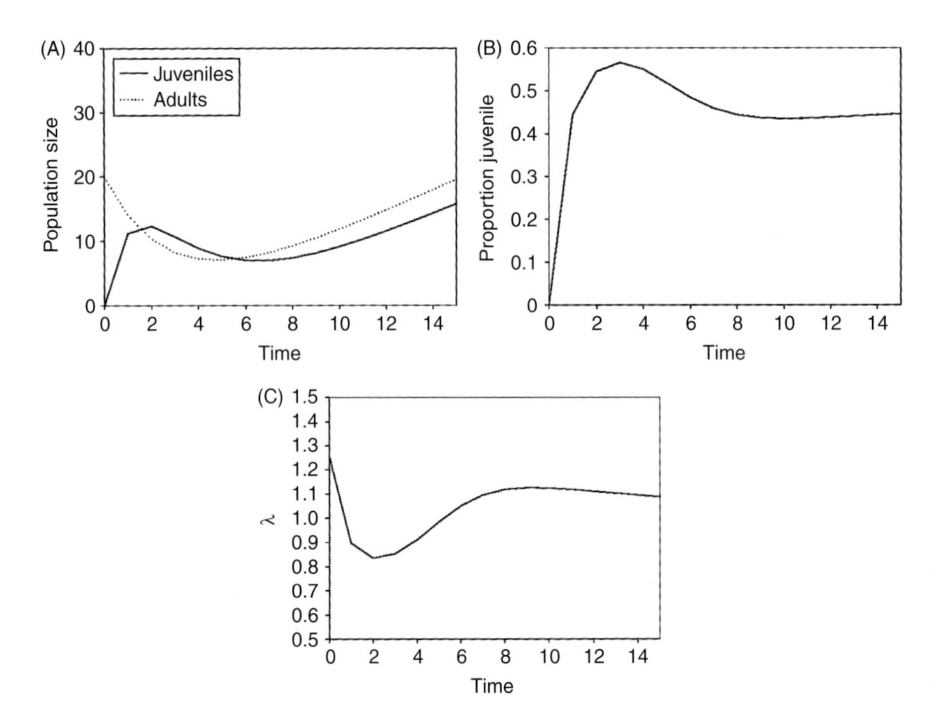

Fig. 3.3 **Age-structure and population growth. $S_a = 0.7$, $S_j = 0.5$, $b = 0.8$, $N_a(0) = 20$, $N_y(0) = 0$. (A) Population trajectory, (B) proportion of juveniles, (C) growth rate (λ).**

The reason is that both growth rates now depend on the relative numbers of juveniles and adults that are in the population, known as the **age distribution**, and this number itself is potentially changing. Only when the age distribution stops changing over time, a condition known as a **stable age distribution**, can we reliably calculate a constant growth rate for the population. This situation is illustrated in Figure 3.3, where the population settles down to a steady rate of growth under density independence after about 7 years. How long it takes the population to reach age stability depends to some extent on how far from stability the population was initially. However, regardless of these initial conditions, the population will always reach the *same* stable age distribution and growth rate as long as the age-specific birth and survival rates remain constant. Populations with many age-classes tend to take longer to reach stability. Techniques for solving for stable age distribution involve matrix operations beyond the scope of this book and are covered in Caswell (2001) and Williams *et al.* (2002). However, a simple way to demonstrate and understand the concept of the stable age distribution is by computing population growth in a spreadsheet; we provide a simple, three-age example in Box 3.3.

Stochastic (random) effects on population growth

So far, all of the models that we have covered have been **deterministic**; therefore there are no random effects, and all future values for the population are exactly determined by

Box 3.3 Age-dependent population growth: an example with three age classes.

Here is a simple three-age example to see how to generate age-specific population growth in a spreadsheet. As suggested in the last box, we will use the "name" convention found in spreadsheet programs to assign labels to our initial population values and parameters:

S_0	0.2
S_1	0.3
S_2	0.8
b_1	1
b_2	3
N_00	0
N_01	5000
N_02	0

For the age-specific survival rates, birth rates (b_2 for ages 2 and higher), and three initial population sizes in each age class (0, 1, and 2) we used underscores (S_0, etc.), because otherwise spreadsheet programs would confuse these cell names with cell locations (S1, S2, etc.) Initial values are placed in cells B2, C2, and D2 ($t = 0$). The population model then creates values at $t = 1$ for age 0 (cell B3; animals born to surviving age 1, i.e., last year's juveniles) and age 2 (last year's age 1 and age 2 animals) as follows:

$$= \mathbf{S\_0} * B2 * b\_1 + (S\_1 * C2 + S\_2 * D2) * b\_2$$

age 1 (cell C3; surviving juveniles from last year) as:

$$= S\_0 * B2$$

and age 2 (cell D3; animals surviving age 1 and 2 from last year) as:

$$= S\_1 * C2 + S\_2 * D2$$

We also compute proportion of age 0 and age 1 (p0 and p1; p2 is by subtraction) and population $\lambda = N(t+1)/N(t)$.

The projections of the population and demographic parameters look like this:

t	N0	N1	N2	tot	p0	p1	λ
0	0	5000	0	5000	0	1	1.2
1	4500	0	1500	6000	0.75	0	1.1
2	4500	900	1200	6600	0.681818	0.136364	1.018182
3	4590	900	1230	6720	0.683036	0.133929	1.019643
4	4680	918	1254	6852	0.683012	0.133975	1.019615
5	4771.8	936	1278.6	6986.4	0.683013	0.133975	1.019615
6	4865.4	954.36	1303.68	7123.44	0.683013	0.133975	1.019615
7	4960.836	973.08	1329.252	7263.168	0.683013	0.133975	1.019615
8	5058.144	992.1672	1355.326	7405.637	0.683013	0.133975	1.019615
9	5157.361	1011.629	1381.911	7550.9	0.683013	0.133975	1.019615

The complete spreadsheet example can be found in the electronic companion to the book (see enclosed CD and website address on p. ii).

the parameter values and the initial conditions. That is, for a particular set of numbers used as input, and specified model parameters, the model will always give you the same answer – whether you run the model once or a hundred times. For instance, with the age-structured model above, even though the population growth may look random, it is varying simply because the population did not start out at a stable age distribution.

By contrast, **stochastic** models allow for effects that are not entirely predictable. These might be weather conditions or other factors whose future outcomes are uncertain, but may affect the population in some way. We handle these kinds of effects by modifying our models to allow for chance outcomes. For example, numbers of offspring produced by females of many species in the family Canidae are quite variable depending on the condition of females as a result of environmental conditions. Therefore we might have an average number of offspring produced per female, but with some incorporation of potential variability in this value to take variation into account. This can be done in a number of ways. For example, we can take a deterministic growth model like Equation (3.4) and simply add a random number to it. For example,

$$N(t+1) = N(t)(1+r) + X_t$$

where X_t comes from a statistical distribution [e.g., a normal distribution with a mean ($\bar{x}$) and standard deviation (SD)]. Another approach (which we tend to prefer) is to model random variation in one or more model parameters. So, we might take:

$$N(t+1) = N(t)(1+r_t)$$

where r_t comes from a normal distribution with $\bar{x} = 0.1$ and $\text{SD} = 0.10$. This produces the sort of effect represented in Figure 3.4, where the population is generally increasing,

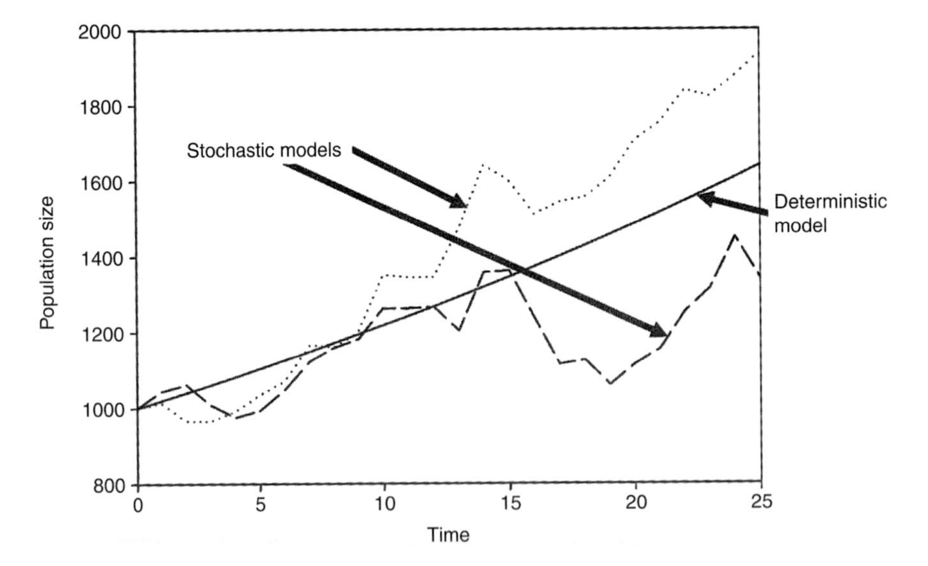

Fig. 3.4 **Stochastic population growth. $N_0 = 1000$. Two stochastic simulations with realized growth drawn from a normal distribution having $\bar{r} = 0.02$, $SD(r) = 0.05$; smooth line in middle is deterministic growth ($r = 0.02$).**

but not in the sort of completely smooth manner as in the deterministic case seen in the smooth solid line or in Figure 3.1. In this model we then see that the same starting conditions and same parameter estimates can provide quite different population trajectories and outcomes. Using the analogy from above, now 100 runs of our model will give us 100 different outcomes. This is obviously quite useful for identifying outcomes such as extinction probability or the impact of hunting on a population or the impact of some type of management (see Box 3.4).

Spatial structure and population growth

So far we have pretended that the population is a single unit in space, potentially with age (and sex) structure, but otherwise homogenous. Increasingly, conservation biologists are appreciating the importance of spatial variation in populations, and how consideration of space is integral to understanding and managing populations.

To see how space can influence population dynamics, suppose that we have two populations of the same species, isolated enough from each another so that they occupy different habitats, but with occasional exchange (movement of animals between the populations). A classic example of this is populations on different islands of the same archipelago, but the idea transfers to terrestrial habitats as well. Suppose too that the populations on different islands, or habitat patches, at least potentially exhibit different birth rates and death rates, so that growth rates (r_1, r_2) may be different, and finally suppose that any animals that survive to the next time period either remain in the population they started in or move to the other population. We can modify Equation (3.4) to deal with this more complicated situation, while still assuming density independence, by creating additional parameters $\pi_{ij}, i = 1, 2; j = 1, 2$, representing the expected proportion (or **probability**) of movement of animals from population i to population j. Then, the number of animals at $t + 1$ in population 1 will be the number of animals produced by population 1 between t and $t+1$ that stay in population 1 *plus* the number of animals produced between t and $t + 1$ in population 2 that move from 2 to 1:

$$N_1(t+1) = N_1(t)(1+r_1)\pi_{11} + N_2(t)(1+r_2)\pi_{21}$$

Likewise, abundance in population 2 at $t + 1$ will be the number produced by 2 and remaining, plus the number exported by population 1:

$$N_2(t+1) = N_1(t)(1+r_1)\pi_{12} + N_2(t)(1+r_2)\pi_{22}$$

Spatial stratification can lead to interesting and sometimes unexpected results, depending on the relative growth and movement rates. An important special case of this model is **source–sink** dynamics, in which there are two populations, a source with $\lambda_1 = (1 + r_1) > 1$ and a sink with $\lambda_2 = (1 - r_2) < 1$. Pulliam (1988) solved this model assuming that (i) there is an upper limit N_1^* to the source population, (ii) all excess "source" animals move to the sink once N_1^* is reached, and (iii) "sink" animals remain in the sink (or die). Given these assumptions, the equilibrium abundance in the

Box 3.4 Stochastic population growth.

We can illustrate stochastic population growth with a slight modification to the model in Box 3.1, where we now draw r from a random variable distribution. As before, we need columns for t and N; we will create an additional column for storing the random values of r. For the stochastic model, we need the following parameters: $N(0)$ (the initial population size), and a mean ($\bar{r}$) and standard deviation (σ) for the normal distribution used to generate values of r. In this example we will use the "name" convention in Excel, assigning labels "$N0$", "rbar," and "SD" to the cells containing values for these parameters. These labels are then used in subsequent computations, below. In our example, $N0 =$ 1000, rbar $= 0.10$, and SD $= 0.05$.

To generate a random value for r we used the inverse normal function in Excel, which, given a probability, mean, and standard deviation for the random variable, generates its value from the normal distribution. The probability is simply a uniform (0,1) random variable, and we have already specified $\bar{r}$ and σ. The statement to generate the random values for r is then

= NORMINV(RAND(),rbar,SD)

and is copied to all the cells up to year 25 in the second (B) column. We will place the population values in the third (C) column. The first of these is simply $N0$, so we establish this value by entering

$$= N0$$

in cell C2. We then compute subsequent values of N by entering

$$= \text{C2} * (1 + \text{B2})$$

in cell C3 and copying this formula down the page. The last value ($t = 25$) should be

$$= \text{C26} * (1 + \text{B26})$$

(in this example we used the first row of the spreadsheet for column labels, adding a row to the 26 population values). Notice that if Excel is set for automatically updating formulae, you will get new values each time you open the spreadsheet or make any changes. You can also "refresh" (generate new numbers) by hitting F9.

The complete spreadsheet example for this can be found in the electronic companion to the book (see enclosed CD and website address on p. ii). The syntax will differ a bit for other spreadsheet programs (e.g., Quattro), but this will give you the idea.

sink population is:

$$N_2^* = \frac{\lambda_1 - 1}{1 - \lambda_2} N_1^*$$

and overall abundance is:

$$N^* = \left[\frac{\lambda_1 - 1}{1 - \lambda_2} + 1\right] N_1^* \tag{3.8}$$

We will return to spatially stratified models, and source–sink dynamics, when we apply population models to conservation problems in the next section (see Box 3.5).

Models for two or more species

Many conservation problems involve dealing with the dynamics of two or more species that interact with one another, so that one species' dynamics influence the other's. The two most basic versions of species-interaction models are the Lotka–Volterra **predator–prey** models and **competition** models (Williams *et al.* 2002). Both types of models have both differential (continuous-time) and difference (discrete-time) forms; we present only the discrete-time forms here:

$$N_{prey}(t+1) = N_{prey}(t) + [r_{prey} - d_{prey}N_{pred}(t)]N_{prey}(t)$$

and

$$N_{pred}(t+1) = N_{pred}(t) + [b_{pred}N_{prey}(t) - d]N_{pred}(t) \tag{3.9}$$

In these equations, $N_{prey}(t)$ and $N_{pred}(t)$ are the abundance of prey and predators at each survey time t. For prey, we assume that population growth occurs at a constant (density-independent) rate r_{prey} in the absence of predation. The coefficient d_{prey} determines that the death rate of the prey will increase linearly as the abundance of predators increases, with the entire term in bracket operating as a growth multiplier on prey. The equation for predators works in more-or-less the opposite fashion, with birth rates (b_{pred}) of predators presumed to increase as prey abundance increases, but death rates (d_{pred}) of predators not influenced by prey abundance.

The relationships in Equation (3.9) give rise to some interesting predictions regarding the dynamics for predators and prey. First, equilibrium abundance is predicted to occur at

$$N^*_{prey} = d_{pred}/b_{pred}, \quad N^*_{pred} = r_{prey}/d_{prey}$$

Second, abundance for each is predicted to oscillate around these equilibrium levels (Figure 3.5). In the discrete-time model, these oscillations increase over time, with populations "overshooting" their maximum and minimum values. This type of model instability is avoided in the continuous-time models, which, however, are a bit more difficult to construct. Finally, density limitation on the predators, prey, or both can be introduced to predator–prey models, analogous to the logistic assumptions for single populations (Williams *et al.* 2002).

Box 3.5 Spatially stratified population growth with three population strata.

This example has three population strata, initial population sizes of 5000 in each stratum, stratum-specific growth rates of $r_1 = -0.1, r_2 = 0, r_3 = 0.2$, and movement rates of $\pi_{12} = \pi_{13} = 0.25, \pi_{21} = \pi_{23} = 0.3$, and $\pi_{31} = 0.1, \pi_{32} = 0.2$ (in all cases, since there are only three possible populations to move to, the probability of movement to the last one population (i.e., staying put) is calculated by subtraction from 1, e.g., $\pi_{11} = 1-\pi_{12}-\pi_{13} = 1-0.25-0.25 = 0.5$). In the spreadsheet, initial population values are set in cells B2–D2. Then population size at $t = 1$ is calculated by

$$= \mathrm{B2} * (1 + r\_1) * (1 - pi\_12 - pi\_13) + \mathrm{C2} * (1 + r\_2) * pi\_21 + \mathrm{D3} * (1 + r\_3) * pi\_31$$

for population 1;

$$= \mathrm{B2} * (1 + r\_1) * pi\_12 + \mathrm{C2} * (1 + r\_2) * (1 - pi\_21 - pi\_23) + \mathrm{D2} * (1 + r\_3) * pi\_32$$

for population 2; and

$$= \mathrm{B2} * (1 + r\_1) * pi\_13 + \mathrm{C2} * (1 + r\_2) * pi\_23 + \mathrm{D2} * (1 + r\_3) * (1 - pi\_31 - pi\_32)$$

for population 3. As before, these formulae are then copied down the page. Total population size, proportion in each area (area 3 is by subtraction of p1 and p2 from 1), and λ are calculated in columns E–H. These initial values and parameters give values for the first 10 years of

t	N1	N2	N3	tot	p1	p2	λ
0	5000	5000	5000	15,000	0.333333	0.333333	1.047933
1	4569	4325	6825	15,719	0.290667	0.275145	1.067188
2	4320.573	4396.025	8058.525	16775.12	0.257558	0.262056	1.077486
3	4350.277	4664.585	9060.097	18074.96	0.24068	0.258069	1.082347
4	4555.641	5019.07	9988.67	19563.38	0.232866	0.256554	1.08455
5	4866.306	5429.928	10921.22	21217.46	0.229354	0.255918	1.085533
6	5246.543	5887.983	11897.72	23032.25	0.227791	0.255641	1.08597
7	5680.254	6391.119	12940.96	25012.33	0.227098	0.255519	1.086163
8	6161.345	6940.334	14065.8	27167.47	0.226791	0.255465	1.086249
9	6688.746	7538.227	15283.67	29510.64	0.226655	0.255441	1.086287
10	7263.97	8188.34	16604.72	32057.03	0.226595	0.25543	1.086304

You can see from this that the proportion of animals in each population, as well as λ, stabilize within about 10 years. So, geographic stratification creates a situation similar to age stratification, in which the population potentially takes several years to settle down to a "stable space distribution" and growth rate (assuming that population-specific growth rates do not change).

The complete spreadsheet example can be found in the electronic companion to the book (see enclosed CD and website address on p. ii).

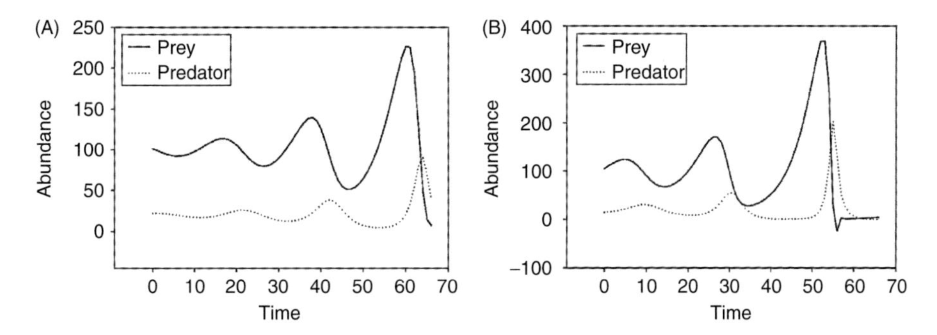

Fig. 3.5 **Discrete-time Lotka–Volterra predator–prey model.** $r_{prey} = 0.2, d_{prey} = 0.01, b_{pred} = 0.005, d_{pred} = 0.5$. **(A)** $N_{prey}(0) = 101, N_{prey}(0) = 22$; **(B)** $N_{prey}(0) = 105, N_{prey}(0) = 15$.

Lotka–Volterra models have also been constructed for the dynamics of two competing species. In discrete form these equations predict abundance for two competing species as

$$N_1(t+1) = N_1(t) + r_1 N_1(t)[K_1 - N_1 - a_{12}N_2]/K_1$$

and

$$N_2(t+1) = N_2(t) + r_2 N_2(t)[K_2 - N_2 - a_{21}N_1]/K_2 \qquad (3.10)$$

Here the model includes growth rates (r) and carrying capacity (K) for each species, and coefficients a_{12} and a_{21} representing the competition effect of one species on the other's population growth. As with predator–prey models, the values of the model parameters determine how the model behaves, and where equilibrium occurs. Equilibrium occurs at

$$N_1^* = \frac{K_1 - a_{12}K_2}{1 - a_{12}a_{21}}$$

and

$$N_2^* = \frac{K_2 - a_{21}K_1}{1 - a_{12}a_{21}}$$

Depending on the sign of the numerators of these equations, the model can either result in a stable coexistence of both populations, competitive exclusion of one or the other, or unstable equilibrium (depending on initial population sizes). Figure 3.6 illustrates the first two of these, along with the case where there is no competition ($a_{12} = a_{21} = 0$).

Both predator–prey and competition models can be extended to interactions of multiple prey and predator species, or three or more competing species. Such models can obviously get enormously complex very rapidly, and thus are beyond the scope of this book (see Box 3.6). However, readers who understand the two-species models

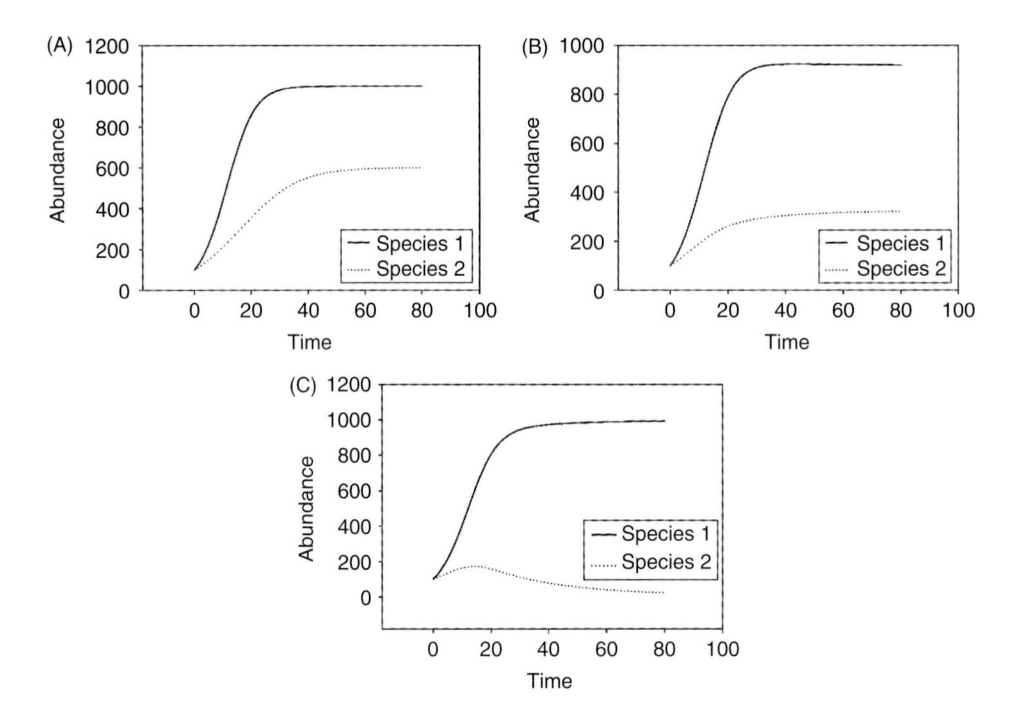

Fig. 3.6 **Discrete-time Lotka–Volterra competition model. $r_1 = 0.2, K_1 = 1000$; $r_2 = 0.1, K_2 = 600$. (A) No competition $a_{12} = 0.0, a_{21} = 0.0$. (B) Stable coexistence $a_{12} = 0.25, a_{21} = 0.1$. (C) Competitive exclusion $a_{12} = 0.25, a_{21} = 0.75$.**

Box 3.6 Two-species modeling: predator–prey and competition.

Here we used spreadsheet programs to calculate two-species models for predation and competition. In the first (predator–prey) Excel worksheet we use Equation (3.9) to produce predictions under the discrete-time Lotka–Volterra model for user-specified values of r_{prey}, d_{prey} , b_{pred}, and d_{pred}, as well as initial values for abundance $N_{prey}(0)$ and $N_{pred}(0)$. These parameters are specified in column G. The program then calculates equilibrium abundance for prey as

$$= d\_pred/b\_pred$$

and for predators as

$$= r\_prey/d\_prey$$

Finally, abundance in each year following the first (row 2) is given by

$$= \text{B2} + \text{B2} * (r\_prey - d\_prey * \text{C2})$$

for prey (initial value in B2)

Box 3.6 Continued.

and

$$= \mathrm{C2} + \mathrm{C2} * (b\_pred * \mathrm{B2}\text{–}d\_pred)$$

for predators (initial value in C2).

In the second (competition) worksheet we perform similar calculations for the discrete-time Lotka–Volterra competition model. The user specifies values for $r_1, K_1, r_2, K_2, a_{12}$, and a_{21}, and initial population values for each species, $N_1(0), N_2(0)$.

The program calculates equilibrium abundance for species 1 as

$$= (K\_1\text{–}a\_12 * K\_2)/(1\text{–}a\_12 * a\_21)$$

and for species 2 as

$$= (K\_2\text{–}a\_21 * K\_1)/(1\text{–}a\_12 * a\_21)$$

The numerators of these expressions are evaluated to determine whether the model leads to stable coexistence, competitive exclusion, or instability (cell H27). Finally, the initial abundances (cells B2 and C2) are projected over time as

$$= \mathrm{B2} + r\_1 * \mathrm{B2} * (K\_1\text{–}\mathrm{B2}\text{–}a\_12 * \mathrm{C2})/K\_1$$

for species 1 and

$$= \mathrm{C2} + r\_2 * \mathrm{C2} * (K\_2\text{–}\mathrm{C2}\text{–}a\_21 * \mathrm{B2})/K\_2$$

for species 2.

should have no problem grasping these more complicated forms (Williams *et al.* 2002).

In this chapter, we have described how to build basic dynamic population models, and to use these models to explore how populations might behave under various assumptions about parameter values, density dependence, age structure, stochasticity, and other factors. In Chapter 4 we will turn our attention to specific applications of population models to important questions in conservation.

4
Applying population models to conservation

In this chapter we discuss two major types of applications of population models to conservation. First, we cover those situations in which populations are generally large, widely distributed, and often increasing. These populations are often ones for which it is reasonable to extract a harvest, so we will emphasize what is termed **sustainable harvest**. However, the "large population" problem also occurs in wildlife control, where the objective is to reduce or eradicate populations that are pests, invasive exotics, or simply locally too abundant [for example, beavers (*Castor canadensis*) or Monk parakeets (*Myiopsitta monachus*), which cause damage to forestry plantations and agriculture, respectively]. Modeling of these populations tends to emphasize large numbers and achievement of equilibrium conditions. They are particularly useful as "models" for other types of applied questions because these are species and questions where data can and often have been collected in large quantities.

The other type of population includes those that are rare, patchily distributed, decreasing in abundance, and/or otherwise in trouble demographically. Unlike the "large population" case, these populations potentially have a real chance of becoming extinct, at least locally, within the foreseeable future. Modeling of these species tends to emphasize the problems of small numbers, which include chance extinction, isolation, and inbreeding, among others.

Clearly these categories – "large" versus "small" populations – are artificial, and many species fall into both categories at different times and other different situations. Our favorite local (Georgia, USA) example is that of the white-tailed deer (*Odocoileus virginianus*), which in our lifetimes (and we are really not that old!) has gone from being nearly extinct locally, to fully capable of sustaining harvest – even heavy harvest – to being "overabundant" (e.g., an economic and safety threat due to agricultural and landscaping damage, and deer–vehicle collisions).

Harvest models

Some readers at this point may be thinking that they will never have an interest in harvest models, because they only work on "rare" species. We argue here that many of the basic principles are the same in dealing with population dynamics and some of the

Quantitative Conservation of Vertebrates, 1st edition. By M.J. Conroy and J.P. Carroll. Published 2009 by Blackwell Publishing, ISBN 978-1-4051-8228-7 (pb) and 978-1-4051-9098-5 (hb).

best examples of integrating models with population dynamics have been done with harvested species.

Now returning to our technical discussion, we begin by looking at our basic population growth equation [Equation (3.3)]:

$$N(t+1) = N(t) + N(t)r(t)$$

We can modify this to include a harvest $H(t)$ taken each year:

$$N(t+1) = N(t) + N(t)r(t) - H(t) \quad (4.1)$$

By rearranging this equation slightly, we can discover the conditions under which harvest will result in the population staying at a constant level (equilibrium), which is met when $N(t+1) = N(t)$:

$$N(t) = N(t) + N(t)r(t) - H(t)$$

or

$$H(t) = N(t)r(t) \quad (4.2)$$

From this, we can easily see that equilibrium is maintained whenever the per-capita harvest rate exactly equals the growth rate $r(t)$:

$$h(t) = \frac{H(t)}{N(t)} = r(t) \quad (4.3)$$

What Equation (4.3) tells us is that if we somehow knew what the population growth rate would be for any year t, we could exactly balance this rate if we could control harvest rates $h(t)$. Equation (4.2) tells us that the size of the harvest we get will also depend on population size.

Any harvest that meets these conditions [Equations (4.2) and (4.3)] is by definition **sustainable** – population growth will be exactly balanced by harvest and a stable population maintained (in theory, forever; but see stochastic models and the next section). These relationships are not all that useful, however, because $r(t)$ usually varies over time, and often in unpredictable ways. If growth rates are constant over time, we go back to our density-independent model [Equation (3.4)] and can see that population growth is exactly balanced by $h(t) = r$. Therefore, if we know what r is we can maintain a constant population by harvesting at a constant rate:

$$h = r$$

Of course, the actual *size* of the harvest will still depend on population size:

$$H(t) = N(t)h(t)$$

or

$$H(t) = N(t)r$$

when $h = r$, which means that we will always get a larger harvest under this model (as long as $r > 0.0$; if $r \leq 0.0$, any harvest will deplete the population) by waiting for the population to grow to a larger size.

A more interesting (and useful) situation arises when the harvested population follows the logistic model [Equation (3.7)]. Now we get population equilibrium by satisfying the following:

$$N(t) = N(t) + N(t)r_{\text{max}}\left[1 - \frac{N(t)}{K}\right] - H(t)$$

which happens when we take a harvest of:

$$H(t) = N(t)r_{\text{max}}\left[1 - \frac{N(t)}{K}\right] \tag{4.4}$$

Unlike density-independent growth, this equation specifies a parabolic relationship between harvest and population size (Figure 4.1), which reaches a maximum yield

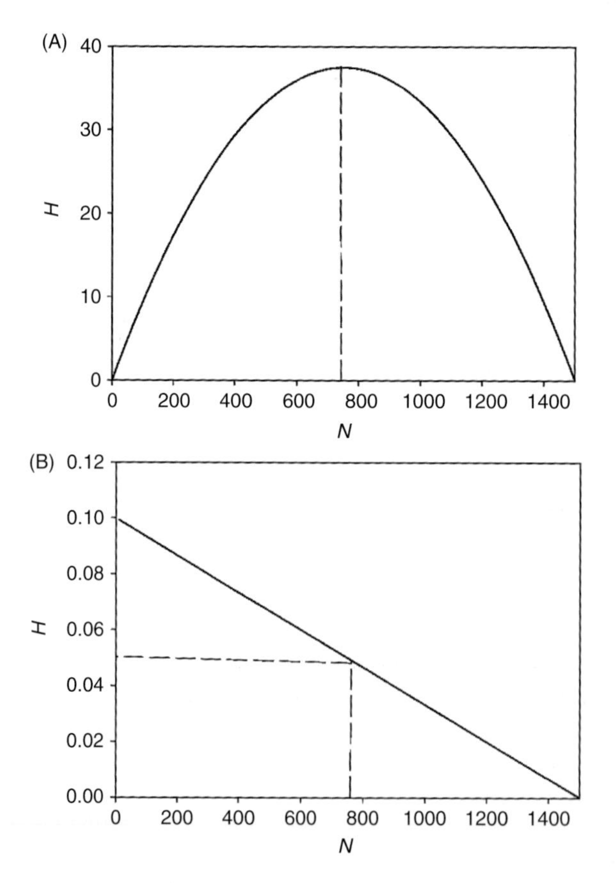

Fig. 4.1 **A maximum sustained yield model showing yield (A) and harvest rate (B) as a function of population size. Parameters for this MSY model include $r_{\text{max}} = 0.10$, $K = 1500$.**

when $N^* = K/2$ (the $*$ refers to this being an optimal value); the value of this yield is $r_{max}K/4$. At all other population sizes (from 0.0 to K), there is a "mirror image" N that gives the same yield, but all of these yields are lower than the maximum yield obtained at N^*, known as **maximum sustainable yield (MSY)**. Also, the per-capita harvest rate that will result in MSY is $h^* = r_{max}/2$. Putting this another way, if our goal is to obtain MSY, we can do so by maintaining the population at $N^* = K/2$ and taking a harvest of $H^* = r_{max}K/4$, at an optimal rate of $h^* = r_{max}/2$; if we are above or below $K/2$ and take h^*, the population will tend to return to the equilibrium value of N^* (because it is actually being harvested at a rate lower or higher than the current population level can tolerate, causing the population to increase or decrease depending on which side of N^* the population currently is. A numerical example makes this clearer (Box 4.1).

As attractive as the idea of MSY can be, it is important not to get carried away with this concept as has been done in the past (Larkin 1977). Always remember that

Box 4.1 Calculating MSY using the logistic model.

As we have seen, under the logistic model, harvest yield can be modeled solely as a function of N, given values for the parameters r and K. That is, harvest yield can be modeled as

$$H(N) = Nr_{max}(1 - N/K)$$

This function can be maximized (solved for the value of N that gives maximum yield) by calculus. However, we can use a spreadsheet and graphics to find this maximum, for example in which $r_{max} = 0.1$ and $K = 1500$. In column A of the spreadsheet we have values of N from 0 to 1500 (there is no point in plotting past K since there can be no yield in this range). In column B we compute:

$$= \text{A2} * r_{max} * (1 - \text{A2}/K)$$

(we previously used spreadsheet naming convention to set the values for r and K as 0.1 and 1500; we can change these if we like). We can also calculate harvest rates in column C:

$$= \text{B2}/\text{A2}$$

(note that the first of these is a bit problematic because we are trying to divide by zero!) Finally, we can plot columns B and C versus A. When we see that there is a clear peak to the yield curve. With a little trial and error you can convince yourself that this peak *always* happens at $K/2$ and always gives a yield equal to $r_{max}K/4$ (in this example $K/2 = 750$ and $H^* = 150/4 = 37.5$). The harvest rate associated with this yield is $r/2$ (in this example, 0.05).

The complete spreadsheet example can be found in the electronic companion to the book (see enclosed CD and website address on p. ii).

MSY completely depends on the assumptions of the logistic model [Equation (3.7)]. Among other things, MSY applications typically assume that the values r_{max} and K are known exactly, and that these do not change over time. This in turn rules out (at least in this simple form) stochastic effects on the environmental carrying capacity or demographic rates, or variation in growth due to age instability. Obviously, if MSY is used even as an approximation for yield determination, the logistic model must have empirical support as a credible model, and not be taken on blind faith, since even mild deviation from an assumed model or parameter values could have enormous consequences for harvest decisions. For example, the models outlined here have not included any age structuring, although this has been done in fish exploitation using Beverton–Holt models (Beverton and Holt 1957). We especially are skeptical of some of the applications of MSY ideas to the population dynamics of vertebrates in tropical conservation biology, where broad claims are made for "sustainable" harvest levels with little or no empirical data (e.g., Robinson and Redford 1991). At a minimum, biologists should be willing to entertain a plausible range of model forms and parameter values, and explore the implications of uncertainty among these in decision making. In the following example we show how one model of harvest (with an assumption of logistic growth) can yield quite different results from another model (where we assume that growth rate is density independent, but has a mean value and varies randomly around that mean – random walk). In both cases the basic model inputs of r_{max} and K are the same (Box 4.2).

Box 4.2 Exploring model uncertainty: an example of harvest under logistic versus "random walk" growth.

As we keep trying to emphasize, models are only abstractions of reality – they are not reality. Furthermore, different models can lead to very different conclusions regarding management. In this spreadsheet we have got predictions of population growth under two different models, one (in columns B through D) under logistic growth ($r = 0.1$, $K = 1500$), the other (columns F through H) under density-independent, random growth (average of $r = 0.1$, SD $= 0.05$). We can explore different harvest rates (in the spreadsheet the decision is a constant rate h each year; if we want to get really complicated we can explore different rates for each year). For example, a harvest rate of 0.05 will under the logistic model result in the population stabilizing at about $K/2$, but under the "random walk" model the population will continue to increase. Increasing the harvest rate to 0.10 will roughly stabilize the population under the random walk model, but will result in the population under the logistic model declining. The spreadsheet also keeps track of cumulative harvest, in this case for 100 years. Under "sustainable harvest" we should try to maximize this cumulative harvest over the long term. Clearly this cannot be done while the population is declining!

The complete spreadsheet example can be found in the electronic companion to the book (see enclosed CD and website address on p. ii).

Small population models

As suggested earlier, a dominant "theme" of small population conservation is the concern that the population will go extinct, at least locally, over the foreseeable future. Of course *all* populations (and species) will eventually go extinct with certainty. In a practical sense we are actually more concerned with extinctions over reasonable periods in the future, typically in the 100- to 500-year range. As conservation biologists we are also principally concerned with extinction events that are driven by human actions, such as habitat destruction or over-harvesting. Naturally, if an asteroid were to impact the Earth, we would miss the species extirpated (assuming that we were among the humans to escape "Armageddon"). However, we suspect there is little that we could do about it (Hollywood films, starring Bruce Willis, to the contrary).

Stochastic, birth–death process models have been developed to study the mathematical conditions leading to extinction. These models tend to be rather complicated, so we will not repeat them here (see Williams *et al.* 2002, Chapter 11, for more details), but rather we will focus on some key elements. Under some simplifying assumptions (such as constant birth and death rates, and no sources of randomness except for the birth–death process) we can write a general prediction for the probability of extinction by time t:

$$p_0(t) = \left[\frac{de^{(b-d)t} - 1}{be^{(b-d)t} - d} \right]^{N_0} \quad (4.5)$$

where d and b are constant, instantaneous death and birth rates and N_0 is initial abundance (typically taken as the current population level). We can use this expression (and the mathematical idea of *limits*) to evaluate the probability of eventual extinction ($t \to \infty$) for two situations. First, if death rates exceed birth rates ($d > b$) we get

$$p_0(\infty) = \left[\frac{-d}{-d} \right]^{N_0} = 1$$

Therefore we have a 100% probability that the population will go extinct eventually (again, we are talking mathematically here: *all* populations go extinct eventually). Conversely if $b > d$:

$$p_0(\infty) = \left[\frac{d}{b} \right]^{N_0}$$

which we can see is a fraction with a value always less than 1 and this value becomes smaller as N_0 gets bigger. This brings out one of the essential ideas of "small population" biology: small populations are at greater risk of extinction than large populations, and extinction risk (due to random demographic events) rapidly decreases as abundance increases (Figure 4.2). Interestingly, if we make $b = d$ then our resulting probability of extinction is also 1 (Box 4.3).

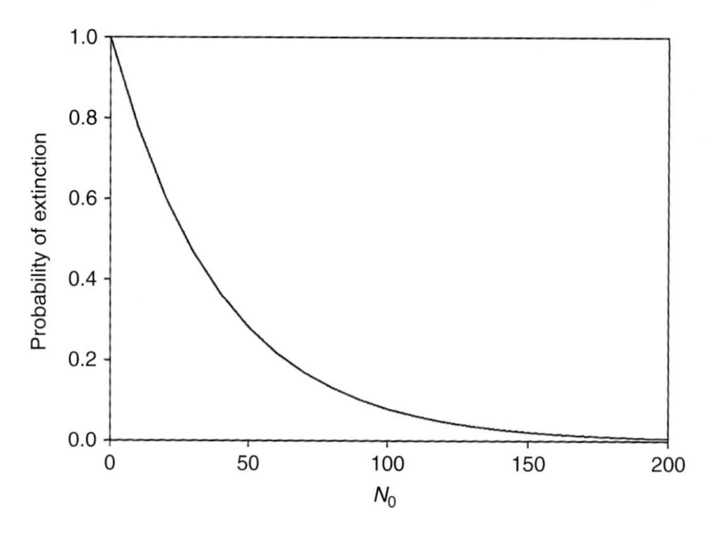

Fig. 4.2 **Example of the probability of extinction as a function of birth, death, and initial population size (NB_{0B}). $b = 0.4$, $d = 0.39$.**

The same ideas (but a slightly different mathematical model) can be used to ask the question "What is the average (expected) time to extinction if birth rates and death rates are constant?" This leads to the formula:

$$T_E(N_{max}) \cong \frac{1}{bN_{max}} \left(\frac{b}{d}\right)^{N_{max}} \tag{4.6}$$

where N_{max} is maximum abundance (e.g., carrying capacity). Just as the probability of extinction decreases, expected time to extinction T_E rapidly increases as N_{max} gets larger (Figure 4.3). Because this number quickly exceeds several thousand years for any reasonably healthy (births exceeding deaths) population, this has led to the idea of a **viable** or "**minimum viable population**," above which the risk of extinction is substantially reduced or, conversely, postponed until the very distant future. However, there are several things to keep in mind here before getting caught up with arbitrary viability rules. First, these *are* only models, and thus they are abstractions: real populations are much more complicated. Even assuming that the models are reasonably good approximations of the real world, they require estimates of b, d, N_{max}, or other parameters, and these estimates may be very poor – *often not much more than simple guesses.* Finally, several authors have pointed out that Equation (**??**) captures only *demographic* uncertainty – not uncertainty due to environmental variation, and definitely not the risk of a catastrophic event (yes, the asteroid impact has a more than 0.0 probability of happening: the probability of this happening in our lifetime is quite small, but it is still not 0.0). It also does not include the effects of factors that may be predictably increasing over time, such as human population increase and resulting habitat degradation. If we include some of these sources, then we can see that just increasing N_{max} alone does not necessarily postpone extinction indefinitely (Figure 4.3).

Box 4.3 Single small-population model.

Here we construct population models for a "small" population under two types of assumptions: (i) density-independent growth with random r, and (ii) density-dependent growth with random r and K.

This example just combines ideas from previous examples (Boxes 3.1, 3.2, and 3.4), incorporating exponential growth, logistic growth, and random effects. We have added a couple of features to accommodate very small populations. Under 'density-independent' (columns B–D):
Column B calculates random r

$$= \text{NORMINV(RAND()}, r_{\text{max}}, \text{SD\_}r)$$

Column C (starting in row 3) is initialized to NN0
We have added code to deal with a common problem in modeling small populations, in which the model can be still numerically "extant" but biologically extinct. Unless we fix this, in the model the population can decline below 2 (or 1 for an asexual organism) and still "recover" mathematically. If this ever happens for a real population it is doomed. We handle this be creating an additional column D, which checks to see if column C falls below 2. If it does it assigns the value 0 to column D; otherwise it keeps the computed value:

$$= \text{IF(C3} < \text{2,0,C4)}$$

Finally, the new population value in column D now becomes the basis for projecting next year's population as:

$$= \text{D3} * (1 + \text{B3})$$

We have used a similar device to compute logistic, random growth (columns F–I); note that the r values are computed independently of those for exponential growth.

Try running this model with small starting populations (NN0 < 10) and low growth rates ($r = 0.01$). Click F9 repeatedly to see how many of these go extinct before 100 years. Try increasing NN0 and r and varying SD_r and SD_K to see how initial abundance, growth, and growth variation affect extinction (see enclosed CD and website address on p. ii).

The complete spreadsheet example can be found in the electronic companion to the book (see enclosed CD and website address on p. ii).

This last point leads to a very important contribution of theoretical ecology to conservation biology, that of **island biogeography**. Very simply, whether we are talking about actual oceanic islands or "islands" of habitat, individuals in local populations tend to interact more with other locals than they do with distant or even relatively nearby neighbors, especially when there is a degree of fragmentation or other barriers to movement. However, individuals do occasionally disperse from local populations and settle in neighboring islands. Sometimes these islands are vacant, so actual

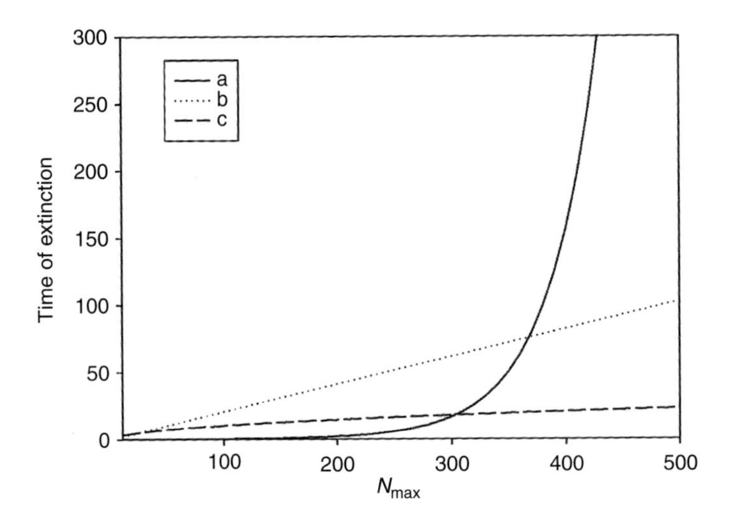

Fig. 4.3 **Expected times to extinction, including several types of stochasticity. (a ——) Demographic stochasticity only, (b ······) demographic plus environmental stochasticity, (c – – –) demographic plus environmental stochasticity plus catastrophic events.**

colonization (and even range expansion) occurs. Sometimes the islands had been populated in the past, but the population disappeared for some reason: perhaps it was wiped out by disease or an exotic predator, or perhaps it hit a population bottleneck and went extinct by chance (see above). Unless this was the only island where the species occurs, "extinction" in these cases is local, not global, and colonization from a neighbor represents a second chance.

We can see this by considering a **metapopulation** (a "population of populations") comprised of three population "islands." Overall abundance is given simply as the sum of the abundances on the three islands; therefore,

$$N(t) = N_1(t) + N_2(t) + N_3(t)$$

Obviously, this population will *only* be extinct if all three populations go extinct. Under our simple extinction model we know that

$$p_{0i}(\infty) = \left[\frac{d_i}{b_i}\right]^{N_i(0)}$$

where $i = 1, 2, 3$ indexes the birth rates, death rates, and initial abundance for each island. Even if there is *no* interchange among the islands, global extinction requires all three populations to go extinct. In the simple case where extinction on each island is independent of what happens on the other islands, but assuming that birth rates and death rates are the same among islands, we get:

$$p_0(\infty) = p_{01}(\infty)p_{02}(\infty)p_{03}(\infty) = \left[\frac{d}{b}\right]^{(N_1(0)+N_2(0)+N_3(0))}$$

which is just the same as:

$$p_0(\infty) = \left[\frac{d}{b}\right]^{N_0}$$

In other words, each island adds to the metapopulation's overall probability of persistence, with the overall effect the same as pooling all three populations.

Of course, real situations will be more complicated, and require more realistic modeling. For example, islands that are closer to one another are likely to experience similar weather and other environmental conditions, but may have different habitats. Thus, one would expect the birth rates to be different but correlated, and more realistic modeling would allow for this type of situation. Also, islands that are near to one another likely exchange more individuals than distant islands, so distance or barriers between islands (or habitat patches) need to be included. Spatially stratified models like the ones considered in the previous section could be useful here. Naturally, the more complicated these models become, the more parameters have to be specified. Mark-recapture methods can be used to estimate parameters such as population-specific survival and movement rates (see Williams *et al.* 2002, Chapter 17, for some examples). We present a simple three-population metapopulation example in Box 4.4.

The main idea, however, is that as long as population "islands" have some degree of connectivity, local extinction is "not forever": there is always the potential of

Box 4.4 Three-population metapopulation model.

Here we return to the three-population example in Box 3.5, now adapted as a "small population" problem. This is accomplished by two modifications. First, rather than assuming constant population-specific growth rates of $r_1 = -0.1, r_2 = 0, r_3 = 0.2$, these are used as the means for selection of random growth rates each year, with the amount of variation controlled by standard deviations for each population. This results in three columns of random growth rates (columns H–J). Second, as with Box 4.3, we have programmed the spreadsheet to force populations that fall below 2 to zero. Of course, with movement between populations, even if this happens the population may recover, but this prevents the nonsensical situation of 1 (or fewer) animals in the total population. The adjusted population values are displayed in columns E–G.

The spreadsheet displays population growth for 50 years. Try running this with small initial populations (<10) in each population, or even 0 for some. Increase or decrease the growth rates and standard errors. Change the movement rates: notice what happens when there is *no* movement, lots of random variation, and small initial values.

In this example, we kept things relatively simple by assuming that movement rates were constant over time, and that growth rates, while variable, varied independently among the populations. In reality, movement rates likely would vary over time, and growth rates would probably be at least somewhat correlated, requiring more complex modeling.

The complete spreadsheet example can be found in the electronic companion to the book (see enclosed CD and website address on p. ii).

rescuing colonization from one of the extant populations. This also relates to the commonsensical notion of "not putting all of one's eggs in the same basket." No matter how abundant a local population is, it is always at risk of local extinction. If it is the only population in the world, extinction is now global. Thus, species that have widespread geographic range are automatically more resistant to extinction than, say, island endemics. These ideas also come into play when trying to maintain and restore populations via reserve networks. The "single large versus several small" (**SLOSS**) controversy still rages, and probably cannot be settled universally (since animals are so different in their dispersal abilities). Keeping these ideas in mind – but remaining open to contrary views and evidence – will be key to objective, scientific conservation.

Modeling genetic effects

Much attention in conservation biology has focused on the genetic aspects of small population biology. Populations that experience low numbers are at higher risk of experiencing loss of genetic diversity, due to random mutations and genetic drift. Also, individuals in small populations have fewer choices for mates, leading to **inbreeding**, the mating of individuals who are closely related (and thus genetically similar), not to mention the Allee effect noted earlier. In extreme cases inbreeding leads to a phenomenon known as **inbreeding depression**, in which the reproduction rates, survivorship, or both of offspring are impaired. Classic examples of this have occurred in extremely small (less than 100 individuals) populations, for instance some of the big cats like Asian tigers (*Panthera tigris*) and the Florida panther (*Puma concolor coryi*).

Coverage of population genetics and genetic impacts on demography is beyond the scope of this book. A few points are worth keeping in mind, however. First, the issue of genetics is, from a species survival point of view, an issue of *population* impacts. Regardless of the interesting or even bizarre genetic outcomes that may occur among individuals, it is only the degree to which these affect birth rates or death rates that is relevant to conservation biology. Thus, the claim that low abundance leads to genetic "defects" must be taken a step further: these "defects" must be shown to affect demographic rates. Second, even where such impacts have been demonstrated, the role of genetics in conservation must always be kept in perspective. It seems obvious to us that populations that are at such low levels that inbreeding and drift are occurring are already critically imperiled, probably due to habitat loss or overexploitation, or a host of other reasons. Focusing solely on genetics in conservation is a bit like treating a terminal cancer patient's blood pressure. It may keep the patient from dying right away, but the main problem is still there. By removing or mitigating the "ultimate" causes of population demise, we will have solved the "proximate" problems of genetic abnormalities. Of course, if populations have already declined to the critical stage, genetics probably will need to be managed by captive breeding, reintroductions, or other methods, but the ultimate salvation for the population lies elsewhere.

Including habitat or other factors in models

Wildlife managers have recognized for years that habitat is a key requisite for the sustenance of animal populations. By definition, habitat provides food, shelter from predators, structures for denning or nesting, or other life requirements, and therefore presumably influences survival rates, reproductive rates, or carry capacity of populations. Therefore, it makes sense to incorporate habitat into population models, particularly if management decisions may influence habitat in ways that alter population dynamics.

We can start with the simple, density-independent model of population growth in Equation (3.4). To incorporate habitat (X) we could redefine this equation as:

$$N(t+1) = N(t) + N(t)r = N(t)[1 + r(X)]$$

where $r(X)$ defines growth rates as a function of habitat X. This might be as simple as expressing a linear relationship between r and X, for instance:

$$r(X) = b_0 + bX$$

If data are available, it might be possible to develop relationships between X and the components of growth rate, birth (b) and death (d) rates, keeping in mind that both of these rates are logically constrained to be in certain ranges ($b \geq 0; 0 \leq d \leq 1$). Again we provide a simple spreadsheet example in Box 4.5.

The same kind of ideas can be extended to the logistic model [Equation (3.7)]. Here, it might make sense to view habitat as principally influencing carrying capacity (K). We could then modify Equation (3.7) as

$$N(t+1) = N(t) + N(t)r_{\max}\left[1 - \frac{N(t)}{K(X)}\right]$$

where again $K(X)$ specifies that K is a function of habitat (see Box 4.5 for an example). A similar approach could be taken with the source–sink model, where N_1^* (carrying capacity in the source) might be raised or lowered, depending on habitat management (Box 4.6).

Use of "canned" modeling software

In the last few decades, several computer packages have increasingly been used by conservation biologists to conduct population modeling for conservation. These have been especially prevalent in the area of population viability analysis for small populations. Notable examples include VORTEX (Lacy and Kreeger 1992), RAMAS (Akçakaya *et al.* 1999), and WALEX (Possingham and Davies 1995), but there are many others. These programs typically are reasonably "user-friendly" in that they provide menus or graphical user interfaces, enabling users who are not particularly computer savvy to provide inputs with relatively little pain.

Box 4.5 Building a model to predict population growth from habitat conditions.

A very basic idea in wildlife management is that management of habitat translates into an increased potential for a population to sustain individuals. If we assume that the population operates under the logistic model (Box 3.2), habitat improvements can translate into either increased growth potential r_{max}, or, perhaps more reasonably, increases in the maximum numbers that the population can support (carrying capacity, K). In fact, K is often referred to as "habitat carrying capacity," even though the logistic model itself says nothing directly about habitat (only that there is an upper limit to growth).

To include habitat as a factor influencing the population, we need an explicit model relating habitat (X) to a parameter in the population model. In this example we have chosen to specify that relationship via a simple linear model:

$$K(X) = b_0 + b_1 X$$

where $K(X)$ indicates that the parameter K is now a function of habitat X, which in this case we take as acres of habitat added to (+) or subtracted from (−) the present habitat level (0). The parameters b_0 and b_1 determine the intercept and slope of the linear relationship. For example, $b_0 = 5000$ and $b_1 = 0.5$ determine that K will be 5000 with no additional habitat, and will increase (decrease) by 50 animals for every 100 additional acres added (lost).

Of course, it is one thing to propose a model relating habitat to carrying capacity, and a far different thing to demonstrate the relationship empirically. For now we leave the empirical issue aside, noting that, for instance, simply demonstrating that abundance is higher or lower in some habitat than another does *not* make the case (see source–sink and the next example).

The complete spreadsheet example can be found in the electronic companion to the book (see enclosed CD and website address on p. ii).

We admire the creativity of the developers of these programs in rendering fairly complicated mathematics accessible to those who would normally be frightened away from simulation modeling. Indeed, we have used programs such as WALEX and VORTEX as teaching tools in undergraduate and graduate courses on population modeling. Our quarrel is not with these programs *per se*, but rather with the fact that they can foster a rather blind, and we think, naïve approach to applied population modeling. Often, these programs provide little in the way of understanding of underlying model assumptions; indeed, they typically make a large number of critical assumptions "by default." In some cases, marketers of some of this software seemingly encourage uncritical use of the packages, in ways that we think are counterproductive to scientific conservation (Conroy 1992).

In many if not most cases, we believe that the complexity of "canned" computer packages for conservation modeling far outstrips the reliability of data to determine parameter values, while hiding critical assumptions within the proverbial "black box." We are firmly convinced that most conservation biologists would be far better served by constructing simple, understandable models, whose assumptions (and deficiencies) are

Box 4.6 A simple model demonstrating source–sink dynamics.

Under source–sink dynamics, populations in source populations (by definition where $\lambda_1 > 1$) grow exponentially up to a limit N_1^*; beyond this limit excess individuals disperse to sink habitats (by definition where $\lambda_2 < 1$). Conversely, in the absence of source animals, sink populations decline exponentially (to extinction, eventually).

We have constructed a spreadsheet model that allows investigation of source–sink dynamics. The user specifies λ_1, λ_2, and N_1^* and initial values for the source and sink abundances. Initial values are stored in cells B2 and C2 for source and sink. The next year's source population is then calculated as:

$$= \text{IF}(\text{l\_source} * \text{B2} > N_{max}, N_{max}, \text{B2} * \text{l\_source})$$

and sink population as:

$$= \text{IF}(\text{l\_source} * \text{B2} > N_{max}, \text{C2} * \text{l\_sink} + \text{l\_source} * \text{B2} - N_{max}, \text{C2} * \text{l\_sink})$$

(this requires some familiarity with branching "IF" statements in Excel). In the example spreadsheet we specified $\lambda_1 = 1.3$, $\lambda_2 = 0.85$, $N_1^* = 1000$ and initial values in each habitat of 10. Columns B and C project from this abundance to equilibrium levels in less than 20 years. A direct solution to equilibrium is also provided in cells J9–J11 from Equation (3.8)

$$= N_{max}$$

by definition for the source and

$$= N_{max} * (\text{l\_source} - 1)/(1 - \text{l\_sink})$$

for the sink.

Try a range of values for λ_1, λ_2, and N_1^* and initial values. See how the sink population can equilibrate above – or below – the source population, and how fast equilibration occurs. Be sure though not to allow $\lambda_1 < \lambda_2$, $\lambda_1 \leq 1$, or $\lambda_2 \geq 1$ (any of which would violate source–sink assumptions).

The complete spreadsheet example can be found in the electronic companion to the book (see enclosed CD and website address on p. ii).

transparent. If a biologist builds a model, even a simple spreadsheet model of the types demonstrated in this chapter, that model will capture the biologist's understanding of the system. More importantly, the biologist will be in a position to critically evaluate the assumptions used to build the model and, if possible, to collect data appropriate for the proper model parameterization. If, at a later point, the biologist wishes to use one of the more "sophisticated" modeling programs, he or she will be doing so with at least a kernel of understanding of the underlying assumptions involved – and, we hope, with a critical eye toward testing model assumptions.

In this chapter we outlined some fairly simple models using contrived data. As conservation biologists we are much more interested in moving away from theory and toward creating models that will be useful for describing real processes. Therefore in Chapter 5 we discuss the design of sampling strategies that allow us to collect data in the most practical and useful manner.

5
Basics of study design and analysis

Heretofore we have focused on building and using models, but have given little or no attention to how the values used in these models were derived. That is, we essentially assumed that values for abundance and other state variables, and important parameters such as survival and reproductive rates, were available and accurate. Now we begin to focus attention on how to obtain these values from field data. In Part II we will focus much attention on the specifics of how to collect and analyze field data to obtain these values. In this chapter, we lay out some basic principles of study design and analysis that we will carry through in Part II.

Proper design of conservation studies, as in any scientific endeavor, is needed to make reliable inferences about populations and communities. **Reliable** means that the results will provide evidence that is *repeatable* and *defensible*. Studies that are not based on these basic principles will fall short: both scientifically and with respect to the extent that their conclusions are comparable to those of other studies, or may be used to support conservation decisions.

Field biologists often focus solely on the details of techniques used in the field to observe, capture, or otherwise detect the presence of animals. We do not wish at all to minimize the importance of field techniques: proper identification, measurement, and quantification of presence or other attributes is a key part of study methodology. However, conservation biologists sometimes fail to correctly place their field observations in the context of a larger system. Thus, it will hardly ever be of specific interest that a species of bird is detected at a particular sampling point on a particular day. Instead, a single observation has meaning because of its context as part of a larger study (e.g., a series of sample points in a selected forest type). Conversely, biologists almost always seek to generalize their field observations to a larger system of interest. Thus, a series of detections or misses of birds on sample points will usually lead to broader conclusions about the presence, abundance, or other parameter of the species in the region of the samples. Regardless of the specific field method used to gather the data at each sample, the results will only provide reliable information about this larger system (e.g., a population or a community) if they are applied as part of a valid **sampling design**. The purpose of this chapter is to provide guidance as to what constitutes a valid sampling design, with relevant examples from biodiversity sampling.

It is absolutely essential that conservation biologists apply these principles *before* rather than after embarking on field sampling. As noted above, failure to follow basic sampling principles results in data that will not stand up to scientific scrutiny, and may be useless for the purposes intended, thus wasting valuable resources that could

Quantitative Conservation of Vertebrates, 1st edition. By M.J. Conroy and J.P. Carroll. Published 2009 by Blackwell Publishing, ISBN 978-1-4051-8228-7 (pb) and 978-1-4051-9098-5 (hb).

have been used elsewhere. Moreover, problems created by improper sampling cannot be fixed by application of clever statistical techniques. Regrettably, it is still common for biologists to gather field data with no design (indeed, often with no real scientific question) in mind, or to use *ad-hoc* sampling methods that inevitably lead to biases. These biologists are then upset when they bring their data to a statistician, only to be told that the data are totally inadequate for the desired application. Rather ironically during university education most students in conservation biology take courses in statistical analysis early on, and if they ever take a course in experimental design it is often when they are more advanced students. Since the former depends on the latter it is a bit like setting the "cart before the horse." Because research in conservation biology is often complex, and formal experimentation is difficult, many field studies, if not carefully designed, result in "messy data" that are difficult to handle with statistical analyses.

Statistical models

Throughout most of the discussion to this point, we have either pretended that parameter values for our models are known with certainty, or deferred the problem of estimating these values with data. In this section we consider **statistical models**, models that use sample data to address population questions. The name "statistical" comes from the fact that these models are built up around random values or **statistics** that are observed as sample data (a statistic is just any function of the sample data, including the individual observations themselves). For now we will assume that our data come from a valid sampling design; later in this chapter we will discuss how to achieve a valid design.

Frequency distributions

If we observe any characteristic (say, body length) about individuals in a population, that characteristic will vary from individual to individual. The number of animals that take on a particular value (say, 500 kg) is the frequency of those values, and the distribution of frequencies over all N (say, 10,000) animals in the population is the **frequency distribution** (Figure 5.1). If we take a random sample (of say 100 animals), we should expect that the relative frequencies in this sample closely represent the frequency distribution (if not, we probably do not have a good sampling design: see the next section). This relationship between the population we are interested in and the sample frequencies in our data is the basis for all our statistical models (see Box 5.1).

Descriptive statistics

Although it is a good idea to examine the "raw data" (e.g., with frequency plots), usually we will want to summarize our data in various ways. Summary statistics are useful for several reasons. First, they are often good, compact descriptions of the data and of

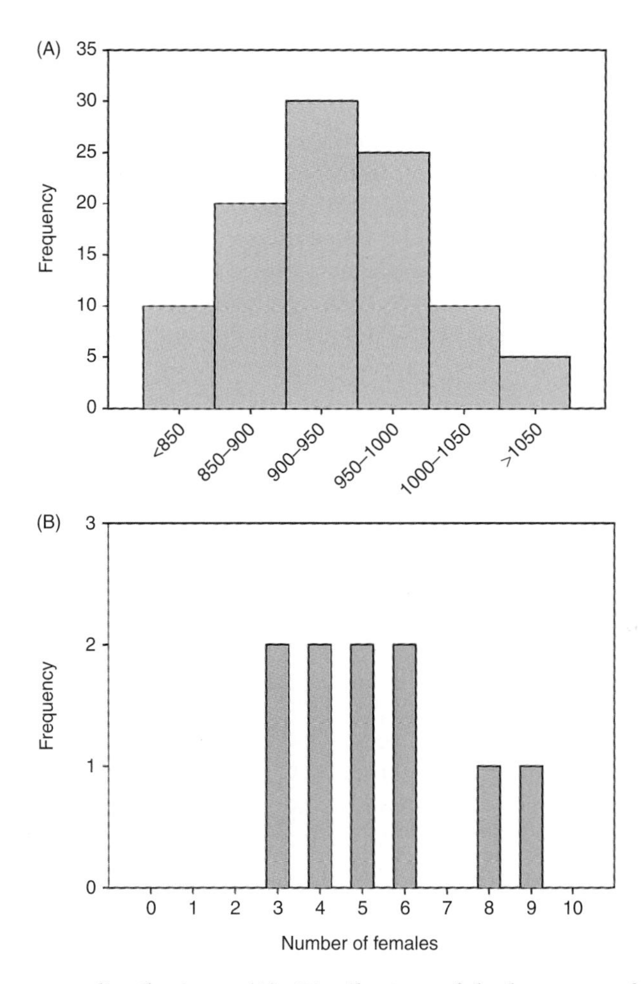

Fig. 5.1 **Frequency distributions. (A) Distribution of body masses for 100 ducks; (B) distribution of number of female ducks in 10 samples of 10 each.**

population characteristics, such as central tendency and variability. Second, sample statistics are often useful for more detailed statistical modeling, either because they are directly related to parameters we are interested in estimating or because they summarize the data in ways that are more efficient for modeling than the raw observations. The sample **mean** $\bar{x}$ is a useful measure of central tendency, and is computed simply as the average of the observation values:

$$\bar{x} = \frac{\sum_{i=1}^{n} x_i}{n}$$

The sample mean is a natural estimator of the *population mean* μ:

$$\mu = \frac{\sum_{i=1}^{N} x_i}{N}$$

Box 5.1 Spreadsheet example of frequency distributions.

The **frequency distribution** describes the relative frequencies at which different values occur in a sample data set. It is one of the most basic and useful ways of describing sample data, and it is the backbone for most of our statistical models. We illustrate how the frequency distribution works with a sample data set of 100 measured body masses (g). The first thing to notice is that the masses are recorded to the nearest 0.001 g, and that in fact no two sample masses are identical; this is a common feature of continuous variables. Here for simplicity we consider the data rounded to nearest 1 g. Therefore, in order for the idea of frequency to make sense, we have to group the data into intervals or "bins." In this example we chose bins in intervals of 50 g, resulting in a summary table of the data that looks like this:

Bin	Frequency
<700	0
700–749	1
750–799	2
800–849	7
850–899	9
900–949	16
950–999	18
1000–1049	14
1050–1099	16
1100–1149	9
1150–1199	5
1200–1249	3

The bins can be formed by hand after ranking data; Excel also provides a handy "histogram" function for doing this automatically. The binned data can then be plotted and examined visually. A quick inspection (of either the table or the graph) reveals that the most frequent observations occur right around 950–1000 g, with few observations either <800 g or >1200 g.

The complete spreadsheet example can be found in the electronic companion to the book (see enclosed CD and website address on p. ii).

which is simply the average attribute value over all the individuals in the population. The mean tells us what the attribute's value tends to be "on average." We also need to know how the values vary over the sample (and population). The *variance* is a standard way to express this, computed as:

$$s^2 = \frac{\sum_{i=1}^{n}(x_i - \bar{x})^2}{n-1}$$

The sample variance is a natural estimator of the population variance:

$$\sigma^2 = \frac{\sum_{i=1}^{N} (x_i - \mu)^2}{N}$$

The mean and the variance completely determine the shape of the **normal distribution**, one of the most familiar and important statistical models.

There are many other useful descriptive statistics. Among these are the **mode**, which describes the most frequently observed value, and the **median**, which describes the value that is located halfway through the ordered values of the data. More generally, **percentiles** describe the location of ranked values (e.g., the 35th percentile indicates that 35% of the observations are equal to or less than the indicated value). Box 5.2 gives examples of how some of these common statistics are computed.

Major statistical models

A complete coverage of statistical models is beyond the scope of this book. Interested readers can refer to Williams *et al.* (2002), especially Appendix E. Here, we describe a few of the most common and important statistical models.

The normal distribution, already mentioned above, is used to model continuous attributes that can take on any real values (so, positive or negative). The normal distribution takes on the familiar bell-shaped curve, being symmetric about the mean (μ) the width or dispersion of the distribution determined by the variance (σ^2) (Figure 5.2). These two parameters completely determine the normal distribution; the mean is also identical to the mode and the median (50th percentile). Some attributes (e.g., body mass) cannot be negative; for these a lognormal distribution (the observations are normally distributed when log-transformed) is appropriate (see Box 5.3).

The normal and several other distributions model observations that are continuous, and take on infinitely many potential values. Some kinds of attributes take on discrete (countable) values.

The **Poisson distribution** models the discrete random variable x, where x is a non-negative integer ($x = 0, 1, 2, \ldots$). The Poisson distribution is appropriate for counting event occurrences (number of births or deaths in an interval or numbers of eggs in nests, for example) and, potentially, for modeling the distribution of abundance (which by definition is a nonnegative integer). Interestingly, as the mean value of data following this distribution increases, it begins to look more like a normal distribution.

Another type of discrete random variable is defined when there are two or more mutually exclusive outcomes, and x represents the frequency of n observations in one of the outcomes. The simplest case is the **binomial distribution** (Figure 5.3) in which x represents the number of "successes" (e.g., heads in a coin toss, survival, males and females, or alive and dead) in n independent **Bernoulli trials**, each with probability of success p. By subtraction, $n - x$ is the number of "failures" (e.g., tails in a coin toss, mortality), each with probability $1 - p$; p is the parameters of the binomial model, and x and $n - x$ are the data used to estimate p. The binomial extends readily to the situation where there are k>2 outcome classes, with frequencies $x_1, x_2, x_3, x_4, \ldots$ each with

Box 5.2 Basic descriptive statistics for data collected in the field.

In Box 5.1 we introduced the frequency distribution, which is actually one type of descriptive statistic. We can use the frequency distribution to get a statistic that is often used to describe central tendency – the **mode** (most frequently occurring observation); in our example the mode is around 1000 (this will change depending on how the observations are binned).

Several other descriptive statistics can be computed, more or less easily, and we will illustrate these with the same data we used in Box 5.1. Probably the most familiar (and easiest) of these is the sample mean, which is computed simply by summing up the observations and dividing by sample size. Most spreadsheets can perform these calculations easily, for example in Excel® we get the sample mean by

= SUM(A2:A101)/100

where the data are in D2:D101. Excel® actually makes this even easier with a built-in "average" function:

= AVERAGE(A$2:A$101)

We have computed the mean both ways in the spreadsheet example. The variance is also an important statistic. It is computed by (i) subtracting the mean from the observations, (ii) squaring the result, (iii) adding these values across the data, and (iv) dividing by $n-1$, where n in this case is 100. We have performed these calculations in column D of the example. As with the mean, there is also a built-in spreadsheet function in Excel® which does this all in one step:

= VAR(A$2:A$101)

The variance is also used to compute two other statistics: the **standard deviation** (SD), computed simply as the square-root of the variance, and the **standard error of the mean**, computed by dividing *SD* by the square root of n; these statistics are also computed in the spreadsheet.

Our final descriptive statistics are based on ranking the observations from lowest to highest value, and then determining the values, known as **percentiles**, below which specific percentages of the observations fall. The most familiar percentile is the 50th, also known as the *median*. For an odd number of observations the median is just the observation in the middle; e.g., if there are 101 observations, the 51st has 50 below and 50 above. With an even number, it is a little trickier: the "middle" is halfway between observations 50 and 51, and is simply calculated as the mean of these two observations. Other percentiles are similarly computed. For example, the 25th percentile has 25% of the observations lower and 75% higher. Excel® has a convenient built-in function for percentile, which we illustrate in the example. The 25th percentile in this example is computed by

= PERCENTILE(A$2:A$101,0.25)

where the percentage is expressed as a proportion (i.e., 25% = 0.25).

The complete spreadsheet example can be found in the electronic companion to the book (see enclosed CD and website address on p. ii)

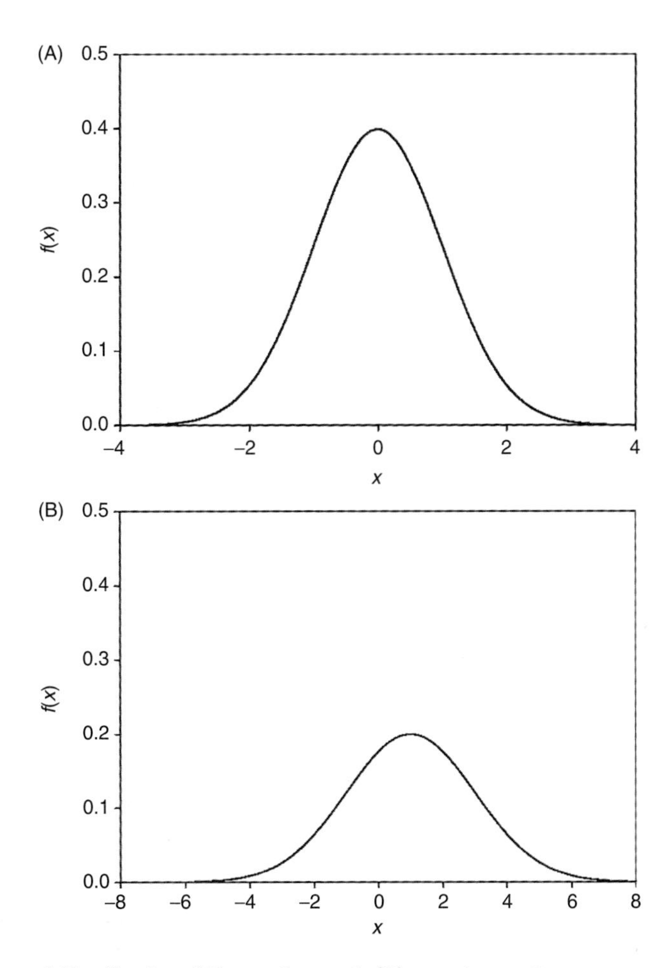

Fig. 5.2 **Normal distribution. (A) $\mu = 0, \sigma = 1$, (B) $\mu = 1, \sigma = 2$.**

probabilities $\pi_1, \pi_2, \pi_3, \pi_4, \ldots$. The binomial and **multinomial** distributions are particularly important for survival estimation and for the modeling of capture–recapture data (see Chapters 10–12 and Box 5.4).

Estimation approaches

Statistical models, including those described above, can be thought of in two different ways. If we assume a particular model (say, the binomial distribution) and parameter value (say $p = 0.7$), we have a model that essentially predicts what we should expect if we were to sample from a population that followed this model. In this case, we would expect in a sample of $n = 100$ to get about 70 "successes" (we would probably get a few more, or a few less by chance, and this outcome would vary slightly from sample to sample).

On the other hand, we as field biologists are often confronted with the opposite problem: we have observed the outcome (say, 69 successes in 100 trials) and we would

Box 5.3 Normal distribution, only one type of distribution that may describe the data collected by field biologists.

The normal distribution has two parameters that completely define the distribution: the mean (μ) and the standard deviation (σ). Standard statistical tables for the normal distribution are usually based on what is called the **standard normal distribution**, which has a mean of 0 and standard deviation of 1; all other normal distributions can easily be obtained from the standard normal, essentially by multiplying by the desired standard deviation and adding the mean.

Many spreadsheet programs have built-in normal functions that make this even simpler. In our example, we have used built-in functions to generate probability densities, cumulative probabilities, and quantiles for user-selected normal distributions (so, the user selects μ and σ). The *probability density* $f(x)$ expresses the relative likelihood of sample values of x from the specified normal distribution. This is easily created in Excel® by

$$= \text{NORMDIST(A3,mean,sd,0)}$$

where A3, etc. are valued for x (we selected values in the range of -6 to 6 for this example; these would have to be changed for distributions with larger or smaller means) and mean and sd are named values for these parameters (so the user can change these). The spreadsheet then plots $f(x)$ versus x; the user can change μ and σ and see how this affects shape.

Quantiles (percentiles) of the normal distribution are obtained from the inverse normal distribution, and are values below which specific percentages of the observations are predicted to fall (note that observed percentiles, from Box 5.2, are the actual observations associated with these percentages). We use the spreadsheet to create several standard quantiles for the normal distribution (0.01, 0.05, 0.25, etc.); for example,

$$= \text{NORMINV(0.25,mean,sd)}$$

returns the 25th quantile for the specified mean and standard deviation.

The *cumulative probability distribution* $F(x)$ is also useful for many purposes. It expresses the probability that a sample value lies below a specified value. Mathematically, $F(x)$ is obtained by integrating (summing for a discrete variable) over the density function, but Excel® once again provides a shortcut. For example,

$$= \text{NORMDIST(2,mean,sd,1)}$$

provides $F(2)$, the probability that a value lies below 2 [note that the 4th value of the function is 1; this distinguishes $F(x)$ from $f(x)$, where the value is 0]. The cumulative function can be useful for many purposes. For example, we can use it to easily evaluate the probability that a sample value occurs in a certain range. Thus, for example, the probability that a value from a normal distribution with $\mu = 2$ and $\sigma = 1$ falls between 2 and 3 is given by $F(3) - F(2)$, computed in Excel® as

$$= \text{NORMDIST}(3, 2, 1, 1) - \text{NORMDIST}(2, 2, 1, 1) = 0.341$$

The complete spreadsheet example can be found in the electronic companion to the book (see enclosed CD and website address on p. ii).

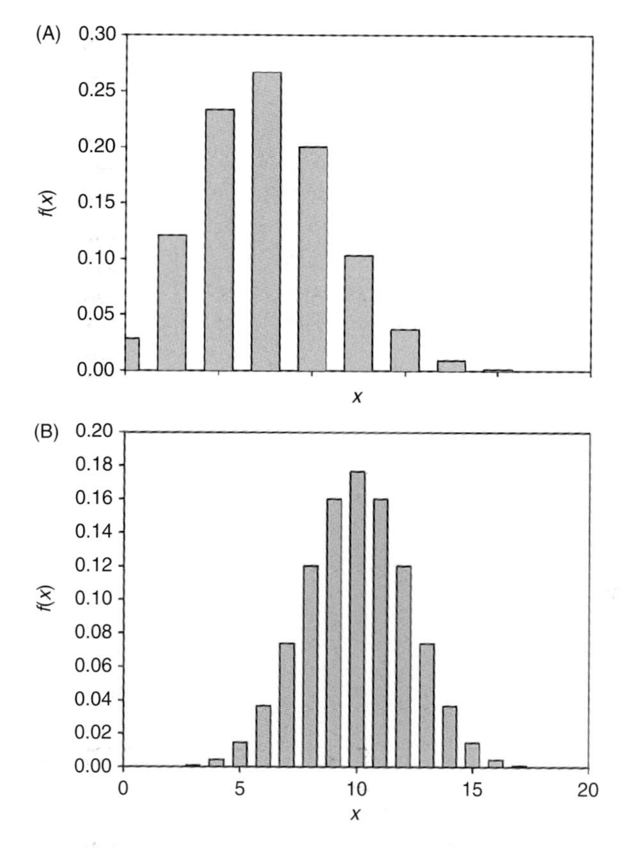

Fig. 5.3 **Binomial distribution. (A) $n = 10, p = 0.3$, (B) $n = 20, p = 0.5$.**

like to describe the outcome with a statistical model. In essence, there are two steps. The first is picking an appropriate model. In this simple case, there is an obvious choice, the binomial. Given this choice, the next task is to select a value for the parameter(s) that does the best job of representing the frequency distribution of the data. The usual technique is known as **maximum likelihood** and essentially involves treating the data as constants and finding the value of the parameter(s) that maximizes the model, now known as the **likelihood**. Most (but not all) of the familiar statistical methods, including those we use in Part II, are based on maximum likelihood estimation. In reality, the goals of **model selection** and **estimation** are closely intertwined, and we typically will use the data both to estimate parameters under competing models and to evaluate how well each model performs (and, thus, to pick a "best" model). For a book such as this, these ideas are best illustrated by concrete examples, in each of the next few chapters, but we provide some simple examples here to illustrate the basic ideas (Boxes 5.5 and 5.6).

Statistical hypothesis testing

In this book, we emphasize the estimation of parameters of models, and do not give perhaps as much attention to the formal testing of hypotheses using data. However,

Box 5.4 Binomial distribution.

The binomial distribution is the appropriate distribution when the data are n trials where each trial has an outcome of 0 or 1 (failure or success, died or lived, etc.), the trials are independent, and the probability of success at each trial is the same (p). Here we show how to calculate estimates of p and its standard error, as well as two methods for calculating confidence intervals on p. We also use the estimate with an Excel® function to produce a probability distribution $f(x)$ under the binomial model.

For a binomial sample with x successes in n trials, the maximum likelihood estimate of p is

$$\hat{p} = \frac{x}{n}$$

and the estimated standard error is

$$SE(\hat{p}) = \frac{\hat{p}(1-\hat{p})}{n}$$

These quantities are calculated in cells I6 and I7 in the spreadsheet and given input values for n and x in cells I3 and I4.

Confidence intervals are calculated via two methods. The first is a normal approximation:

$$\hat{p} \pm SE(\hat{p}) z_{\alpha/2}$$

where $z_{\alpha/2}$ is the standard normal deviate for a $1-\alpha$ confidence interval (1.96 for a 95% confidence interval). These values are calculated in cells I8 and I9. The second is based on the exact binomial distribution for n and p and provides 2.5 and 95.7% lower and upper critical values for this distribution. These are then divided by n to provide associated values for p (lower and upper); the calculations are performed in cells K8 and K9. In this case, the normal approximation and the exact solution are close. However, notice that the lower limit for the normal approximation is negative, obviously an impossible outcome. The exact value, although tougher to compute, will avoid this, and will also perform better in general at low sample sizes, and away from $p = 0.5$.

The complete spreadsheet example can be found in the electronic companion to the book (see enclosed CD and website address on p. ii).

readers by now should realize that all models, including statistical ones, can be viewed as **hypotheses** about how a system is structured or behaves. In fact, the same methods that we described above for parameter estimation and model selection can be thought of from a hypothesis-testing point of view. The common idea – whether we are using traditional tests such as t-tests and ANOVA or information-theory approaches such as AIC (favored by us) – is that our models are used to compute alternative predictions, which we can then support (or not) with our data. We will pursue these ideas further when we use alternative models to estimate parameters (Part II) and to predict the consequences of conservation decisions (Part III).

Box 5.5 Goodness of fit.

Once we have collected data and estimated the parameters of a statistical model, we need to verify that the model really is an adequate representation of the data. A standard way of going about this is called **goodness of fit**. Basically, the process involves (i) specifying a statistical model, (ii) estimating the parameters of that model with the data, (iii) using the parameter estimates to predict the sample data under the assumed model, and (iv) comparing how well the predictions match the observed values.

We illustrate goodness of fit using the data in Box 5.1. Here we have computed the sample mean as 995.95 and SD as 108.56. We use these together with the cumulative normal distribution function to generate expected frequencies for each "bin" of the observed data. These expected frequencies are computed simply as

$$n[F(x_u) - F(x_l)]$$

where x_u, x_l are the upper and lower limits of each bin, respectively, and n is the total number of observations in the sample. In the spreadsheet these values are computed in column H, and are compared in the graphic to the observed frequencies in the plot above. The observed and predicted values match quite well for most of the data range, agreeing to within 1 or 2. This suggests that the normal model is quite appropriate for these data. Larger differences between observed and expected (which can be formally tested by a chi-square test) would suggest violations of the normality assumptions, and perhaps the need for an alternative, better fitting model might be sought.

Box 5.6 Model comparison using AIC.

For many of the procedures we use for estimating abundance and other parameters, several statistical models are available to estimate the same parameter (e.g., abundance). Typically, these models involve different underlying assumptions, for example, about sources of variation in capture probabilities or other types of detection. In order to obtain accurate estimates of the parameters that we are interested in, we should use models that fit the data (Box 5.5) but also do not contain an unnecessary number of parameters. A standard approach is to use several models and to compare how each performs. Then one selects the model that seems best supported by the data but uses as few parameters as possible.

A useful statistic for this purpose is **Akaike information criterion**, or AIC. AIC is computed using the log-likelihood for each model:

$$AIC_i = -2 \ln L_i + 2k_i$$

where L_i is the likelihood (evaluated at the maximum likelihood estimates) for each model and k_i is the number of parameters in the model. The models are ranked from

Box 5.6 Continued.

lowest to highest and the difference computed between each model's AIC value and that for the lowest model to compute ΔAIC_i. Finally, a model weight is computed as

$$w_i = \frac{\exp(-\Delta AIC_i/2)}{\sum_{j=1}^{n} \exp(-\Delta AIC_j/2)}$$

where there are n models under consideration.

We illustrate the application of AIC with a simple example from three independent binomial samples, each involving 100 trials. The number of successes in the three samples is 50, 25, and 20, respectively. We use these data to fit three alternative models: (i) a model assuming that each sample's probability of success is different, having three parameters; (ii) a model assuming all three have the same probability, for one parameter; and (iii) a model assuming that sample 1 has a different probability than 2 or 3, which are identical to each other (two parameters). The estimates of parameters under the three models are as follows:

	Model 1	Model 2	Model 3
p1	0.5	0.316667	0.5
p2	0.25	0.316667	0.225
p3	0.2	0.316667	0.225

and the computation of AIC is

Model		Log likelihood	Number of parameters	AIC_i	ΔAIC_i	w_i
1	All different	−7.22863	3	20.45726	1.281977	0.345016
2	All equal	−18.9395	1	39.87909	20.70381	0.00002
3	1 vs. 2&3	−7.58764	2	19.17528	0	0.654963

In this example model 3 provides the lowest AIC values (highest model weight) and should be used for inference from these samples. However, model 1 has a fair amount of support, and a good procedure is to take into account "model uncertainty" by computing the weighted average of parameter values over models with nonnegligible weights. Here there is little point in doing so because models 1 and 3 produce the same estimates for the parameters. In many situations we will want to do this averaging, and also take into account model uncertainty when computing variances and confidence intervals.

Sampling designs

Now that we have a basic idea of where data collection needs to be headed – that is, toward the collection of data that can be used to make reliable statements about populations – we need to discuss some basic principles of how to achieve this result. A good sampling design will ensure that the data we collect can be used to make valid inferences for our study system. Conversely, critical errors made at this stage cannot be undone at some future point: in other words, no amount of statistical "magic" will remedy a faulty study design.

Defining the study objectives

The first step in developing a sampling design is to define the study objectives. At a minimum this requires:

1. defining the quantities that are being estimated (e.g., abundance, density, presence/absence, etc.);
2. establishing the spatial and temporal scope of the study (e.g., size of the study area, duration of the study);
3. establishing criteria for reliability (e.g., **precision**);
4. identifying practical constraints such as cost, manpower limitation, and safety.

For example, an ill-defined study might be "quantify the abundance of tigers (*Panthera tigris*) in India." A more appropriately defined study would be "obtain an unbiased estimate of density of tigers on the Corbett Tiger Reserve (Figure 5.4A) during July 2009, with a coefficient of variation of less than 25%, and for a cost of under $5,000US."

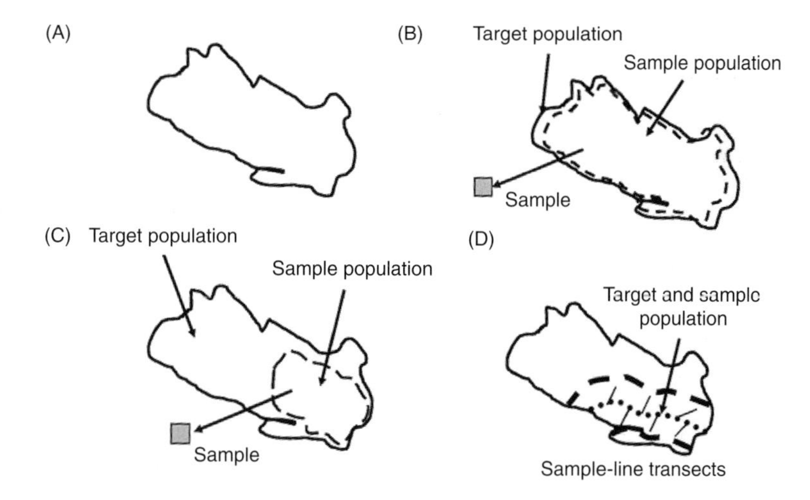

Fig. 5.4 **Target and sample populations and sampling units. (A) Corbett National Park and surrounding areas. Dark outer line indicates boundary of hypothetical study area for estimating tiger density. (B) Close agreement of sample population to target population. Sample plots for pheasant counts are selected from sample population. (C) Poor agreement between sample and target population. Sample inference is not applicable to target population. (D) Target population is redefined to be that portion of CNP within reach of the central road and coincident with sample population. Sample inference is now applicable to target population as redefined.**

The first statement leaves a great deal to the discretion of the field biologist as to what is being measured (abundance? density? presence?), where (everywhere in India?), when (all year? today?), and what are the criteria for success. The second statement leaves no doubt as to any of these questions, but still gets us only part of the way, since we have not really said *why* it is important that we have an estimate of density. We suggest that the "need" for an estimate must itself be part of a scientific or management question of interest. If so, then we now have an excellent starting point for developing a rigorous design. It is obvious now there is a conundrum with the first statement because often we do want to know the abundance of tigers in India with some assigned level of confidence – what we point out is that the first statement is often what policy makers and the public want answered. The key is recasting that in such a way that we can "defend" statements we might want to make about tigers in India. Better yet, we have clearly defined a scientific or management objective, and the estimate of tiger density is one step towards helping us reach that objective.

Target and sampled populations

Unless a population or other system of interest is exhaustively and/or completely sampled, conclusions (inferences) about the population of interest must be based on a sampled subset. The manner in which this sample is taken is critical to the validity of these inferences. We refer to the population about which we are making inferences as the **target population**. In the previous example, the target population was "tigers on Corbett Reserve during July 2009." In this way sampling can be designed to meet study objectives by assuring that samples indeed represent this "target" population. Mismatch between the "target" and "sampled" populations is a very common and serious problem in conservation, and results in the data that are collected not being applicable to the population of interest. Figure 5.4B illustrates a situation where the sampled part of the population closely matches the target population (here, Corbett Tiger Reserve, CTR). By contrast, in Figure 5.4C, only the southeastern portion of CTR is sampled. Clearly, it would be very risky to base inference about all of CTR on samples from only this portion, which may be nonrepresentative of CTR as a whole. Of course, it may not be practicable to sample all of CTR because of costs and logistical constraints. Indeed, much of CTR is inaccessible by road. A road traverses much of the eastern portion of the reserve (Figure 5.4D), and could be used to access sampling plots that are located within a specified distance of the road. However, it would be necessary to take these restrictions into account in extending inference to a target population, which legitimately should be redefined so that it matches the sample population. Researchers would also have to consider the effects of the road itself, as it potentially either alters tiger behavior or makes tigers more detectable, or both.

Replication and randomization

Once the target and sampled populations are properly defined, sampling units must be delineated, and a method for sampling devised. Often sampling units are units of space (e.g., plots, segments of lines, or other divisions of space) whose number is finite and known or determinable (e.g., 1000 1-ha^2 plots in a 1000-ha study area). Sometimes the sampling units are the animals themselves, in which case the number of units is not known in advance. **Replication** is needed to assure that our sample is spread throughout the sample population, and does not represent conditions at just a single point. The goal is that we want to be able to apply what we learn from places that we sample, to places where we do not sample. Most statistical models also assume that the sample data are collected according to a **randomization** scheme, in which a sample of units is drawn at random from the total list in the sampled population. A **sampling design** is a method for assuring that adequate replication and randomization of samples occur, so that the resulting data can be validly used to estimate parameters. Below, we focus on two closely connected issues: (i) the reliability of sample-based estimates of parameters, and (ii) sampling designs to assure that the sample data are adequate for estimation.

Estimate reliability

Estimates of parameters such as abundance, density, survival, etc. are computed from sample data that have been collected. Samples are selected according to a randomization process, and therefore *the collection of sample values, and any calculations using these values, are also random events.* Because sample data are used to calculate parameter estimates, the values of these estimates are also random outcomes: if we were to repeat the sampling and compute another estimate, almost certainly it would take on a different value. Furthermore, that value might or might not be close to the true parameter value.

To the extent that estimates of parameters are close to the true parameter value *on average* they may be said to be **unbiased.** On the other hand, to the extent that sample estimates are close *to one another*, they are said to have low **variance** (and thus be highly repeatable). To the extent that sample estimates tend on average to be both close to the true parameter value (unbiased) and close to each other (repeatable), they are said to be **accurate.**

The relationship of sampling to bias, variance, and accuracy can be seen by a target shooting analogy (Figure 5.5), where the "bulls eye" represents the true value for the parameter (Θ). Sample estimates will usually vary from sample to sample, but ideally they will be close on average to the true parameter value (Figures 5.5A and C). In both of these cases, the estimation procedure is unbiased. However, in Figure 5.5A, the estimates are close to one another (and to the true parameter value), whereas in Figure 5.5C the estimates have high variance, and any single estimate may be quite far from the true parameter. By contrast, in Figure 5.5B, variance is quite low and the estimates are highly repeatable but far, on average, from the true parameter. Finally, in Figure 5.5D, the estimates are both highly variable and biased.

Usually we will have a single sample from which to estimate our parameter, and it is important that this estimate has a high probability of being close to the true parameter value, which of course will be unknown. We can increase the repeatability of our estimates by our sampling design, mainly by increasing the number of samples taken, but also by stratification and other methods. Bias is usually controlled by

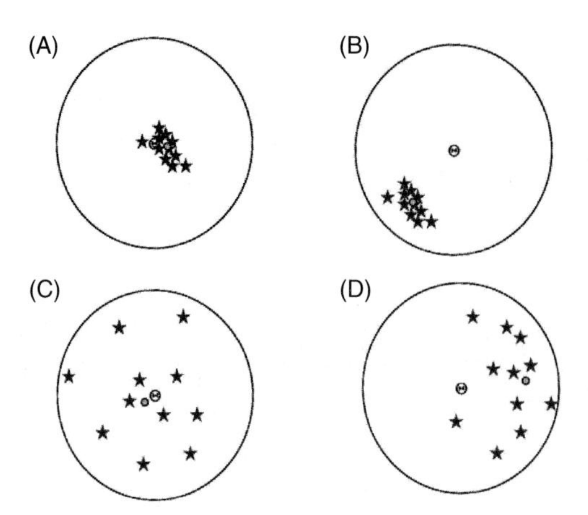

Fig. 5.5 **Relationship of hypothetical sample estimates to bias and precision. In each case the sampling and estimation procedure is repeated several times, and an average of the sample estimates is computed. (A) Estimates are close on average to true parameter value (low bias) and are highly repeatable (low variance). (B) Average of estimates differs from true parameter value (biased), but estimates are highly repeatable (low variance). (C) Estimates are close on average to true parameter value (low biased) but have high variance. (D) Average of estimates differs from true parameter value (biased) and estimates have high variance.**

meeting the assumptions of the statistical model used to estimate the parameter, and using a good model, together with data that have been properly collected according to an appropriate sampling design. Two common ways that estimates can be biased are (i) using an inappropriate sampling design, and (ii) failing to account for systematic biases in our sample data, such as incomplete detection of animals. We will see below how both of these can be avoided through proper sample design, collection of appropriate field data, and use of appropriate statistical models. One final note here from Figure 5.5 is that we suggest that the worst-case scenario is Figure 5.5B, which might superficially be counterintuitive. However, some would argue that highly repeatable and biased estimates imply that we have better data than we do possibly, leading to the researcher having great confidence in a wrong answer. When we ask our students which of these scenarios is the worst case most reply naively that it is "D." However, when we explain reasoning we suggest that at least in Figure 5.5D we know that we have poor data.

Standard sampling designs

Returning to the CTR example, a single, unreplicated sample (Figure 5.6A) would be of little use for inference, regardless of how it is selected. Likewise, replicated samples that are selected non-randomly may perforce be nonrepresentative of the target population, leading to biased estimates (Figure 5.6B). Most sampling schemes will combine replication with randomization. Here we describe the most important sampling designs: simple random sampling and stratified random sampling.

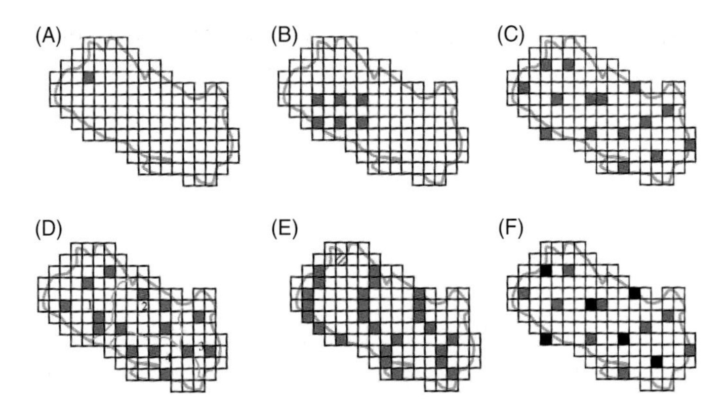

Fig. 5.6 **Sampling schemes. (A) Single, unreplicated sample plot taken at random from study area. (B) Replicated, non-random sampling. (C) Replicated sample plots selected according to simple random sampling. (D) Replicated sample plots selected according to stratified random sampling. (E) Systematic sampling; initial sample at random (shaded plot) with every 5th plot. (F) Double sampling. Inexpensive but inaccurate measure (e.g., aerial counts) taken on all sampled plots; expensive and accurate measure (e.g., mark–recapture estimates) taken on a randomly selected subset of plots (dark plots).**

Simple random sampling

In **simple random sampling**, sample units are drawn at random from the entire sampled population, with equal probability. This is accomplished first by numbering all the Npotential sample units, and then randomly selecting n units, each with the same probability n/N of being selected. For example, suppose we are sampling a 10,000-ha study area using 10-ha sample plots, and we decide to sample $n = 100$ of these plots. Potentially, there are 1000 such plots that could be sampled, each with probability $100/1000 = 0.1$ of being selected. A simple method for selecting the plots to sample would be to go down the list of plot and select a uniform random number between 0 and 1; if this number is less than or equal to 0.1, select the plot, if not go to the next, until 100 plots have been selected. Another approach would be to randomly order the 1000 plots, and then select the first 100. Either approach should produce a spatial distribution of sample plots that is random appearing [(Figure 5.6C), i.e., dispersed throughout the sample area with no obvious patterns (in contrast to Figure 5.6B)].

Stratified random sampling

Frequently, the population being sampled is heterogeneous, but regions or strata that are relatively homogeneous can be identified. For example, forest cover types may be mapped in advance using aerial photographs or other techniques. Random samples are then assigned to each of the strata, as for example with CTR (Figure 5.6D). **Stratified random sampling** can result in improved estimates of the population parameters of interest, by "absorbing" some of the variability among the sample units in the strata. This improvement occurs when the strata do in fact account for a significant amount of variation among the sampled units; otherwise, there is no improvement over simple random sampling. An issue that arises with stratified sampling is how to allocate the sample among the strata. We will return to this issue when we discuss sample size determination in later sections.

Systematic sampling

In **systematic sampling**, sample units are selected according to some regular ordered scheme, usually after the first sample is selected at random. For example, rather than simple random sampling of CTR (Figure 5.6C), the first plot could be selected at random, followed by every fifth plot thereafter (Figure 5.6E). Systematic sampling usually has the advantage of being easier to implement in the field, because sample units typically occur at regular intervals of distance or time. Systematic sampling can also be useful when the main objective is to address questions about the spatial distribution of animals or other objects. Systematic sampling is equivalent to random sampling when the attribute being sampled is distributed randomly over the sampled population. Otherwise, gradients and other patterns will cause the data to be spatially autocorrelated. Field biologists often "cheat" by using this type of sampling because in theory it can provide results the same as random sampling. However, we know that ecological nonrandomness is the rule, rather than the exception, and therefore random sampling ordinarily should be preferred over systematic sampling.

Double sampling

Often the ecological attributes in which we are interested are very difficult or expensive to measure exactly, but other, correlated attributes are cheaper or easier to measure. For example, if we are interested in estimating the total volume of trees in a forest stand, we can do so very accurately by sample plots, on each of which we measure the diameter and height of every tree. A much less expensive (but also less accurate) estimate of volume could be obtained from aerial photography. Likewise, accurate counts of nesting ducks are possible via direct observation on the ground of nesting ducks, but it is much less expensive (albeit also less accurate) to count ducks from airplanes. In both cases, a primary attribute of interest (Y) is predictable from an auxiliary measure (X). In **double sampling**, we take advantage of these features by an overlapping sample in which X is measured on all n sample units, and Y is also measured on a subset ($n' < n$) of units. The n' overlapping units on which X, Y observations are taken are then used to build a statistical model to predict Y from X; often this is a simple linear or even ratio model. Besides being an efficient approach when resources are limited, double sampling can directly address the issue of incomplete detection, when Y and X are, respectively, an unbiased and a biased estimate of abundance or other attribute (Figure 5.6F). In conservation research we believe that double sampling is significantly underutilized. Much more efficiency could be gained in answering conservation questions at large scales by combining accurate and more expensive techniques on smaller study areas with widespread and potentially less accurate techniques at the large scale.

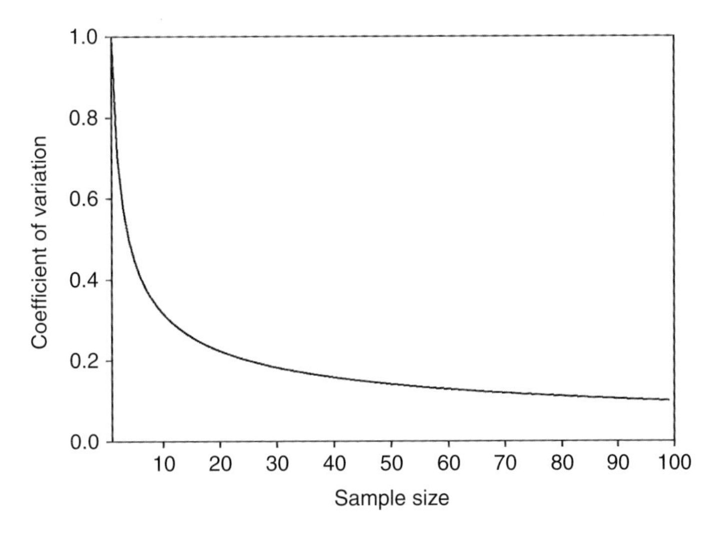

Fig. 5.7 **Example relationship between precision (CV = SE/$\bar{x}$) and sample size. This highlights the rapid increase and nonlinear relationship effects of sample size on CV.**

Determining sample sizes needed

Simple random sampling

The sample size needed will depend on the precision required of parameter estimates. This in turn depends upon study objectives. Precise estimates will, under appropriate study designs, allow detection of important spatial and temporal differences. Conversely, estimates that are very imprecise will allow only the crudest descriptive inferences about parameters, and even these will be subject to great uncertainty because of wide confidence intervals. Sample size computation will depend upon the particular method being used for estimation, and hence will be taken up in the individual chapters devoted to particular approaches. Often, sample size (n) will be expressed as a function of variance or **coefficient of variation** ($CV = SE/\bar{x}$), with n increasing as SE or CV decreases. A typical relationship between precision and sample size is given for estimating the mean of a continuous variable (Figure 5.7). A rapid increase in precision is achieved in moving from $n = 1$ or 2 to n of around 30 (CV decreasing from 1 to less than 0.2). However, additionally sampling up to $n = 100$ does not reduce CV to 0.1. Additional precision beyond $CV = 0.1$ would require other approaches, for example stratification, because of underlying variability in the sampled population. Please note that this is merely an example of the relationship between precision and sample size.

Specific sample size guidelines often will depend on the actual field data collected and the statistical model used, and therefore will be discussed in the chapters on estimation (Part II). However, we provide here some basic approaches for estimating the sample size needed to determine mean μ with a given level of precision, based on simple random sampling. More formally, we wish to ensure that the estimated mean is within a fraction r of the true mean, with confidence $(1 - \alpha)$. If we assume that the sample mean $\bar{y}$ is approximately normally distributed, then we can use the formula:

$$n = \left(\frac{z_{\alpha/2}}{r} C\hat{V}\right)^2 \tag{5.1}$$

where r is desired precision (as a proportion of the true mean), $C\hat{V}$ is an estimate of the population coefficient of variation (σ/μ), often obtained from a pilot study, and $z_{\alpha/2}$ is ordinarily the upper α point from the standard normal distribution. If we are sampling without replacement from a finite population (as ordinarily would be the case in plot sampling), then an adjustment is needed for finite sampling:

$$n' = \frac{n}{(1 + n/N)} \tag{5.2}$$

where n is obtained from the first expression and N is the number of units in the sampled population.

Stratified random sampling

As noted earlier, stratified sampling can be an improvement over simple random sampling, because some of the variability that would otherwise be part of the error in estimating the mean is accounted for by the survey strata. As with simple random sampling, the total sample size needed can be approximated using data from a pilot study. However, a decision must then be made as to how to allocate this sample among the strata. The two basic approaches are **proportional** and **optimal allocation**. Under proportional allocation, the sample is allocated to strata based on their size, as determined by numbers of sampling units available (N_i) or equivalently total area per stratum i. Thus the formula for proportional allocation is

$$n_i = n\frac{N_i}{N} \tag{5.3}$$

where n is the total sample size and n_i is the sample size for stratum i, for $i = 1, \ldots, I$ strata. Optimal allocation also takes into account differences among the strata in variability and cost of sampling:

$$n_i = n\frac{N_i\sigma_i/\sqrt{C_i}}{\sum_{m=1}^{I} N_m\sigma_m/\sqrt{C_m}} \tag{5.4}$$

where σ_i is the stratum-specific standard deviation and C_i is the stratum-specific cost of sampling.

Comparison of time and space (monitoring)

In conservation we are often as interested in how populations or communities vary over time and space as we are about the particular values at any given location or time. Care must be taken that sample data are collected in a way that leads to valid interpretation of population variation. Two important principles must be followed in order to assure interpretable results. First, the estimates of population size or other parameters must be comparable between study areas and over time, meaning that the sampling and estimation methods lead to estimates that are in the same units and can be meaningfully compared. Most of the methods we advocate in this book lead directly to unbiased estimates of parameters, and these should by definition be comparable over space and time, if appropriate assumptions are met. However, in some cases the sample data do not provide unbiased estimates or, because of assumption violations, are not consistently related to the parameters of interest. In these cases, estimates may or may not be useful in making comparisons, since these comparisons may be confounded by other factors. In particular, we believe that heterogeneous detection is likely to confound spatio-temporal comparisons, as discussed further in the next section.

Comparisons over space and time also require **controls** to take into account that some differences occur just by chance. For example, we might take simple random samples from each of two study areas and compare the results (e.g., an estimate of mean biomass of prey per hectare) (Figure 5.8A). However, even ruling out differences within statistical uncertainty, differences between the two areas might be of little interest, and may say nothing about the inherent nature of either area, because of uncontrolled temporal variation. By observing the two areas through time to see the range of temporal variation of each, one will gain insights as to the true differences between areas. Likewise, a single study area may be observed through time and seen to vary, perhaps in response to climatic factors (Figure 5.8B). However, more general conclusions about temporal variation could only be reached if similar patterns were also observed in other study areas (Figure 5.8C). Sometimes, different areas respond differently to some environmental or other factor that varies through time. In such cases, monitoring both areas through time may yield important information about time–space interactions. These ideas extend to practical situations in which the impact of management is being monitored. Here, it

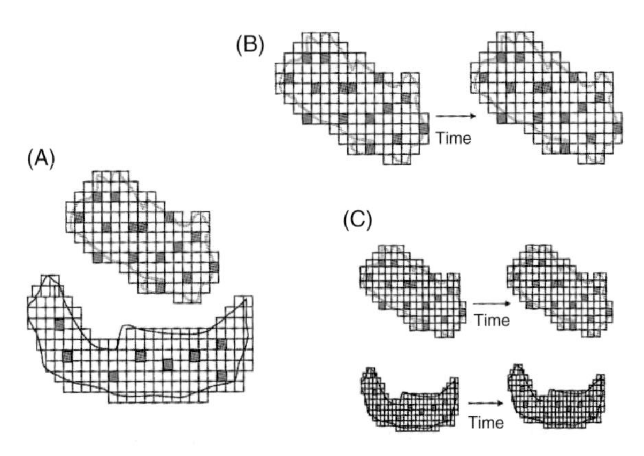

Fig. 5.8 **Examples of spatial and temporal controls. (A) Comparison of two study areas at a single point in time, (B) comparison of a single study area over time, and (C) comparison of two study areas at multiple points in time.**

is most useful if study areas or other units can be followed through time, both before and after the management intervention, and measurements taken on units that are subject to the management and some that are not (controls). In the ideal situation, such a design would involve replicated study units and, best of all, random assignment of study units to treatments and controls. This last situation would constitute a bona fide experimental design, and, while often unachievable in practice, remains the "gold standard" for making causal inferences about factors under management control. To the extent that a sampling and monitoring program can even approach this standard, via spatial and temporal controls and some degree of replication, the conclusions will be immensely more supportable than would be otherwise.

Accounting for incomplete detection

In virtually every study that we are familiar with, it is impossible to ensure that all animals in the sampled units are detected. This is assuming what we call a "census" of a population, meaning that all individuals in a population are counted without error or omission. We argue throughout this book that this is a rare occurrence, and that we should not typically pretend that we are undertaking complete counts. Typically, if we are conducting sample counts, not only do we not sample the entire study area, but also in those areas we do sample we *absolutely* miss some fraction of the animals present (Figure 5.9A). The fraction that is actually detected is generally given the symbol $\boldsymbol{\beta}$ throughout the rest of this book; however, in certain cases (e.g., capture–recapture) the symbol p is used to mean the same thing. Unfortunately, many conservation study designs ignore the issue of incomplete detection of animals in sample surveys, or assume that **detection probability** is homogeneous over space and time, so that the survey data represent valid indices to abundance or other quantities. We emphasize that such assumptions are likely to be untrue in practice, lead to serious biases and potentially false conclusions, and are in any case unnecessary. *These assumptions are not met by standardizing techniques or field methodology.* Failure to deal adequately with detection probability has been an enormous weakness of conservation research. We have found this to be a serious disconnect between field biologists and statisticians when the former are obtaining advice from the latter. The statistician without understanding the detection problems of simple standardization of field methods may conclude that basic assumptions of statistical tests are met when in fact they are not.

If detection rates are heterogeneous, then two samples taken at different points in space may be impossible to compare, unless detection rates are taken into account (Figure 5.9B). In this example, comparison of the total number of some animal detected on six randomly selected plots yields 23 in one case and 8 in the other, suggesting that abundance is higher in the first sampled area. However, this apparent difference in our example is due nearly entirely to differences in detection rates: the numbers of our study animal actually present on the six plots are 28 and 27, respectively. Unless appropriate adjustments for detection are made, sample counts may "reveal" differences that do not

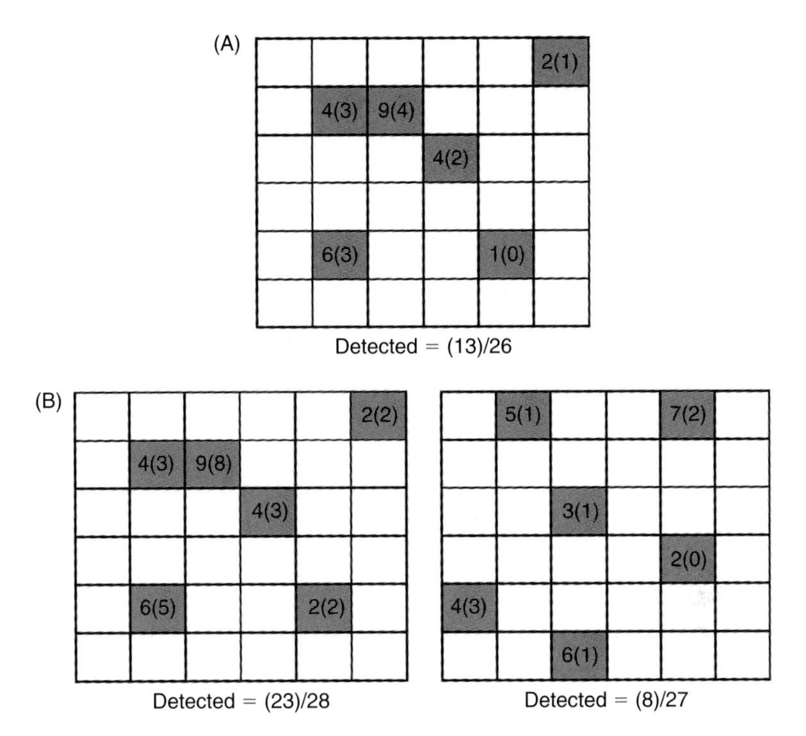

Fig. 5.9 **Example demonstrating incomplete detection. First digit indicates number of individuals counted per sample plot, with parenthetic number the number actually detected. (A) Incomplete detection on a single simple random sample, and (B) incomplete detection on two simple random samples, each with different rates of detection.**

exist. In other cases, detection heterogeneity can mask real differences over space and time. Because it is not generally known whether detection is homogeneous over time and space, it is best to assume that it is not and use the methods described in Part II to estimate detection and provide unbiased estimates of abundance and other parameters, at least on subsamples (as in double sampling).

Summary

In this chapter we discussed the basic principles underlying the design of studies, in order to obtain data that will allow investigators to reach reliable (that is, repeatable and defensible) conclusions. Specific methods for estimating population and community parameters will be covered in the chapters that follow, but all these methods have in common the principles brought forth in this chapter. All study designs require the following and will help to ensure that collected data are useful: (i) definition of the study objectives, including the spatial and temporal scope of the study; (ii) proper definition of a target and a sampled population; (iii) a method for selecting samples, generally by randomization, from the sampled population; and (iv) measures of reliability to assure that the resulting estimates relate to parameters of interest in a predictable way.

In connection with this last issue, most field samples will only provide partial detection of the subject present on study plots or other sampling units, and the rates of detection often vary in time and space. In Part II we emphasize sampling designs and statistical models that allow for the estimation of detection rates and the correction of sample estimates to provide more reliable estimates of parameters.

Part II

Conservation studies and monitoring programs

6
General principles of estimation

In Part II, we develop the basic principles elaborated in Part I into specific methods for quantifying populations and communities as part of research, inventory, and monitoring programs. Chapter 6 begins by discussing the fundamental principles for estimating abundance. Again, as emphasized in Chapter 5, our sampling data must produce information that meets study objectives; it must be repeatable and take into account detection probabilities of our target population.

Virtually all estimation methods used by conservation biologists are based on counts or binary observations (detected or not) from sampling units. Extrapolations from these observations to conclusions about the population involve taking into account both the fraction of the total area sampled and the probability of detection at each sampling unit. We also consider "indices" in which either counts or other measures are assumed to be proportionally related to abundance or density. We show how index assumptions are almost sure to be violated in practice, and how the application of uncalibrated indices to comparisons over space and time can be very misleading. Again, this is related to the assumptions about detection probabilities that we discussed in the previous chapter.

Chapter 7 focuses on methods used to estimate species distribution and finer-scale occupancy (presence–absence) studies. Species distributions are usually developed based on "occurrence records," which catalog locations at which animals have been observed to occur over some defined period of time. Ordinarily, these records are not obtained via any sort of sampling approach that assures representative coverage of areas where animals potentially could occur, nor do they take into account that search efforts, and thus encounter probabilities, tend to be highly heterogeneous over space and time. Therefore the resulting maps of distribution typically confound actual animal distribution with the distribution of search effort, for example resulting in many distribution records near universities and museums, and fewer in sparsely populated areas away from academic habitats. The same phenomenon occurs at a local scale, where occupancy (presence/absence) methods are often used in lieu of abundance estimation. In either case, occurrence (presence) is the result of two processes: the animal's occurrence in some region of interest, and the discovery of the animal by an investigator. Whereas a "presence" at least conveys positive information about the occurrence of one or more individuals, an "absence" record is ambiguous: the animal may indeed be absent, or it may be present but not detected. Thus, presence/occurrence information is of limited value, unless detection probabilities can be taken into account. In particular, it is meaningless to compare distribution or presence record over space or time without accounting for potentially heterogeneous detection. Fortunately, with some planning

Quantitative Conservation of Vertebrates, 1st edition. By M.J. Conroy and J.P. Carroll. Published 2009 by Blackwell Publishing, ISBN 978-1-4051-8228-7 (pb) and 978-1-4051-9098-5 (hb).

and care it is possible to collect presence data to estimate detection probabilities and provide valid estimates of actual occurrence. We provide several examples illustrating both invalid and valid approaches for using presence data; for the latter we use recently developed and freely available software.

Chapters 8–10 specifically deal with the estimation of abundance. Some of the methods start with the simple (but unrealistic) assumption that all animals in the sampling units are detected, but we emphasize methods that permit estimation of detection and provide unbiased estimates of abundance.

Census versus estimate

One topic that we must discuss and one that creates a great deal of confusion among field biologists is the distinction between census and population estimate. Even the various dictionaries we consulted provided ambiguous and contradictory definitions. Interestingly, there appears to be some conflict between British and American usage of the terms. We use a more narrow American definition, which we believe clarifies the distinction between the colloquial meaning of the word "census" and its technical meaning in population estimation. We define a **census** as a complete count of individuals. Thus, if there are 100 animals in a population, then exactly 100 animals are counted. There is by definition no sampling or sampling error associated with this number. In wildlife conservation work this should be an extremely rare occurrence, simply because animals are difficult to count. We suggest assertions that a "census" number is actually a complete count are nearly always unsupportable. Even studies by biologists of large ungulates in enclosures with natural habitat found it almost impossible to undertake a complete census. However, we will admit that there are occasions when the population is so small that counting all individuals is possible and warranted.

For most biologists, even those working on rare or endangered species, we will contend that the correct term for our reporting of abundance is an abundance or population **estimate**. In fact, by following defined protocols and not violating assumptions of sampling techniques we should find that an abundance estimate will be better than a census. This apparent ambiguity is clarified by the case where we have attempted to census humans. Even here with a relatively cooperative population and usually many more resources available to undertake the endeavor, we find that they do not meet the goal of a complete count. A census, by definition, cannot account for missed individuals – that is, there is no detection rate estimate if detection is less than 1.0. Interestingly, most large-scale human censuses, such as the one undertaken every 10 years in the USA, must actually attempt to incorporate correction factors for detection probability – exactly what we have to do in sampling. When we use good sampling designs and estimates, we are admitting that we cannot count all individuals. We instead collect data so as to estimate detection probabilities, providing unbiased estimates of true abundance. Another important point here is that a true census is not a very wise or efficient use of scarce resources in conservation, because attempts to count all individuals of even relatively small populations is an enormous undertaking – siphoning resources from other conservation uses.

Indices

Commonly in conservation science we are faced with limited resources and time to undertake and develop estimates of abundance of our target species. Researchers face a dilemma of having to choose between quantitative estimators of abundance described in the following chapters and indirect measures of abundance which might or might not provide them with reliable information.

An **index** is any measure or count of a species based on direct observation or observation of sign of the species that provides some numerical scale of observation without a measure of detection rate (β). This means that counts represent some number equal to, or less than, the true number of individuals present. The actual relationship between an index and the true population may take an infinite number of forms (examples of several are shown in Figure 6.1). What biologists often assume is that this relationship is positive and linear (Figure 6.1A); however, the relationship may instead be nonlinear (Figure 6.1C and D), nonmonotonic (Figure 6.1E), or there may even be no relationship whatever (Figure 6.1B).

The key in making indices truly useful is to link the observed numbers in the index to some true estimate of abundance or density. Unfortunately this is rarely done. What is more common is the application in management of the "unsubstantiated index" with assumption of some underlying distribution. There are a number of ways, both direct and indirect, to make this linkage between index numbers and abundance. Probably the best and most cost effective is to use **double sampling** (see Chapter 5) with one of the quantitative estimators described in the following chapters. This is where a subgroup of the sample sites is subject to both the index and quantitative estimator and then the relationship between them determined. The quantitative estimator is then taken as the "true" estimate.

General relationship between counts and abundance or occupancy

Here we take a brief but important detour to explore a bit more formally the idea that sample counts may or may not be exactly, or even consistently, related to what we are trying to enumerate at our sample sites: namely, abundance or, more crudely, occupancy.

Let us consider any sample take from a portion (e.g., 1 ha) of our study area at a particular time (say June 1, 2008), and give this sample a label i. We may take a large number of these samples, say 100, and in which case we would label the samples $i = 1, 2, 3, \ldots, 99, 100$. In Chapter 5 we saw how to select such a sample in a way that validly represents the population. Suppose we are interested in abundance over our study area, so that on each sample plot we take a count C_i of the animals present. Likewise, if we are simply interested in assessing presence, we would create an indicator I_i, which would be 1 if $C_i > 0$ and 0 otherwise. So, for example, in 10 samples we might get values for C_i of 10, 0, 2, 40, 1, 17, 0, 2, 1, 0 for our counts and thus $I_i = 1, 0, 1, 1, 1, 1, 0, 1, 1, 0$ for our indicator of presence. Now suppose that the true number of animals N_i in these 10 samples is actually $N_i = 15, 2, 4, 47, 3, 17, 6, 5, 3, 0$. This means that a fraction of the number actually present ranging from 0 to 100% was detected, depending on the sample plot. If we were to sum up the counts on all the sample plots we would obtain 73 detected of 102 actually present, or 0.72 (72%). In terms of evaluating occupancy we did a little better: animals were actually present on 9/10 of samples, but we detected them on 7/10, so we detected 7/9 (78%) of the presences.

We use this example to make two points. First, ordinarily we expect less than perfect detection, or a detection probability $\beta < 1.0$. In our experience, most animal surveys have detection probabilities much lower than 1.0 and sometimes far below 0.5. Second, we expect that detection often varies from sample to sample, as in this example; that is, we expect detection to be *heterogeneous*. Some heterogeneity is explainable simply by random variation due to sampling (Chapter 5), and can be dealt with by increasing sample sizes. However, detection probabilities also frequently vary over space, time,

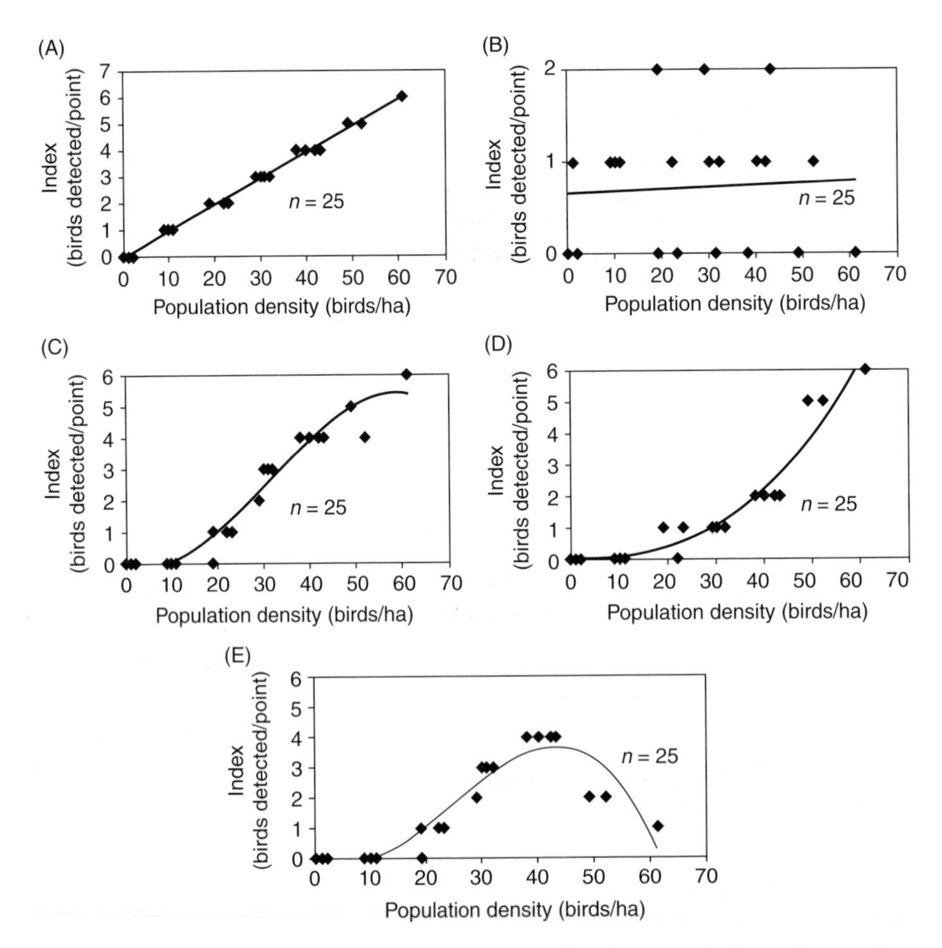

Fig. 6.1 **Several examples of the possible relationship between index values and true abundance. (A) Linear proportional; (B) random (null) relationship; (C and D) nonlinear, monotonic; (E) nonlinear, nonmonotonic.**

between observers, or even among individual animals. In fact, this may be the rule rather than the exception in many situations (Williams *et al.* 2002). Therefore, if we are using a method that depends on visual detection of animals, we might very well expect detection fractions to be different depending on vegetative cover, size, or color of the animals, or experience of the observer. Besides adding to variability in the counts, this can create serious problems if we are trying to use uncorrected counts to make comparisons: perhaps differences we obtain in the counts are not due to actual differences in abundance, but to factors such as cover that enhance or detract from our ability to detect animals.

If we either know what the detection probabilities are or have a way to estimate these, then we can use our sample counts (or occupancy indices) to estimate abundance (or occupancy) by correcting for detection. In the simplest case, detection is *homogeneous*, that is, it does not vary from sample-to-sample (over space, time, among observers, etc.) In this case we could expect that our sample counts are related to true abundance by the very simple relationship:

$$E(C_i) = \beta N_i$$

where $E(C_i)$ is the average or expected value for the count. If $\overline{C}$ is the sample average count from replicate surveys, we can use this relationship to solve for average abundance, provided we know what detection is

$$\overline{N} = \frac{\overline{C}}{\beta}$$

Of course, we usually *don't* know what β is; however, if we can collect additional data to *estimate* β then we have a way of obtaining an unbiased estimate of N (assuming of course that our estimate of detection is unbiased) as

$$\widehat{\overline{N}} = \frac{\overline{C}}{\hat{\beta}}$$

In fact, this is the general form that most of our abundance (and presence) estimators take – simply a sample count value divided by an estimate of detection. These estimates can come from a variety of sources and usually require a bit more effort than just counting animals. However, often these additional data can be obtained with just a small amount of additional effort. In Chapter 7 we focus on sampling designs and estimation for adjusting sample data to estimate occupancy. In the remainder of Part II we use the same principles to estimate abundance and demographic parameters.

Count data as indices

Often, biologists are not so interested in estimating absolute numbers or presence as they are in evaluating whether animals are relatively more abundant or prevalent in one area than another, or over time. For this reason, abundance or presence indices are often considered. It is worthwhile, however, to explore just what needs to be assumed in using an index. We have already seen the relationship between the count and the index when detection is homogeneous. More generally, however, the relationship is

$$E(C_i) = \beta_i N_i$$

so that detection also potentially varies from sample to sample. Suppose that we are interested in comparing sample counts from two different areas, or perhaps at two different points in time. A very sensible idea is that we might wish to use these counts to index the relative numbers of animals in the areas or over time. Therefore, for example, if we have a count C_1 in area 1, and another count C_2 in area 2, we might wish to compare these counts, for example by a ratio, to make conclusions about abundance in the two areas. Can we reasonably do this? It turns out that we can, but only if we are willing to make (and ideally demonstrate) that some very special conditions hold.

To see this, consider that what we are really interested in estimating with the index is the *true* relative difference between the two populations, that is

$$R = \frac{N_2}{N_1}$$

Thus, if $R = 1$ the two populations are equal in abundance; if $R = 2$ then abundance in area 2 is twice that in area 1; and if $R = 0.5$ then abundance in area 2 is half that in area 1. The same idea holds if "1" and "2," rather than being labels for area, are labels for time. In this case, "2" might be next year's abundance and 1 this year's, so that R represents the population rate of increase between the two years.

The idea of the count as an index is that we presumably can use C_i to gauge these types of *relative* differences, even if we cannot use them to gauge *absolute* abundance or presence. In essence, the idea is that we can estimate R by C_i; for the above example:

$$\hat{R} = \frac{C_2}{C_1}$$

The idea here, of course, is that proportional differences in the index reflect corresponding proportional differences in the population. However, as we have already seen, the index on average is related to true abundance by

$$E(C_i) = \beta_i N_i$$

Because the expectation of a ratio is approximately equal to the ratio of expectations for the numerator and denominator, this means that we should expect

$$E(\hat{R}) \approx \frac{E(C_2)}{E(C_1)} = \frac{\beta_2 N_2}{\beta_1 N_1} = \frac{\beta_2}{\beta_1} R$$

We can easily see that the expectation of this ratio involves the thing we are interested in (R) but also some things we are not interested in (detection probabilities for the two areas or times). Ideally, $\beta_1 = \beta_2$, in which case detection probabilities cancel and we have

$$E(\hat{R}) = R$$

However, if detection probabilities are for any reason unequal (heterogeneous), then the index now is completely confounded: real changes in abundance cannot be discriminated from heterogeneous detection. Unfortunately, the common occurrence with wildlife indices, including those from incomplete counts, is just that. As much as we might wish for homogeneity, detection likely is heterogeneous, or at least cannot be shown to be homogeneous. Of course, rather than wishing for something that likely cannot be made to happen, it just may be better to deal with reality as it is. This is why we generally discourage the use of uncalibrated indices in favor of counts that *have* been calibrated to true abundance, by the methods discussed in the remainder of Part II.

"Closed" versus "open" estimation

Another important issue we must address is that of whether sampling takes place in a **closed population** – where abundance is constant over the sampling period – or in an **open population** – subject to changes due to births, deaths, immigration, and/or emigration. For the methods in this chapter we mainly assume that the population is closed. Practically, this means that sampling occurs over a sufficiently short time, or time of year, so that recruitment and mortality are thought to be negligible. Likewise, it means that the study area is sufficiently large that movement into and out of the area is small in comparison to the whole population. Meeting this assumption will depend on the study organism and the study area. Larger, long-lived animals like elephants will tend to be closed to mortality and recruitment over longer periods of time, but will require larger areas to be closed geographically. Migratory populations may be approximately closed over certain periods (e.g., several days to weeks during the nonbreeding period), but obviously will be geographically open during migratory periods. Careful selection of the study interval and scope of the study area may allow the assumption of closed population to be met approximately in some cases. In others, it will be necessary to use methods that allow the population to be treated as open (see Chapters 11 and 12).

Summary

In this chapter we discussed the general principles for estimating abundance and other population parameters based on field data. We emphasized methods that take into account the fact that most sampling approaches do not guarantee that all animals present in the sampled area are counted or otherwise detected, or even that a consistent fraction of animals is detected. For this reason, we emphasized estimation approaches that account for incomplete and variable detection – both to provide unbiased estimates and to enable valid comparisons over space and time.

In the chapters that follow we continue with the themes introduced in this chapter. In Chapter 7, we focus on estimation of occupancy from incomplete sample surveys, taking into account imperfect and unequal detection. Initially in Chapter 8 we focus on methods involving finite-area sampling of populations, in which detection is assumed to be complete on each sampled unit. These methods are generalized to allow for incomplete detection, with detection probabilities estimated by auxiliary data, possibly in a double-sampling design. In Chapter 9 we consider the class of sampling and estimation approaches known as "distance sampling," in which the sample units are lines ("line transects") or points ("point counts") rather than polygons or circles. The data collected are the counts of animals detected by observers traveling along the lines or located at points, together with measures of perpendicular (radial) distance from the line (point) to the detected animal. The distance data are used to estimate detection functions, and thereby correct the incomplete counts so as to obtain estimates of density and abundance. In Chapter 10, we introduce capture–recapture sampling. In capture–recapture, animals are initially marked (usually by capture, but sometimes by genetic sampling or other approaches) on one occasion, and may be recaptured on one or several subsequent occasions. On each occasion, the number captured can be viewed as an incomplete count of the population. Assuming that no population gains or losses occur between samples, and that random mixing of marked and unmarked animals occurs, recapture data are used to estimate the probabilities of detection (i.e., capture) and thus to adjust the capture count to estimate abundance. For two samples (one capture and one recapture occasion), simple models such as Lincoln–Petersen can be used to estimate abundance. More complicated, multiple-sample designs, allowing for **robust** estimation of abundance, modeling behavioral and other forms of capture heterogeneity, require use of computer software such as CAPTURE or MARK (again, freely available). We also consider the special case of removal sampling, where recaptures are removed (physically, or by marking) from the population, thus producing a decaying number of unmarked animals available for capture. We illustrate all these methods with real examples, using a variety of vertebrates sampled under different situations, and with a range of available technology.

7
Occupancy (presence–absence) analysis

In this chapter we focus on methods used to estimate species distribution and finer-scale occupancy studies. Please note here that we are using the term "**occupancy**" to mean that an organism is "present;" however, we are adding the component that this is done with some level of uncertainty because we are sampling. Capturing uncertainty should now be no surprise at all for readers of this book. This area of conservation has seen rapid development during the last few years as biologists have strived to not only better utilize observational and collection data but also provide opportunities to assess these data with more sophisticated analyses – and hence provide us with methodologies for more efficient use of field data. A much more in-depth treatment of this whole class of data has recently been published by MacKenzie *et al.* (2006).

Species distributions are often developed based on "occurrence records," which catalog locations at which animals have been observed over some defined (or often rather ill defined, but not always the fault of the researcher) period of time. Ordinarily, these records are not obtained via any sort of sampling approach that assures representative coverage of areas where animals potentially could occur, nor do they take into account that search efforts, and thus encounter rates, tend to be highly heterogeneous over space and time. Thus, the resulting maps of distribution typically confound actual animal distribution with the distribution of search effort. For example, many distribution records are found near universities or museums, or even larger villages in remote areas where it is easier to hire "collectors," whereas fewer records are found in sparsely populated areas away from academic habitats – or simply as a function of how hard it is to get to a particular locality. The same phenomenon occurs at a local scale, where presence/absence methods are often used *in lieu* of abundance estimation, simply because effort required to obtain true abundance estimation is much greater – or at least perceived to be beyond the means of a typical study. In either case, occurrence records are the result of two processes: (i) the animal's actual occurrence in some region of interest, and (ii) the discovery of the animal by an investigator. Whereas an occurrence record ("presence") at least conveys positive information about the occurrence of one or more individuals, the lack of a record is ambiguous: the animal may indeed be absent, or it may be present but simply *not detected* or *not detectable.* Thus, occurrence records are of limited value, unless detection rates can be taken into account. In particular, it is meaningless to compare distribution or occurrence records over space or time without accounting for potentially heterogeneous detection.

Quantitative Conservation of Vertebrates, 1st edition. By M.J. Conroy and J.P. Carroll. Published 2009 by Blackwell Publishing, ISBN 978-1-4051-8228-7 (pb) and 978-1-4051-9098-5 (hb).

Now that we have said this we need to add some *caveats.* First, we are also field biologists and trying not to cast stones from our academic offices. We are simply reminding the reader that these types of data have some problems; we are not suggesting that historical records are useless. On the contrary, we are suggesting that when mining these records, the researcher should always keep potential problems in mind. Second, we do suggest that when publishing data resulting from old records, or rapid faunal surveys, or other types of information that authors be very clear about distinguishing true presence–absence studies from presence-not surveyed and presence-not detected surveys, where estimates of detection rates are not calculated. These will make conservation planning much easier for those who want to both assess conservation status of species and rate the quality of that assessment.

Fortunately, with some planning and care, it is possible to collect presence data to estimate detection rates and provide valid estimates of actual occurrence. This is the area in conservation that has become quite exciting in the last few years and where development of new methodologies has provided field biologists with additional tools. Finally, there are now extensions to simple occupancy data constructs that allow us to use heterogeneity in detection, as well as to count data, to extend these analyses to estimates of abundance. We provide several examples illustrating both invalid and valid approaches for using occupancy data; for the latter we use recently developed and freely available software.

Design and analysis of occupancy studies

Occupancy data can be enormously useful for assessing conservation questions, provided that the data are collected and analyzed properly. Compared to other quantitative estimators, these techniques tend to be less labor intensive and more cost effective to apply, and therefore in future may be some of the most important tools for conservation research. There are many forms of this type of data and actually a number of categories besides presence and absence – as we alluded to above. We will begin here with some definitions of the various sorts of terms associated with presence data.

1. **Present and detected** – refers to the situation where an animal is both present at a site and detected in a sample at a particular place and time. We distinguish **detection** from **presence** for the important reason that animals may be present, but not detected; or even not detectable. Detection may involve direct observation or inference by means of sign such as calls, tracks, dens, marks, feces, and/or shed body parts. Detection is generally considered to be error free, that is, ordinarily detection implies presence, and thus is commonly equated with "presence." However, there are potential errors that can be included in detection data. For example, in undertaking meta-analysis of data using museum records there might be reporting errors for collected localities. In fact, especially for older specimens, this rate may actually be quite high. When detection is determined in a field study there are also potential errors associated with misidentification

of the target species by field personnel. For example, we have a colleague who found on some of his study areas that a bird known to be a very vocal good mimic was adept at the call of his target species, so that he found it difficult to use calls for identification. Surveys of his species carried out by naïve field workers might actually detect the species where it does not occur – because they are detecting the mimic. Finally, detection also has a time function because a species may be present at some historical period, but not now, or the reverse might occur. This might also be on shorter time scales, the most obvious being presence on breeding or wintering sites by migratory species.

2. **Absent** – refers to the actual absence of a species, not simply failure to detect the species. This is more difficult to assess and needs to be determined with some estimation of detection (β or some other symbol depending on the specific estimator). Where we can get into trouble here is when we confuse absence with the following.
3. **Present, but not detected** – this occurs when we attempt to find the species in a locality, but do not find it. A variation of this is when a species is present, but not detectable. We may do a pretty good survey of a location and simply not find the animal. Or we might mistakenly run our surveys at the wrong time of day or year and the species is simply not observable (e.g., animals that might be hibernating). Obviously we cannot know absolutely this outcome, which is why this whole area of research becomes more complicated. This result is especially important when we are attempting to determine the status of a species and potentially create some protected status to habitats. Utilizing some of the techniques described later in this chapter we can assign a detection probability (β) to our field surveys, allowing us to estimate the probability of this outcome. Obviously, if β is low then our naïve results may underestimate the true occurrence of the species. If it is high then we might have a great deal of confidence that we actually know where the species is truly found for making conservation decisions. We suggest that many of the rapid surveys being undertaken, although definitely worthy of being done in many areas, are plagued by this problem. Often areas are surveyed only once, providing lists of species that are detected, but with no way of linking these detections with how difficult particular species might be to find, or how this might be biased by techniques used by the researchers.
4. **Not surveyed** – again for species conservation research this is critical. A species cannot be detected in places where researchers have not looked. Again this creates an artificial underestimation of the distribution or presence of a species. We believe that in conservation assessments this category is just as important in data presentation as presence–absence.

Types of data

Occurrence and occupancy data can come in many forms with a wide range in data quality. Many of the data we have available are not of the highest quality, but help provide a knowledge base. One of the common types of data available is museum or other collection records. These data, although often of low quality, are extremely important in providing an historical context for particular species. Although rarely are there any data on abundance associated with these records, they do give us valuable information on the presence of a species at a particular location and time. These data are weak in the sense that we usually have no information on survey effort or potential locality errors, areas surveyed or not surveyed, or information on detection probability (β; see Chapter 6). These data can be and are commonly overlaid on known habitat for a species to provide even more useful information.

Two other sources of information also provide us with base knowledge on the presence or absence of our target species. These are simply incidental or anecdotal reports by researchers working in a particular area and, for avian biologists, the records of bird watchers. In both of these cases we are generally obtaining more recent information than museum records, but these have the same common weaknesses in data quality. These are weak for a number of reasons including, but not limited to, a lack of research design, no controls on effort, lack of estimates of β, and generally no information on areas surveyed versus areas not surveyed. The only thing this information tells us is that the species in question has been found in certain locations. These issues do not even cover the quality control questions relative to factors such as misidentification. For example, Gordillo-Martinez (1998. Patrones de distribución de la Familia Pahsianidae (Aves: Galliformes) en la Republica Mexicana. Unpubl. Bach. Diss, UNAM, Fes-Zaragoza, México., D. F.) A.T. Peterson and A.G. Navarro (unpublished data) plotted the historical location data from museum species of the relatively unstudied Douglas quail (*Callipepla douglasii*) in Mexico (Figure 7.1A). Plotting the localities alone suggests that this species is restricted to western to northwestern Mexico. However, we also see that there are many gaps which might represent several different things. We see a concentration of locations near the southern end of the purported distribution and a thinning of specimens from the north that end in just a few localities near the US border. Now in Figure 7.1B, we see the addition of data that helps to improve the value of this map. Based on some information known about the habitat of the species, Gordillo-Martinez (1998) overlaid a vegetation map representing suitable habitat. We now see more clearly that this species is likely limited to a suitable habitat band in western Mexico and that the thinning of observations to the north might be a result of more remote areas and/or more subtle changes in habitat. Reconstruction of the data this way, while not ideal, provides us with some base information on the likely distribution of the species. This particular species also highlights the value of even this type of weak data because in the larger conservation picture it is fairly unlikely that dedicated surveys of the Douglas quail will ever be undertaken.

Stepping up from these methods are the rapid biological surveys now being undertaken in many areas, especially for birds. These potentially provide additional information on survey areas and standardization of effort, but generally we do not see these being applied. Most often these are done using some sampling framework, but generally lack repeated surveys or ancillary data which might assist in developing detection functions. Again providing presence data, but lacking conditions that will allow separation of the four potential outcomes that we presented above, we would suggest

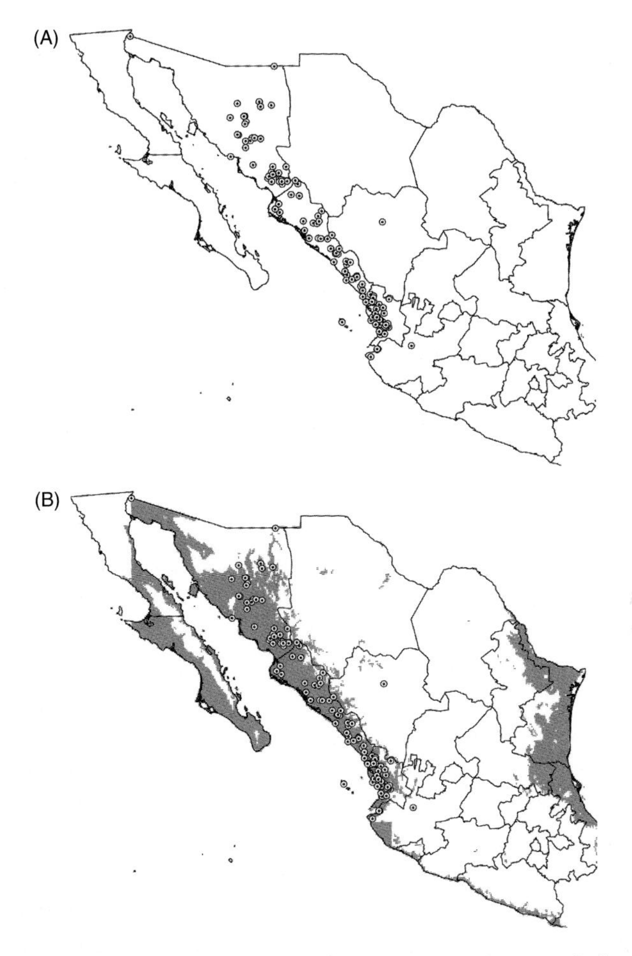

Fig. 7.1 **(A) Example of the distribution of museum specimens of the Douglas quail (*Callipepla douglasii*) from Mexico. This relatively unstudied species initially appears to be restricted to a band near the west coast of Mexico to the USA border. (B) Some data on habitat were used to derive a spatial model of suitable habitat, then overlaid on the data, and then overlaid with suitable habitat. It is apparent that some of the "thinning" of observations in the northern parts of the distribution represents either lack of effort or maybe some more subtle habitat differences. Either question is worth investigating when issues of the species conservation status are addressed.**

that some simple upgrading of survey designs would allow these surveys to be much more valuable – again improving data quality and efficiency of application of limited conservation funding.

Occupancy estimation

The most valuable data are when occupancy (more accurately, "detection-non-detection) data are collected using the sampling designs outlined in previous chapters

Table 7.1 Surveys of a hypothetical species among a number of reserves, demonstrating that the detection rate for each survey is less than 1.0. This data structure is typical of presence–absence studies, where absence is often coded "0" and presence coded "1." The naïve estimate for each survey is less than half the naïve estimate of the three surveys combined, but even this will underestimate true presences of the species among these reserves. Simply looking at these data we see that even when present we often do not detect the species in all three surveys. Although seven of the nine sites are occupied based on our raw data, we see that any one survey does no better than five reserves detected. These two factors used together provide the basis for presence–absence analysis of occupancy and detection rates

Reserve	Survey 1	Survey 2	Survey 3	Combined
1	Y	Y	Y	Y
2	Y	N	N	Y
3	N	N	N	N
4	N	N	Y	Y
5	N	N	N	N
6	N	Y	Y	Y
7	Y	Y	Y	Y
8	N	Y	Y	Y
9	Y	N	N	Y
Number of reserves where detected	4	4	5	7

and estimation approaches described below and in the following chapters. Theory development and analytical techniques have seen quite rapid change over the last few years and the more advanced reader should definitely read MacKenzie *et al.* (2006). They depend on use of well-established criteria for providing estimates of detection, which we generically referred to as β in Chapter 6, but it is given the symbol d in this chapter. This is the critical step that allows these types of data to be much more useful and defendable for conservation research.

At this point, we will formally define some terms and parameters commonly used in occupancy estimation. A site is **occupied** if one or more animals are observed at a specified time; probability of occupancy is ψ. An animal is **detected** if it is both present at a site and detected in at least one of k samples. The probability of detection is

$$d = 1 - (1 - p)^k$$

where p is the detection probability on each of the samples. Therefore, the probability that an animal is both present and detected ("1") is $\psi \times d$. An animal is **not detected** ("0") if it is either not present or present but not detected in at least one sample. The probability of this happening is $(1 - \psi) + \psi(1 - d)$. The alert reader will recognize this as the binomial distribution (Chapter 5), crucially important in the chapter and those to follow.

A typical scenario for these types of data is where we might be surveying a series of reserves for our target species (Table 7.1). In this example, we have nine reserves where we have surveyed the species. We have completed three surveys in each of the reserves and end up finding this species in seven of the nine sites. Our naïve estimate for occupancy (ψ) is therefore 7/9 or 0.778. However, in looking at the data we see that in any particular survey we never detect the target species in all of the sites where it was ultimately present. In fact, using one of the programs described later we find that our probability of detecting this species in one survey is only 0.570, which of course is quite a great underestimate of true occupancy. In our experience single-survey detection rates can be much lower, which reenforces our earlier criticism of unreplicated, rapid surveys. With the results from the three surveys we completed, we can use the detection rate we estimated above to estimate true occupancy at 0.845 ($\pm$0.164 SE), thereby suggesting that we might have missed this species in one or both of the remaining reserves. From these contrived data we actually have quite good detections rates and in fact our target species is likely found in most or all of the reserves. A more realistic data set, but still based on a common species that is reasonably easy to detect, is outlined in Table 7.2. Here we see surveys of the blue grosbeak (*Guiraca caerulea*), a species associated with shrub and field habitats in the southeastern USA (B. Gates, J.P. Carroll, and R.J. Cooper, unpublished data). In this example, we carried out three surveys during the 2001 breeding season on 41 former crop and grass fields being converted by a government program to longleaf pines (*Pinus palustris*). These fields were surveyed during the first 2 years after trees were planted. We find here that blue grosbeaks were detected in no more than 22 fields in any single survey and the three surveys combined reveal that they were detected in a total of 33 of the 41 fields, giving us a naïve occupancy rate of 0.805. We review this data set again later in this chapter to demonstrate use of occupancy analysis (see Box 7.1).

Not only can we use direct observation data, but also in a real-world example using camera-trapping data we see that Winarni *et al.* (2005) found a number of species of lowland forest pheasants on Sumatra, Indonesia. They observed detection and occupancy rates among closely related species of Galliformes in lowland rainforest.

Extending occupancy to abundance estimation

One aspect of occupancy analysis that has recently received more in-depth treatment is the extension of presence–absence data to abundance estimation. A number of authors have been publishing in this area, including models of detection heterogeneity and count data. Royle and Nichols (2003) outlined a way to use detection heterogeneity in per-sample detection rates (p) to provide estimates of abundance. In this scenario we are assuming that abundance has a Poisson distribution and that p is related to abundance. This has been extended to count data, such as what might be collected in bird point counts, by Royle (2004). We outline an example using the same blue grosbeak data from above to demonstrate the usefulness of these models for estimating abundance in Box 7.2.

Table 7.2 Detections of blue grosbeaks during three surveys of 41 old agricultural fields in southern Georgia during 2001. The surveys were undertaken during the breeding season and represent a single 250-m transect of the field. These data are explored in more detail in the example boxes

Survey field	Survey 1	Survey 2	Survey 3	Combined
A	1	1	1	1
B	1	1	0	1
C	0	0	0	0
D	0	1	0	1
E	1	0	1	1
F	0	0	1	1
G	0	0	1	1
H	1	1	1	1
I	1	1	0	1
J	1	1	1	1
K	1	1	0	1
L	0	0	0	0
M	0	0	0	0
N	0	0	1	1
O	1	1	1	1
P	0	0	1	1
Q	0	0	1	1
R	0	0	0	0
S	0	1	1	1
T	0	0	0	0
U	1	0	0	1
V	0	1	0	1
W	1	0	0	1
X	1	1	1	1
Y	1	1	1	1
Z	0	1	1	1
AA	0	0	1	1
AB	0	1	0	1
AC	1	1	0	1
AD	0	1	1	1
AE	0	0	0	0
AF	1	1	1	1
AG	1	0	0	1
AH	1	1	0	1
AI	0	0	0	0
AJ	0	0	0	0
AK	0	1	0	1
AL	0	1	1	1
AM	1	1	1	1
AN	1	0	1	1
AO	0	1	0	1
Number of fields where detected	18	22	20	33

Box 7.1 Single-season occupancy analysis with homogeneous detection probability.

We applied occupancy analysis to observations of blue grosbeaks (*Guiraca caerulea*) on 41 old fields planted to longleaf pines (*Pinus palustris*) in southern Georgia, USA. Surveys were undertaken on 500-m transects across each field and were completed three times during the breeding season in 2001. The data are presented in Table 7.2. For this example we used program PRESENCE 2.0 to analyze the data. Initially we used the basic occupancy model with no covariates and a single homogeneous detection parameter to estimate occupancy from the three surveys combined. The output from PRESENCE is provided below. First, if we ignore detection, we obtain a naïve estimate of occupancy of 0.8049. The occupancy analysis, however, indicates that even this common and easy to find species is not perfectly detected on our samples (probability of detection 0.553 for each survey period). Now taking this imperfect detection into account we obtain an estimate of occupancy of 0.8848 ($\pm$0.0764), considerably higher than our naïve estimate.

The following is output from program PRESENCE:

Predefined model: detection probabilities are NOT time-specific.
Number of groups = 1
Number of sites = 41
Number of sampling occasions = 3
Number of missing observations = 0

Number of parameters = 2
−2 log(likelihood) = 168.189754
AIC = 172.189754
Naïve estimate = 0.804878

Proportion of sites occupied (Psi) = 0.8848 (0.076390)
Probability of group membership (theta) = 1.0000
Detection probabilities (p):

Group	Survey	p	se(p)
1	1	0.551317	(0.059721)

Variance–covariance matrix

psi	p(G1)
0.0058	−0.0021
−0.0021	0.0036

Bootstrap variance–covariance matrix

psi	p(G1)
0.0049	−0.0022
−0.0022	0.0041

Bootstrap estimate of SE for proportion of sites occupied = 0.069960
Complete input and output for PRESENCE for this example are provided in the electronic companion to the book (see enclosed CD and website address on p. ii).

Assumptions and important considerations

Like all the methods we discuss in this book, there are some important assumptions in using occupancy models and analyses. The authors cited throughout this chapter have investigated assumptions and impacts of violations of those assumptions rather extensively. There is an excellent review in MacKenzie *et al.* (2006). The key assumptions any researchers undertaking these types of projects must keep in mind are as follows:

1. These models assume that we are dealing with sites that are closed to changes in occupancy. That is, during a particular "season" or period, sites are either occupied or not – they do not switch status.
2. Occupancy probability across sites is assumed to be constant. However, if we have covariates that might explain differences in occupancy then we meet the assumption.
3. Detection probability either can be modeled with covariates or survey period or does not vary across sites.
4. Detection among sites is independent, unless of course we specifically model this.

Box 7.2 Estimation of abundance using occupancy sampling.

Finally, we return to the blue grosbeak example to illustrate how, under certain assumptions, occupancy data can also provide estimates of abundance. The analysis now incorporates, in addition to "detected" or "not detected" data for each site, counts of the number of individuals detected. We then used by Royle and Nichols, which models variation in counts, heterogeneity, and the assumption of a Poisson distribution in the program PRESENCE 2.0, to estimate abundance as well as occupancy for blue grosbeaks. We applied two models, the Royle repeated count model and the Royle–Nichols single season heterogeneity model (which does not include counts as auxiliary data, and so has stronger assumptions). The model selection table below suggested that the Royle model had more support – see the model weight column (w_i). Therefore we present that model output. This provides an estimate of 182.25 (46.29–318.21, 95% CI) blue grosbeaks on the 662.4 ha of fields we surveyed. Interestingly, distance sampling methods which use more data, provided similar estimates of abundance, but with narrower confidence intervals (B. Gates, J. Carroll, and R. Cooper, unpublished data).

Royle model w/species counts ($k = 200$)
Number of groups = 1
Number of sites = 41
Number of sampling occasions = 3
Number of missing observations = 0
Matrix 1: rows = 3, cols = 3

p	1.000000	0.000000
lambda	0.000000	1.000000

Box 7.2 Continued.

Number of parameters = 2
Number of function calls = 58
Final function value = 161.950321
−2 log(likelihood) 323.900642
AIC = 327.900642
Naïve estimate = 0.536585

Untransformed (beta) parameters:
Estimated parameter: estimate std. err

Beta0 = −1.3675 0.4804
Beta1 = 1.4918 0.3806

Beta variance–covariance matrix:

0.2307	−0.1749
−0.1749	0.1449

Model parameters:

Parameters	Estimate	SE	95% CI
Estimated			
Detection probability (c)	0.2030	0.0777	0.0507–0.3554
Average abundance/sample unit (lambda)	4.45	1.69	1.13–7.76
Derived			
Occupancy (psi)	0.9883	0.0199	0.9493–1.0272
Total abundance (N)	182.25	69.37	46.29–318.21

Model	AIC	ΔAIC	Model weight (Wt.)	Model likelihood	No.	−2 ∗ LogLike
Repeated count data (Royle Biometrics)	327.90	0.00	0.9920	0.9841	2	323.90
Abundance induced heterogeneity (Royle/Nichols Het) model	337.55	9.65	0.0080	0.0079	2	333.55

Complete input and output for PRESENCE for this example are provided in the electronic companion to the book (see enclosed CD and website address on p. ii).

Application and programs

We describe several different **estimators** for use with presence–absence data. These estimators were generally developed by their authors for particular purposes, and therefore have slightly different applications in the field. They all have a common approach of using multiple surveys of the same sites to provide estimates of detection rate. We believe that most field applications that biologists would undertake would work with these, although with continued development the freeware program PRESENCE seems to be a valuable and easy-to-use tool for field biologists. Again, more advanced models, such as dealing with a single species over multiple field seasons or years, or those dealing with multiple species interactions are better described elsewhere (MacKenzie *et al.* 2006).

Estimating single species occupancy using the program PRESENCE

The program PRESENCE was developed by a group of biologists when faced with determining the occupancy of wetlands by various species of frogs (MacKenzie *et al.* 2002, 2003). This program has common application to types of data we often find where habitats are fragmented units over space. It is also important to remember that this method still maintains the assumptions of closed population abundance estimation. This means that during any particular sampling period there is no change in occupancy among sites. In addition, we must meet assumptions of independence among sites and actually correctly identify our target species.

This is a rather simple program that allows the user to estimate **detection probability** (d) and **site occupancy** (ψ). In addition, covariates can be applied to examine the impacts of environmental or other features on probability of occupancy. In some circumstances the user may allow detection probability to vary among surveys.

MacKenzie *et al.* (2006) provide us with a list of assumptions for this method. The minimum number of survey periods is obviously two. However, they suggest that when visiting sites only twice, true occupancy (ψ) should be >0.7 and per-sample detection rates (p) should be >0.30. These thresholds can be relaxed as the number of repeat surveys increases. Overall detection probability (d) is a function of both per-sample detection (p) and the total sampling effort (k). If p is constant over the k samples, then:

$$d = 1 - (1 - p)^k$$

For example, if $p = 0.3$ then $d = 0.832$ for five samples, but increases to 0.972 when we obtain 10 samples. In the latter case, we could be nearly certain that if any animals occupy the site, at least one will be detected over the course of the study. Likewise, we could say with fairly high confidence that if no animals were detected, none was actually present. Note that if p is low (e.g., $p = 0.10$) or there are only a few surveys, or both, the results may be much more equivocal. For example, if $p = 0.10$, then $d = 0.65$ for 10 samples, but only $d = 0.41$ for five samples, and an even worse value of $d = 0.19$ for two samples. Data in this realm would provide relatively low assurance of detecting animals if they are actually present and, conversely, would not allow high confidence that animals were absent, simply because none was detected.

There can be heterogeneity in detection probability among sites, which in some cases can be partially accounted for by use of habitat or other covariates. Detection may also be related to the relative abundance of animals at sites, and Royle and Nichols (2003) exploit this relationship both to model detection heterogeneity and to estimate abundance under certain assumptions. Missing values are common in this type of survey and they suggest that missing values up to 20% of the total sample generally only impacted precision of the estimate. MacKenzie and Royle (2005) and MacKenzie *et al.* (2006) refined estimation of number of repeat visits needed based on rate of occupancy and detection rate. We created a version of their results in Table 7.3, demonstrating some of the trade-offs involved in making decisions about how many surveys need to be undertaken versus greater investment in improving detection rate per survey. MacKenzie *et al.* (2006) go into design issues relative to effort and alternative sampling approaches in much greater detail than we can here, and Bailey *et al.* (2007) provide software for exploring alternative sampling designs.

PRESENCE is available as stand-alone shareware from a number of software sources listed in Appendix A. Using data from a species of songbird, the blue grosbeak (*Guiraca caerulea*) found in recently planted longleaf pine (*Pinus palustris*), we can see application of this type of data and analysis in PRESENCE 2.0 (Boxes 7.1, 7.3–7.5). In this example we surveyed a rather common bird species on 41 fields that were being planted with trees. Even with this easily detected species it is apparent that a single survey would

Table 7.3 Simplified version of the table of MacKenzie and Royle (2005) outlining the number of surveys required to maximize efficiency of survey design, based on detection rate per survey (p) and occupancy (ψ). The reader should note a number of interesting and important factors that can be gleaned here. First, improvement in detection rate is very important in streamlining occupancy analysis. This is true at both low and high occupancy rates, although the differential in number of surveys is greater for the latter. What is important here is development of the best possible methods for detecting the species when it is present. Tradeoffs of particular survey techniques can have enormous implications. For example, if a cheap and easy to implement survey technique yields a p of 0.5 and an expensive technique only yields a slight improvement of p to 0.7, then limited conservation finances suggest that we adopt the former. However, if these values are 0.1 and 0.3, respectively, for a species that is very difficult to detect, then the research should carefully consider the costs and benefits of spending more effort on each survey or having to complete many more surveys

p	ψ				
	0.1	0.3	0.5	0.7	0.9
0.1	14	16	18	23	34
0.3	5	5	6	7	10
0.5	3	3	3	4	5
0.7	2	2	2	2	3
0.9	2	2	2	2	2

Box 7.3 Single-season occupancy analysis with detection probability varying among surveys.

Here we return to the blue grosbeak data (Table 7.2, Box 7.1), now using a slightly more complicated model that allows detection to vary between the surveys, rather than assuming that it is constant for the whole study. It could be that these birds are harder to detect with changing vegetation over the growing season. We simply do not know this before hand, but can estimate and correct for this effect. The estimate of occupancy (0.8827) is similar to the one we obtained in Box 7.1, but now we have three estimates of detection: 0.4974, 0.6079, and 0.5526, one for each of the surveys, respectively. These estimates appear to indicate different rates of detection among surveys. However, notice that the AIC value for this model is 175.295, but the value for the simpler model in Box 7.1 is 172.190; this suggests that the simpler model should be preferred. Also, the individual detection rates under the stratified model have very large confidence intervals, suggesting that detection rates did not truly differ among surveys.

Predefined model: detection probabilities are time-specific.

Number of groups = 1
Number of sites = 41
Number of sampling occasions = 3
Number of missing observations = 0

Number of parameters = 4
−2 log(likelihood) = 167.295032
AIC = 175.295032
Naïve estimate = 0.804878

Proportion of sites occupied (Psi) = 0.8827 (0.076187)
Probability of group membership (theta) = 1.0000
Detection probabilities (p):

Group	Survey	p	se(p)
1	1	0.497359	(0.089155)
1	2	0.607883	(0.090230)
1	3	0.552621	(0.090092)

Variance–covariance matrix

psi	p1(G1)	p2(G1)	p3(G1)
0.0058	−0.0018	−0.0023	−0.0021
−0.0018	0.0079	0.0013	0.0012
−0.0023	0.0013	0.0081	0.0014
−0.0021	0.0012	0.0014	0.0081

Box 7.3 Continued.

Bootstrap variance–covariance matrix

psi	p1(G1)	p2(G1)	p3(G1)
0.0049	−0.0016	−0.0017	−0.0024
−0.0016	0.0074	0.0030	0.0020
−0.0017	0.0030	0.0091	0.0008
−0.0024	0.0020	0.0008	0.0070

Bootstrap estimate of SE for proportion of sites occupied = 0.070127.

Complete input and output for PRESENCE for this example are provided in the electronic companion to the book (see enclosed CD and website address on p. ii).

have underdetected the species. In addition the collection of other types of data, such as the size of each field, allowed us to examine the potential effect of other parameters on occupancy. Over the last few years MacKenzie and colleagues have developed particular components of these models for single species, such as issues of missing observations, covariate modeling, violation of assumptions, and assessment of model fit that are important, but this is beyond the scope of this book. Extensions to this program are now available to actually estimate abundance based on this same approach – these are described below. Again this allows us to more efficiently use data we collect in the field. Readers who are comfortable with these concepts are encouraged to explore the much greater detail found in MacKenzie *et al.* (2006).

Multiple-season occupancy

So far, we have described occupancy estimation for a single point in time, under the assumption that all sites that are currently occupied remain occupied over the timeframe of the study, and that no unoccupied sites become occupied. This is analogous to closed population estimation models (Chapters 8–10) that assume that no births, deaths, immigration, or emigration occur over the study period. In longer-term studies this will not be realistic, and in fact it may be of interest to model the dynamics of site occupancy. By analogy to population dynamics models (Chapter 3), occupancy modeling extends fairly easily to multiple seasons, where occupancy at time t depends on factors that determine local extinction (ε) and colonization (γ) rates. The basic idea is that sites are initially occupied or not, with probabilities ψ_0 and $1 - \psi_0$, respectively. Sites that are occupied either become unoccupied, with probability ε, or remain occupied with probability $1 - \varepsilon$. Likewise, sites that are currently unoccupied may become occupied (γ) or remain unoccupied ($1 - \gamma$). Of course, estimation of these parameters is complicated by the fact that we do not actually observe occupancy, but rather whether

Box 7.4 Single-season occupancy analysis with occupancy and detection modeled using covariates.

In this analysis we return to the blue grosbeak data (Boxes 7.1 and 7.3) and consider the relationship between occupancy and two site-specific variables: field size in hectares and presence of additional management from a government-funded conservation program (BQI). We constructed a model using a single overall detection rate estimate and two covariates: field size and BQI management. In this analysis neither of the covariates appears to strongly explain differences in occupancy by blue grosbeaks, as judged by comparison of the AIC value from the covariate model (175.114) with the value for the simple model in Box 7.1 (172.19). We can also judge the weakness of the covariate relationships by examining the coefficients for the site covariates and noting that the error estimates for each of the parameters encompasses zero (e.g., field size coefficient of -0.23 ± 2.68 SE).

Custom model:
Number of sites = 41
Number of sampling occasions = 3
Number of missing observations = 0

Number of parameters = 4
$-2 \log(\text{likelihood}) = 167.1138$
AIC = 175.1138

Model has been fit using the logistic link.
Naïve estimate = 0.8049
Untransformed estimates of coefficients for covariates (betas):

		Estimate SE
Beta1: occupancy	psi	2.892973 (2.764246)
Beta2: occupancy	psifieldsize	−0.231087 (2.679067)
Beta3: occupancy	psibqi	−1.317230 (1.704668)
Beta4: occupancy	p1	0.211223 (0.246943)

Variance–covariance matrix of untransformed estimates (betas):

	Beta1	Beta2	Beta3	Beta4
Beta1	7.641058	−6.499217	0.385063	−0.005339
Beta2	−6.499217	7.177398	−2.247388	−0.145060
Beta3	0.385063	−2.247388	2.905894	0.137104
Beta4	−0.005339	−0.145060	0.137104	0.060981

Individual site estimates of Psi:

Site	Psi	SE	95% CI

Overall proportion of sites occupied = 0.8827 (0.0781).

Complete input and output for PRESENCE for this example are provided in the electronic companion to the book (see enclosed CD and website address on p. ii).

Box 7.5 Model comparison for single-season occupancy analysis (Boxes 7.1, 7.3 and 7.4).

Here we summarize the three different models considered in Boxes 7.1, 7.3 and 7.4, including the model with no covariates and a constant detection (Box 7.1), detection rate variable by survey (Box 7.3), and our covariates, log of field size, and whether or not the field is enrolled in BQI (Box 7.4). The results suggest that the best model is our constant detection model with no covariates. There is weak negative support for presence in the BQI program and a weak negative relationship with field size. The latter is not surprising since this is an edge species which likely uses fields for foraging while nesting in woody cover adjacent to the field.

Model	AIC	ΔAIC	w_i	Model likelihood	Number of parameters	$-2 * \text{LogLike}$
1 group, constant P	172.19	0.00	0.4012	0.1609	2	168.19
psi(.), p(bqi)	173.12	0.93	0.2520	0.1011	3	167.12
psi(.), p(fieldsize)	173.92	1.73	0.1689	0.0678	3	167.92
psi(.), p(fieldsize,bqi)	175.11	2.92	0.0932	0.0374	4	167.11
1 group, survey-specific P	175.30	3.11	0.0847	0.0340	4	167.30

Complete input and output for PRESENCE for the three examples are provided in the electronic companion to the book (see enclosed CD and website address on p. ii).

animals are detected. Thus, if we observed "1" at time 1 and "0" at time 2, we know that the site was occupied at time 1, but it may have become unoccupied at time 2, or it remained occupied but there were no detections. These possibilities can be modeled as

$$\varepsilon + (1 - \varepsilon)(1 - d)$$

similar to the idea earlier introduced to model a "0" for single-season occupancy. Modeling of multiple-season occupancy can get rather complicated. We provide an example in Box 7.6 which is an extension to 2 years of our blue grosbeak example. Those who are conducting longer-term occupancy studies should see MacKenzie *et al.* (2006).

Other analyses of occupancy data

There are several variations of the same basic premise found in the program PRESENCE. An Excel program (Wintle *et al.* 2004) provides a simple analysis giving results similar to the program PRESENCE (see Box 7.1).

Another variation is an extension of logistic modeling called "zero-inflated binomial" (ZIB) described by Tyre *et al.* (2003). Applications of this program to field data are similar to the program PRESENCE. The assumptions for this program include a minimum number of visits to each site of three. When deciding between more sites

Box 7.6 Multiple-season occupancy analysis probability.

We have now added three identical surveys from 2002 to our blue grosbeak example from Boxes 7.2–7.4. These models of multiple season focus on occupancy, detection, extinction, and recolonization. Here, we focus on a slightly different question, that of the value of these sites to blue grosbeaks, and that is multi-season use for breeding – i.e., we could argue that if these sites are high quality for this species then we would expect them to be detected in both seasons. Lower quality would increase rates of "extinction" and "colonization." What we found is that our model could not deal with extinction because our data showed none. We also find below that the use of 2 years of data increases the precision of our estimates of occupancy during a particular season. What we find with this model is that our naïve occupancy has increased to 40/41 sites. We believe that the colonization effect described below simply describes a prediction that effectively all these sites can be occupied. The following output is from the PRESENCE 2.0 multiseason model with occupancy, detection, and colonization selected.

Open population model:
Number of sites = 41
Total number of sampling occasions = 6
Number of primary sampling periods = 2
Number of missing observations = 0

Number of parameters = 3
−2 log(likelihood) = 333.346777
AIC = 339.346777
Model has been fit using the logistic link.

Untransformed estimates of coefficients for covariates (betas):

		Estimate	SE
Beta1: occupancy	psi1	1.852108	(0.588368)
Beta2: colonization	gam1	5.364129	(10.471822)
Beta3: detection	P[1–1]	0.364697	(0.162977)

Variance–covariance matrix of untransformed estimates:

	Beta1	Beta2	Beta3
Beta1	0.346177	0.720249	−0.025629
Beta2	0.720249	109.659056	−0.746449
Beta3	−0.025629	−0.746449	0.026562

Individual site estimates of Psi:

Site	Survey	Psi	SE	95% CI
1	1	0.864374	0.068975	0.729183–0.999566

Box 7.6 Continued.

Individual site estimates of Gamma:

Site	Survey	Gamma	SE	95% CI
1	1	0.995340	0.048568	0.900146–1.090534

Individual site estimates of p:

Site	Survey	p	SE	95% CI
1	1	0.590177	0.039419	0.512916–0.667438

Complete input and output for PRESENCE for this example are provided in the electronic companion to the book (see enclosed CD and website address on p. ii).

and more repeated surveys, Tyre *et al.* (2003) found that when false-negative rates are low (<50%, that is when $p > 0.50$) then it is better to increase number of sites rather than number of visits. Conversely, when p is <0.5 then it is better to increase number of visits. They also ran some simulations and found that three visits per site eliminated bias, but to obtain better precision of the estimate then up to six visits should be made. An R-based program is available for running ZIB analyses (Appendix A).

Several variations of **Markov chain Monte Carlo** (MCMC) analyses have been described. Sargeant *et al.* (2005) used an MCMC image restoration estimator with some types of presence–absence/occupancy data. They describe scenarios with which biologists are often faced when the available data represents collection over variable times and with variable effort. This is a special case applicable when study areas can be partitioned into regular grids of mapping units and the species distribution within the area is spatially contagious. This method has the advantage for use with spatially dependent data. With their simulations they found that they had good precision and minimal bias when detection rates for more than one visit were more than 0.65. Augustin *et al.* (1996) used an autologistic model to attempt the same type of analysis.

Another MCMC approach is described by Peterson *et al.* (2004). In this example, the authors were interested in modeling the distribution of bull trout (*Salvelenus confluentus*) relative to several hierarchical classes of environmental variables using occupancy data. The authors explicitly linked distribution of this rare species with a range of environmental variables. Obviously this is something conservationists are interested in doing to increase the value of their data. This highlights the level of sophistication that can be attained by good experimental design within the context of occupancy data.

The binomial structure of occupancy data lends itself to extensions within the MARK (v. 5.0) program (White 2008). This version of MARK includes the same models covered in PRESENCE and has been extended to the **Robust Design** occupancy model, Pledger mixture models, the Royle and Nichols (2003) model, and the Royle (2004) Poisson and negative binomial models. Finally, MARK incorporates the multi-state model described by Nichols *et al.* (2007). For readers who use MARK, this provides opportunities to analyze occupancy data using familiar MARK structure.

Finally, Mordecai (2007) used **Bayesian** approaches to model hierarchical relationships including both occupancy and use.

Summary

In this chapter we outlined some of the important issues in occupancy or presence–absence estimation. Issues of detection probability and occupancy are critically important to understand how relatively minor changes in data collection might improve data value substantially and are key to undertaking better field research in support of conservation. In this chapter we reviewed mainly the simple single species models; extrapolation of these methods to multiple species will be covered in Chapter 14.

We believe that occupancy analysis in conservation research has been significantly underutilized. This is particularly the case where now we are seeing many short-term or "rapid" assessments of wildlife communities where substantially better data quality could be obtained with some simple design modifications. Similar issues also occur with many camera-trapping studies where these methods could provide estimates of detection (d) quite easily, but often that is not done. With recent advances in analytical techniques devoted to this type of data we believe that researchers studying wildlife in many parts of the world will benefit from its application. However, over the next few years as the value of these types of studies is seen to increase we believe that additional quantitative support in terms of analyses and theory development will continue to improve. Nevertheless, no quantitative method is going to allow someone to salvage poorly collected data, and basic principles for experimental design for data collected today should still transmit to quantitative methods developed tomorrow.

8
Sample counts for abundance estimation

One of the most basic ways of estimating abundance is via direct counts. In a few, rare instances it may be possible to completely cover a study area and count all the animals present. However, as we have already seen in Chapter 6, this will hardly ever be practical, and in most cases it will actually be more accurate to select samples of the study area for the counts, and to use estimation procedures to extrapolate these to the entire study area. Here we first consider the situation where animals can be completely detected in all the sample areas selected. We then generalize this to the more common situation where a fraction of the animals present in the samples is not detected.

Complete detection assumed

Suppose we have a study area of size A, we divide the area into M potential sampling units, and we take a random sample (see Chapter 5) of m of these. In the simplest case, each of these sample units would have $a = A/M$ area, but more generally the units can be different sizes, as long as the sizes are known. This results in a fraction of the study area $= ma/A = ma/Ma = m/M$. If we count y_i animals on each of the $i = 1, 2, \ldots, m$ sites, then we can compute an estimate of abundance over the sample area as follows:

$$\hat{N} = M\bar{y} \tag{8.1}$$

$$\hat{\text{var}}(\hat{N}) = M^2 \frac{s^2}{m}(1 - m/M) \tag{8.2}$$

where $\bar{y} = \sum_{i=1}^{m} y_i/m$ is the sample mean count and $s^2 = \sum_{i=1}^{m} (y_i - \bar{y})^2/(m-1)$ is the sample variance of the counts. From this we can see that the precision with which N is estimated depends both on how variable the counts are across the samples and on the fraction of the area sampled; in fact, if we "sample" the entire area, then from Equation (8.2) the term $(1 - m/M)$ becomes zero, as does the sample variance.

We show an example of abundance estimation under these simple assumptions in Box 8.1. The approach readily extends to the situation where the sample areas are variable, and this is illustrated in Box 8.2. Variability in size of sample plots can occur in practice for a number of reasons, and creates no estimation problems as long as

Quantitative Conservation of Vertebrates, 1st edition. By M.J. Conroy and J.P. Carroll. Published 2009 by Blackwell Publishing, ISBN 978-1-4051-8228-7 (pb) and 978-1-4051-9098-5 (hb).

Box 8.1 Estimation of N when detectability is perfect and sample areas are equal.

We can illustrate the estimation of abundance of this simple case with an example from counts of bobwhite quail coveys in Georgia, USA. There are 20 10-ha plots (so, 200 ha sampled in total) selected at random from a 2000-ha study area (so $M = 2000/10 = 200$ possible 10-ha plots, of which $m = 20$ were sampled). Biologists survey the selected quadrates to detect how many coveys are present (so in this case "abundance" is actually number of coveys, and not number of birds). The mean count from the 20 sample plots is $\bar{y} = 1.65$ with sample variance $s^2 = 1.608$. The estimate of abundance for the entire area is obtained by

$$\hat{N} = M\bar{y} = 200 \times 1.65 = 330$$

from Equation (8.1), with variance estimated from Equation (8.2) as

$$\hat{\text{var}}(\hat{N}) = M^2 \frac{s^2}{m}(1 - m/M) = 200^2 \frac{1.68}{20}(1 - 20/200) = 2894$$

Taking the square root of the variance and multiplying by 1.96 we get an approximate normal confidence interval of

$$\hat{N} \pm 1.96 \times \sqrt{\text{var}(\hat{N})} = \hat{N} \pm 1.96 \times \sqrt{2894} = 330 \pm 105$$

or

$$(225, 435)$$

The data for this example can be found in the electronic companion to the book (see enclosed CD and website address on p. ii).

the sample areas are known (or can be determined in the field). However, variable sample areas will also tend to make the counts variable, all other things being equal, and therefore are best avoided if possible.

The above method is appropriate for simple random sampling of m plots from a possible list of M. As illustrated in Chapter 5, there are many situations when stratified sampling reduces the variability of the estimate of the mean, and, therefore, in this case of abundance. Stratification is accomplished by first dividing the study up into areas $j = 1, 2, \ldots, s$ strata, each with area A_j and containing M_j sample plots. The number and nature of the strata will depend on identifiable features that can be used to divide the study area (such as forest cover type) and that are thought *a priori* to influence abundance. Then m_i samples are taken from each of the strata to achieve the necessary overall sample size and allocation (Chapter 5). Estimation from stratified sampling is a fairly straightforward extension of simple random estimation, and is illustrated in Box 8.3.

Box 8.2 Estimation of N when detectability is perfect and sample areas are unequal.

The example is from muskrat (*Ondantra zibethicus*) houses surveyed by boats, on a sample of $m = 10$ of $M = 50$ variable-area plots sampled from a 100-ha marsh (Williams *et al.* 2002, p. 249). The data are summarized as follows:

Counts

$$\bar{y} = 1.65, s_y^2 = 16.94$$

Plot area

$$\bar{a} = 1.65, s_a^2 = 0.27$$

Covariance between counts and areas

$$s_{ay} = \sum_{i=1}^{10} (y_i - \bar{y})(a_i - \bar{a})/(10 - 1)$$

Abundance is estimated by

$$\hat{N} = \frac{\bar{y}}{\bar{a}} A = \frac{7.5}{1.4} 100 = 5.36(100) = 536$$

with variance

$$\begin{aligned} \text{var}(\hat{N}) &= \frac{M^2(1 - m/M)}{m} (s_y^2 + \hat{D}^2 s_a^2 - 2\hat{D} s_{ay}) \\ &= 200[16.94 + 5.36^2(0.27) - 2(5.36)(1.56)] = 1586 \end{aligned}$$

where

$$\hat{D} = \frac{\bar{y}}{\bar{a}} = 5.36$$

This provides a 95% confidence interval on N of (458, 614).

The data for this example can be found in the electronic companion to the book (see enclosed CD and website address on p. ii).

Incomplete detection assumed

As noted in Chapter 6, the assumption that the detection of animals on sample units is perfect is not likely to be met in practice. Furthermore, we showed in Chapter 6 that even assuming detection is constant over time and space (and therefore a homogeneous index) is often not valid. Thus, not only would our counts be biased (probably low) as estimates of abundance, but also they would not even be consistent indicators of relative abundance or "trend." The rest of this chapter and remaining chapters in this section of the book devote attention to sampling designs and models that do not require "heroic" (and usually unverifiable) assumptions about perfect detection, but instead collect appropriate data for estimating detection and thus abundance or density directly.

We describe here three basic approaches that we characterize as (i) calibration, (ii) independent count statistics, and (iii) modeling approaches. These are somewhat

Box 8.3 Stratified sampling.

We illustrate stratified sampling with another example involving bobwhite quail coveys in Georgia, this time for a 2200-ha study area stratified into five geographic strata ranging in size from 300 to 600 ha.

Summary statistics				Count		Area		
Stratum	M	M	A	$\bar{y}$	s_y^2	$\bar{a}$	s_a^2	s_{ay}
1	25	5	400	4	2.5	16	30	7.5
2	36	5	500	1.2	0.7	14	30	4
3	38	5	600	1.8	0.7	16	30	4
4	12	5	300	5.4	4.3	26	130	22
5	15	5	400	3.2	1.7	27	245	17

There are two alternative formulae for computing the estimate of total abundance.

The separate ratio estimator is calculated as:

$$\hat{N}_s = \sum_{i=1}^{s} \frac{\bar{y}_i}{\bar{a}_i}(A_i) = \sum_{i=1}^{s} \hat{D}_{si}(A_i) = \left(\frac{4}{16}\right) 400 + \cdots \left(\frac{3.2}{27}\right) 400 = 320$$

with estimated variance

$$\begin{aligned} \text{var}(\hat{N}_s) &= \sum_{i=1}^{s} \frac{M_i^2(1 - m_i/M_i)}{m_i}(s_{yi}^2 + \hat{D}_i^2 s_{ai}^2 - 2\hat{D}_i s_{ayi}) \\ &= \frac{25^2(1 - 5/25)}{5}[2.5 + (0.25)^2(30) - 2(0.25)7.5] + \cdots \\ &\quad \frac{15^2(1 - 5/15)}{5}[1.7 + (0.118)^2(245) - 2(0.118)17] = 206 \end{aligned}$$

The combined ratio estimator is calculated as:

$$\begin{aligned} \hat{N}_c &= \frac{\sum_{i=1}^{s} M_i \bar{y}_i}{\sum_{i=1}^{s} M_i \bar{a}_i} \left(\sum_{i=1}^{s} A_i\right) \\ &= \hat{D}_c A = \frac{25(4) + 36(1.2) + \cdots + 15(3.2)}{25(16) + 36(14) + \cdots + 15(27)}(400 + 500 + \cdots + 400) = 320 \end{aligned}$$

Box 8.3 Continued.

with estimated variance

$$\begin{aligned}\text{var}(\hat{N}_c) &= \sum_{i=1}^{s} \frac{M_i^2(1 - m_i/M_i)}{m_i}(s_{yi}^2 + \hat{D}_c^2 s_{ai}^2 - 2\hat{D}_c s_{ayi}) \\ &= \frac{25^2(1 - 5/25)}{5}[2.5 + (0.146)^2(30) - 2(0.146)7.5] + \cdots . \\ &\quad \frac{15^2(1 - 5/15)}{5}[1.7 + (0.146)^2(245) - 2(0.146)17] = 246\end{aligned}$$

Notice that the separate and combined estimates are very similar, but that the variance for the separate estimator is lower than the combined (206 vs. 246). This will be the case when densities vary among strata, as they do in this example. If densities are similar among strata, the combined estimator should be used.

The data for this example can be found in the electronic companion to the book (see enclosed CD and website address on p. ii).

artificial distinctions, but may be useful in describing basic sampling designs and approaches.

Calibration approach

Recall from Chapter 6 that the basis relationship between a count statistic C and true abundance N is

$$E(C_i) = \beta N_i$$

or in our case

$$E(y_i) = \beta N_i$$

where y_i are the sample counts in each plot i. If we either knew what abundance was on each plot or had an unbiased way to estimate abundance, we could use this information to estimate detectability, β, and thus adjust our sample counts. If we can assume (for now) that the relationship between y and N goes through zero (so, when the count is zero so is abundance, and vice versa) then one estimate of β would simply be

$$\hat{\beta} = \frac{\sum_{i=1}^{n} y_i}{\sum_{i=1}^{n} N_i} \quad (8.3)$$

that is, the sample total divided by the population total. Other approaches such as linear regression are appropriate if we do not want to make the zero-intercept assumption (e.g., the index might go to zero before the population does).

Obviously, if we had perfect detection on our sample unit, we would not need to deal further with the issue of detection. Likewise, if we had calibration of our counts to an unbiased estimate of N everywhere on our study, we would simply use the estimate. The real utility of calibration comes in when, as is often the case, it is very expensive or difficult to assure complete detection or unbiased estimation of N. In these cases, if we establish a calibration relationship between counts y and true abundance N, we may be able to extend that relationship to a larger sample for which only y is obtained (Box 8.4). This is exactly the idea of double sampling (Chapter 5). It might be tempting to conduct this exercise one time, that is perform a single calibration estimation, and then apply the result to all future samples where only y is obtained. This should be avoided if possible, because it of course depends on the assumption that the relationship between N and y, once established, never changes. Experience with numerous types of surveys and taxa suggests that this would be a bold assumption indeed, and that a much more prudent approach is to design continual calibration by way of double sampling at every sampling occasion.

Independent count statistics

Here we have two methods that produce independent count statistics x and y, each related to abundance but perhaps in a different way; unlike the calibration approach, we do not assume that either method is an unbiased representation of N, but instead that each independently is related to N:

$$E(x) = \beta_x N$$

and

$$E(y) = \beta_y N$$

where β_x and β_y are the detection rates specific to each method. We also assume that our independent counts are conducted at the same time and on the same area, so that they represent the same population. If we assume that these rates are between zero and one (essentially the same as assuming that we can underestimate but not overestimate N with our count) if we can classify our observed counts into the number detected by method x but not method $y(n_{+-})$, those detected by y but not $x(n_{-+})$, and those detected by both methods (n_{++}), and finally if we can assume that the methods are independent, then we have the following expectations for the data:

$$E(n_{+-}) = \beta_x(1 - \beta_y)N$$
$$E(n_{-+}) = (1 - \beta_x)\beta_y N$$

and

$$E(n_{++}) = \beta_x \beta_y N$$

Box 8.4 Calibration of counts and double sampling.

We return to the muskrat example (Box 8.2), this time taking a subsample of five plots (1st, 3rd, 5th, etc.) on which we are able to get complete counts c on muskrat houses.

Calibration sample	
Y	c
15	17
6	7
7	8
3	3
9	11

These data are used to obtain a ratio estimate of β as:

$$\hat{\beta} = \frac{\bar{y}}{\bar{c}} = \frac{8}{9.2} = 0.87$$

with estimated variance

$$\begin{aligned}\hat{\text{var}}(\hat{\beta}) &= \frac{(1 - m/M)}{m\bar{c}}(s_y^2 + \hat{\beta}^2 s_c^2 - 2\hat{\beta} s_{cy}) \\ &= \frac{(1 - 5/50)}{5(9.2)}[20 + (0.87)^2(27.2) - 2(0.87)(23.25)] = 0.79\end{aligned}$$

We can use the estimate of β to adjust $\hat{N}$

$$\hat{N}_{adj} = \frac{\hat{N}}{\hat{\beta}} = \frac{536}{0.87} = 616$$

with estimated variance

$$\hat{\text{var}}(\hat{N}_{adj}) \approx \left(\frac{\hat{N}}{\hat{\beta}}\right)^2 \left(\frac{\hat{\text{var}}(\hat{N})}{\hat{N}^2} + \frac{\hat{\text{var}}(\hat{\beta})}{\hat{\beta}^2}\right) = \left(\frac{536}{0.87}\right)^2 \left(\frac{1586}{536^2} + \frac{0.79}{0.87^2}\right) = 400,495$$

We note that this is a very imprecise estimate of β (CV $\approx$ 100%), and thus also a very imprecise estimate of N, not surprising because it is based on only five samples. Unless the relationship between the calibrated and uncalibrated counts is very stable, small samples such as this will provide unreliable calibration estimates.

The data for this example can be found in the electronic companion to the book (see enclosed CD and website address on p. ii).

These relationships lead to estimation under a simple mark–recapture model (Chapter 10):

$$\hat{N} = \frac{(n_x + 1)(n_y + 1)}{m + 1} - 1$$

$$\hat{\text{var}}(\hat{N}) = \frac{(n_x + 1)(n_y + 1)(n_x - m)(n_y - m)}{(m + 1)^2(m + 2)} \quad (8.4)$$

where

$$n_x = n_{+-} + n_{++}$$

$$n_y = n_{-+} + n_{++}$$

$$m = n_{++}$$

Readers may recognize this as the Lincoln–Petersen estimator of abundance, which we will consider when we discuss mark–recapture sampling (Chapter 10). More complicated models require multiple, independent methods or sampling occasions, and allow modeling of heterogeneous detection probabilities. A special case of the independent methods approach is when we have two or more independent observers (Box 8.5). This method can also be modified to allow for dependent observers (Box 8.6).

Modeling approach

Here we do not necessarily have any way to directly estimate detectability, but instead try to find factors that seem to be related to increasing or decreasing rates of detection and then model incomplete counts as a function of these factors. Assuming that the population itself is relatively stable (or adequately sampled at different levels) we may be able to infer from the relationship between the factors and the counts that counts are no longer increasing as factors presumed to be improved detection increase, and so that perfect detection has been achieved, at least approximately. As a simple example, it is well established that aerial counts become increasingly less accurate (biased low) as aircraft speed and altitude above the surveyed objects increase. For a given population density, one would expect increasing counts as airspeed and altitude decrease. A leveling off of counts (Figure 8.1) might suggest that complete detection has been reached. There are obvious flaws in this example – airspeed and altitude can only be decreased so far because of safety and aircraft limitations, and very low/slow speeds (or switching to helicopters from fixed-wing aircraft) might disturb animals and actually lower detection rates. The main logical flaw is that the methods assume a point at which perfect detection occurs, and that point may never be reached (or if it exists is not observed in the study). Nevertheless, the modeling approach can be very useful, especially when combined with other methods. For example, a calibration sample can be used on a subsample, which then allows estimation of actual detection rates on the subsample. This relationship is then extended to the main sample, via double sampling.

Box 8.5 Estimation of detection based on independent methods or observers.

This approach is appropriate when (i) methods or observers are completely independent (e.g., there is no cross-checking between observers), (ii) detection probabilities are homogeneous among animals or other objects detected, (iii) it can be determined which individuals are seen by each method (but not the other) or both methods or observers, and (iv) the population is closed between observer/method occasions. We illustrate this approach with a two-sample (method) problem, but the approach generalizes to multiple samples, allowing robust estimation of abundance (Chapter 10).

The example involves estimation of osprey (*Pandion haliaetus*) nests using independent aerial and ground observers (Henny and Anderson 1979; Pollock and Kendall 1987; Williams *et al.* 2002, p. 252). A total of $n_x = 51$ nests were seen from the air, $n_y = 63$ from the ground, and $m = 41$ by both methods. Applying Equation (8.4) leads to

$$\hat{N} = \frac{(51+1)(63+1)}{41+1} - 1 = 78.2$$

and variance estimate

$$\hat{\text{var}}(\hat{N}) = \frac{(51+1)(63+1)(51-41)(63-41)}{(41+1)^2(41+2)} = 9.65$$

Note that, unlike calibration, β is not assumed to be 1 for either method, and is estimated for the aerial surveys as

$$\beta_x = \frac{n_x}{\hat{N}} = \frac{51}{78.2} = 0.65$$

and for the ground surveys as

$$\beta_y = \frac{n_y}{\hat{N}} = \frac{63}{78.2} = 0.81$$

The data for this example can be found in the electronic companion to the book (see enclosed CD and website address on p. ii).

Study design

Assuring closure

All of the methods that we describe in this chapter require the assumption that the population is **closed**. This means that not only abundance (N) is constant over the study period, but also there are no gains (births or immigration) or losses (death or emigration) to the population. The assumption would be violated if, for example, there were 100 animals throughout the period, but this number was maintained by balancing 25 deaths against 25 recruits. As we have already noted in Chapter 6, the closure

Box 8.6 Estimation of detection based on multiple dependent observers.

A variation on independent observers occurs when observers are present during a survey, with one designated the primary observer and the other the secondary observer (Cook and Jacobson 1979; Nichols *et al.* 2000; Williams *et al.* 2002, pp. 254–255). The primary observer notifies the secondary observer of each animal detected, and the secondary observer records the number of animals seen by the primary survey and surveys the area him- or herself. The data are animals (i) detected by the primary observer and (ii) missed by the primary observer and detected by the secondary. The roles are then switched and the survey continued. The data are the x_{ij} individuals counted by observer $i = 1, 2$ on sample units when observer $j = 1, 2$ was the primary observer.

We illustrate the method with aerial surveys of wading birds in Florida. The data obtained were

$$x_{11} = 20,\ x_{21} = 24,\ x_{22} = 35,\ x_{12} = 14$$

These data were used to obtain estimates of capture probabilities for the two observers, obtained by a conditional binomial model,

$$\hat{p}_1 = \frac{x_{11}x_{22} - x_{12}x_{21}}{x_{11}x_{22} + x_{22}x_{12}} = 0.306$$

$$\hat{p}_2 = \frac{x_{11}x_{22} - x_{12}x_{21}}{x_{11}x_{22} + x_{11}x_{12}} = 0.371$$

and the probability of detection by a least one observer as

$$\hat{p} = 1 - \frac{x_{12}x_{21}}{x_{22}x_{11}} = 0.52$$

with variance conditional on overall detection of

$$\mathrm{var}(\hat{p}|x_{..}) = \frac{(1-p)^2 p}{x_{..}}\left[\frac{1}{p_1\theta_1} + \frac{1}{p_2\theta_2} + \frac{1}{p_2(1-p_1)\theta_1} + \frac{1}{p_1(1-p_2)\theta_2}\right] = 0.039$$

$$\theta_i = \frac{x_i}{x_{..}}, x_{.i} = x_{1i} + x_{2i}$$

Finally, abundance is estimated by

$$\hat{N} = \frac{x_{..}}{\hat{p}} = 178.85$$

with estimated variance

$$\hat{\mathrm{var}}(\hat{N}) = \frac{(x_{..})^2 \hat{\mathrm{var}}(\hat{p})}{\hat{p}^4} + \frac{(x_{..})(1-\hat{p})}{\hat{p}^2} = 4750$$

This produces a normal approximation for the confidence interval on $N$of

$$\hat{N} \pm \sqrt{\hat{\mathrm{var}}(\hat{N})} \times 1.96 = (44, 314)$$

The data for this example can be found in the electronic companion to the book (see enclosed CD and website address on p. ii).

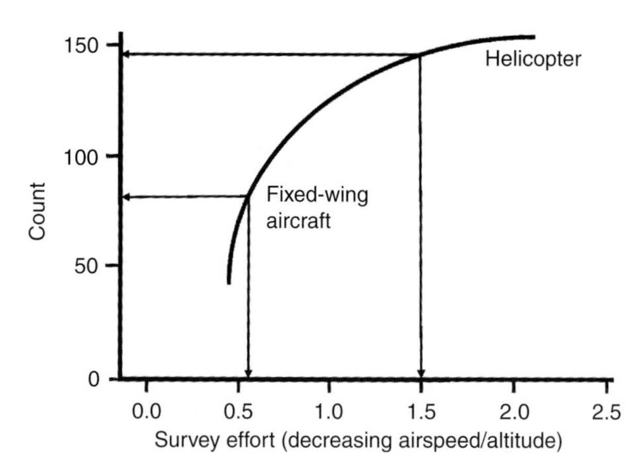

Fig. 8.1 **Hypothetical relationship between survey effort (airspeed and altitude above ground) and count for an aerial survey.**

assumption dictates that sampling should occur over a sufficiently short time, or at a time of year, so that recruitment and mortality are thought to be negligible. It also dictates that the study area be sufficiently large so that movement into and out of the area is small in comparison to the whole population. In both cases, the nature of the study organism and the study area will influence both factors, and so the biologist should have some *a priori* idea of what these should be, at least relatively. For example, a study designed to estimate the abundance of African elephants (*Loxodonta africana*) might be conducted over several months and still avoid violating closure due to their low rates of mortality and/or reproduction, but would require a large area (perhaps many hundreds of square kilometers) to avoid violating geographic closure. By contrast, a study of cotton rats (*Sigmodon hispidus*) in Georgia could reasonably be conducted on a much smaller area (<1 km^2) and avoid violating geographic closure, but would need to be much shorter term (a few weeks perhaps) to avoid violations due to mortality or reproduction. Of course, biologists can never know for certain without quantifying gains or losses whether these occur, so ideally these data would be available to confirm that assumptions are being met, at least approximately. If the study cannot be designed so that area and time span are appropriate for assuming at least approximate closure, then methods appropriate for open population estimation, such as open-population mark–recapture (Chapter 12) should be used instead of the methods in this chapter.

Size, shape, and placement of sample plots

There are many factors that will determine the best size and shape of sampling units, so generalizations are difficult. For shape, the basic choice is between circular or rectangular plots. In some situations circular plots are convenient, because all that is required is the specification of a central point and a radius. Also, circular plots minimize perimeter length relative to area, and thus will tend to minimize errors in determining whether objects are inside or outside the plot. However, a fixed area cannot be divided into M non-overlapping circular plots, an advantage of rectangular or square plots. Square plots have a shorter perimeter to area than rectangular plots, and are often easier to lay out than rectangular plots. However, in some situations, notably aerial surveys, rectangular plots are easier (e.g., by establishing a fixed distance either side of a center line along which an aircraft flies).

Plot size involves opposing considerations. On the one hand, plots with a small area a require more replicate plots to survey the same proportion of the study area A, consequently increasing precision. However, small plots tend to have large perimeter-to-area ratios, inflating the area of inclusion (the area in which animals, if present and detected, will be included in the sample). In addition, small plots frequently will contain one or zero detected animals or other objects, especially when densities are low, thereby inflating estimator variances. The optimal plot size thus will also depend on the biology of the organism under study: quite obviously, a plot appropriate for sampling elephants (e.g., likely to encounter more than one elephant on a reasonable proportion of plots) would be inappropriately large for estimating the density of nesting colonial birds, and vice versa.

Placement of study plots will depend on the study area, the physical layout of the plots (square, rectangular, circular, etc.), whether sampling is stratified, and perhaps other factors, but the end result should be to achieve as closely as possible a random distribution of plots, within the study area overall or within strata (Chapter 5). As described in Chapter 5, randomization is usually achieved by first defining all the M potential plots (e.g., dividing the area up into $M = A/a$ equal-sized squares, e.g., $M = 1000/10 = 100$) and then choosing m at random (e.g., using a computer random number generator, a table of random numbers, or other device that produces a near-random result). Done correctly, each plot will have m/M probability of selection (e.g., $10/100 = 0.10$). Care must be taken that the samples are not simply placed in a haphazard manner, which usually will not be truly random (and often turns into "convenience sampling", which as the name implies may be convenient, but is not reliable), but rather by a scheme devised in advance. Once selected, detailed instructions, including, e.g., GPS coordinates of the selected plots, can be given to the field crews, who should be expected to follow these exactly. Of course, for safety and other reasons it will sometimes be necessary to move plots (M.J.C. recalls doing so on at least one occasion due to hornet nests), but this should be an exception to the rule of random placement.

Sample sizes needed

As emphasized in Chapter 5, choosing the right sample size for estimation is important; if sample sizes are too small, estimates will be imprecise and thus unreliable, and if they are too large, time and money has been spent that could have been used elsewhere. Often, the goal in abundance estimation is to achieve some specified level of precision on the estimate of N. When possible what we need is a pilot sample to get some idea of the variability in our counts, which can then be used to determine how many additional

Box 8.7 Sample size estimation.

Returning to the problem in Box 8.2, we can treat this as a pilot sample of $m_0 = 10$ and use the sample mean and variance to help design a study to achieve a specific coefficient of variation (e.g., CV = 0.10).
We solve Equation (8.5) as

$$m = \frac{50(16.9)}{16.9 + 50(0.10^2)(7.5^2)} = 18.8$$

or 19 total plots, thus requiring nine additional plots to achieve the desired precision.

samples are needed. A simple formula (Cochran 1977) for doing this is

$$\frac{1}{m} = \frac{1}{M} + \frac{CV_0^2 \bar{y}^2}{s^2}$$

or

$$m = \frac{Ms^2}{s^2 + MCV_0^2 \bar{y}^2} \quad (8.5)$$

where CV_0 is the desired CV (standard error divided by mean) and $\bar{y}$, s^2 are the mean and variance from the sample of m' plots. This formula is solved to find the total number m ($m - m'$ additional) of sample plots needed to achieve CV_0. We illustrate this with an example in Box 8.7. If sampling is stratified, then this sample size will need to be allocated across strata, according to either proportional or optimal allocation (Chapter 5).

Incorporating detection rates into study design

As emphasized in Chapter 6, detection rates (β) can hardly ever be assumed to be perfect ($\beta = 1.0$). Failure to account for $\beta < 1.0$ leads to biased estimates of abundance, and invalid comparisons over space and time. However, detection rates also need to be taken into account in study design. First, if possible the same methods for detecting animals (capture, count methods, etc.) should be used for all the samples that are taken. This will help reduce (but not eliminate) variation in the sample data due to detection rates varying across methods. Second, generally speaking, methods with higher detection rates will produce more data, and the resulting estimates of abundance will be more precise than methods that have very low detection rates. Third, estimation of detection should be built into the study design, so that the data that are needed to test for heterogeneous detection, and ideally to correct for detection and produce unbiased estimates, are also collected. In some cases this will involve a calibration approach, for instance using double sampling (Chapters 5 and 6). In other cases the data produced will allow estimation under more formal methods such as distance sampling (Chapter 9) or capture–recapture (Chapter 10). In any case, the time to consider detection probabilities is *before* collecting the field data. Once the data are collected, it will usually be too late to do anything but regret that the necessary data were not collected.

In this chapter we have introduced the first methods directed at estimating abundance. Initially these are based on simple counting approaches on sample units (typically plots or other units of space), assuming that all animals present on the sampled units are perfectly detected. We consider sampling designs including sample size determination and stratification, to assure that study goals are met. We then extend these methods to situations where we do not assume that detection is perfect, but rather attempt to collect data that can be used to estimate detection and correct the counts to obtain unbiased estimates of abundance. Three general approaches are described: (i) calibration of counts to known abundance, (ii) overlapping independent methods that are each incomplete with respect to detection, and (iii) modeling of detection probabilities in relation to covariates.

The chapters that follow continue this theme, by exploring sampling approaches in which different types of data are used to supplement counts in order to obtain reliable estimates of abundance. In Chapter 9, we describe distance sampling, where the data are, in addition to counts of animals or other objects, distances measured from the observer to the detected object. In Chapter 10, we discuss mark–recapture, in which animals are marked (physically, or by some other method) and reobserved at later times, either by capture, resighting, or some other method of detection. The remaining chapters in this part deal with estimation of movement, demographic parameters, community parameters, and habitat selection by a variety of sampling and estimation approaches that mainly have their roots in population estimation.

9
Distance sampling for estimating density and abundance

In Chapter 8 we introduced methods directed at estimating abundance based on counts on sample plots. Initially, we assumed that that all animals present on the sample plots could be perfectly detected, so that detectability was not an issue. We then extended sampling approaches to the more realistic situation, namely that detection cannot be assumed to be perfect, and we instead collect additional data to estimate detection and correct the counts to obtain unbiased estimates of abundance. The methods in this chapter are really just an extension of these ideas to a special class of sampling and estimation known as **distance sampling**. In distance sampling, samples (generally lines or points) are taken and objects (animals, nests, etc.) are detected from these samples. However, in addition to the count of objects detected, we also measure the distance from the sample position to the object detected, and construct models for estimating detection rates and obtaining unbiased estimates of density and abundance. There are two principal sampling methods: line transect, involving sampling along lines that are placed (usually at random) throughout the study area; and point transect, involving sampling from points placed (usually at random) throughout the study area. In fact, both methods are really doing the same thing, resulting in point counts actually being called point transects in the distance sampling literature. For each method we describe how the method in a sense simply generalizes ordinary plot sampling, illustrate sampling procedures and estimation, and discuss study design.

Line transect sampling

In **line transect sampling**, the sampling unit is a line of length L (e.g., 1000 m), placed by the investigator at a location in the study area. We will discuss below how lines should be placed, when we consider study design. The observer walks (or drives, or flies, or boats) along the line and records all of the animals detected, and also records the perpendicular distance from the line to the point at which the animal or other object was first detected. Note that the observer must count *only those objects actually detected from the line*; if it becomes necessary to travel to the animal's detection position and other animals are detected along the way, these cannot be counted as part of the sample. "Detection" can involve actually sighting the animal or object, or detection by other means (e.g., by vocalizations or other sounds), but must enable determination of

Quantitative Conservation of Vertebrates, 1st edition. By M.J. Conroy and J.P. Carroll. Published 2009 by Blackwell Publishing, ISBN 978-1-4051-8228-7 (pb) and 978-1-4051-9098-5 (hb).

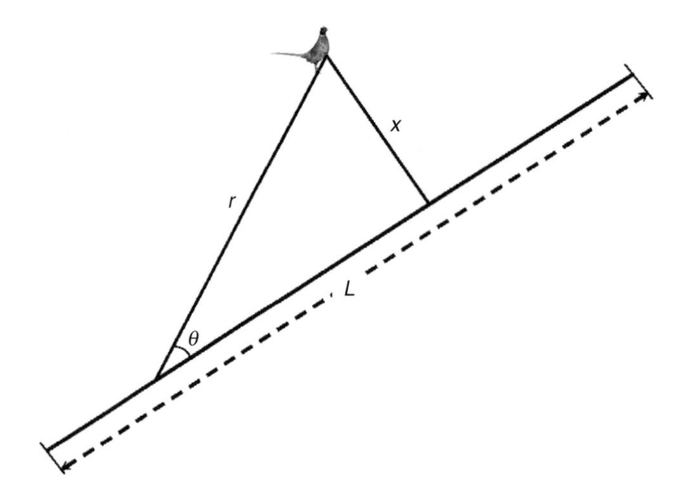

Fig. 9.1 **Example layout for line transect sampling and the field measurements required for analysis. An observer traverses a line of length L and detects animals at a perpendicular distance x from the line. Alternatively, the observer detects animals at a sighting distance r and angle θ, which can be used to compute x via $x = r\sin\theta$.**

the detection position so that perpendicular distance can be recorded. The necessary measurements for line transect sampling are illustrated in Figure 9.1. Notice that it is *not* sufficient to record only the line-of-sight distance from the observer to the animal. Rather, either the perpendicular distance must be directly measured, or both the line-of-sight distance and sighting angle recorded, from which the perpendicular distance can be computed using trigonometry. The latter can potentially add two sources of error to our measurements; that is distance estimation error and angular error from the line.

Basic ideas underlying line transect sampling

Statistical modeling of line transect data to estimate density and abundance can be very complicated, and generally requires specialized software. However, the basic ideas are intuitive and easy to grasp. In essence, line transect sampling can really be thought of as a generalization of sampling from rectangular plots. Suppose that a transect line of length L is in fact the centerline of a rectangular plot, and n animals are counted from the line. If we assume that out to a distance w either side of the line we can perfectly detect animals (Figure 9.2A), then a sensible estimator of density (Chapter 6) is simply the count divided by the area of the plot defined by L and w:

$$\hat{D} = \frac{n}{2Lw}$$

We can also consider the case where detection is less than perfect, but does not vary with distance from the centerline (i.e., is constant out to w; Figure 9.2B), and finally the more realistic case where detection is imperfect, and falls off with decreasing distance

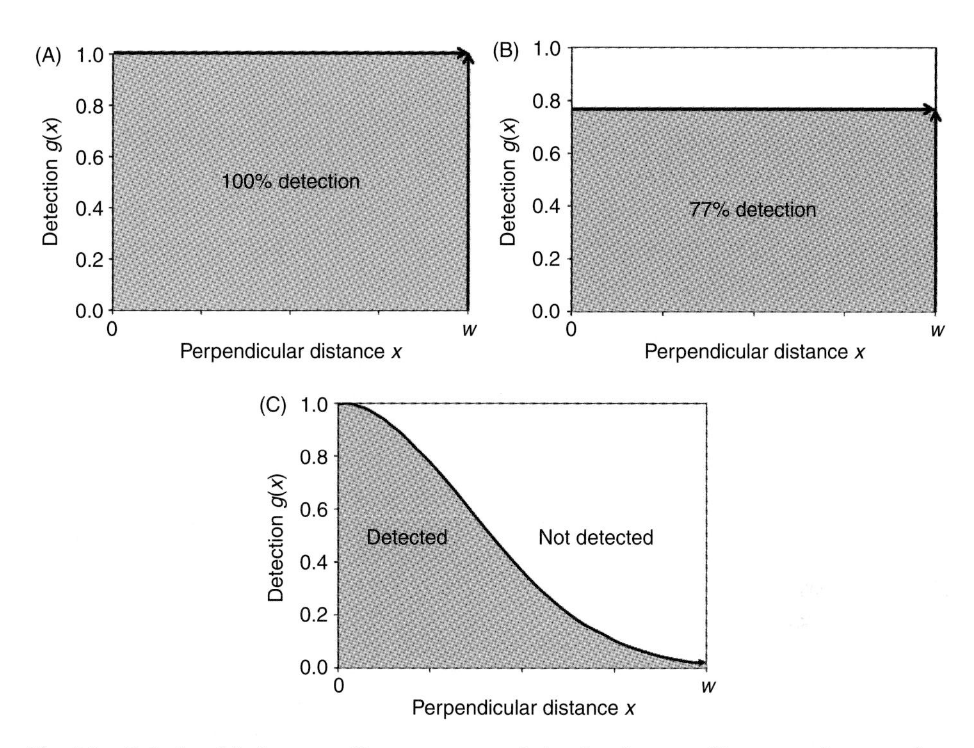

Fig. 9.2 **Relationship between line transect and simple plot sampling assuming complete detection. (A) Detection assumed 100% from centerline to w. Effective area of survey = 2 Lw, same as ordinary plot survey. (B) Detection assumed to be constant but less than 100% from centerline to w. (C) Detection curve showing decrease in detection from the centerline ($x = 0$) to distance $x = w$. Area under curve μ represents effective half-width of survey; effective area of survey = $2L\mu$.**

from the centerline (Figure 9.2C). In all three cases, the area under this curve (whose shape we will assume for now; later we will see how to estimate the curve with data) is known as the "effective half-width" of the plot, μ. For the first (perfect detection) case, $\mu = w$; in the second and third cases $\mu < w$ and is estimated by estimating the mathematical form of the detection curve. Assuming we can estimate this quantity, we can then estimate density as

$$\hat{D} = \frac{n}{2L\hat{\mu}} \tag{9.1}$$

This is the general form of the density estimator we will use for line transect sampling. Notice that if $\mu = w$ we will get the same result as with fixed-area sampling, but if $\mu < w$ our unadjusted counts will underestimate actual density. The problem is, we do not generally know μ, and it likely varies from species to species, within habitats, or even between observers. Thus, the emphasis in this chapter is on estimating μ using sample data, so that we can obtain unbiased estimates of density.

Assumptions of line transect sampling

Before we can properly estimate density and abundance in a line transect study, we must have sample data that meet certain important assumptions. We cannot overemphasize how much researchers need to understand and evaluate these assumptions for their research. The major assumptions of line transect sampling are:

1. Animals or objects directly on the line are counted with certainty. As we will see, violation of this assumption will result in underestimation of density or abundance. In some specialized situations detection probability on the line can be estimated, but this is not likely for most field studies.
2. Animals do not move prior to sampling in response to the observer. Severe violation of this assumption may render distance sampling inappropriate, as will be discussed further under 'Study design'.
3. Distances (and, where needed, angles) are measured accurately. Implications of this assumption will be discussed further under 'Study design'.
4. Transect lines are placed randomly with respect to the animals or other objects. Ordinarily this is guaranteed by random sampling, as discussed under 'Study design'.
5. Observations (counts, distances) of animals or objects are assumed to be independent of one another. In some situations, animals occur in clusters (e.g., coveys of birds) and this assumption is violated. In these cases, the "observation" is more appropriately described and modeled on the basis of clusters rather than individuals, as we will discuss below.
6. There are sufficient samples to construct the detection function. It is this function that inflates the numbers of samples necessary. Often minimum detections of 60–80 are now being cited in the wildlife literature.

Estimation models

For now, we will consider the simplest case of line transect sampling, a single line of length L on which n animals or other objects are detected. The data available for estimating density are:

- n, the sample count on the line;
- $x_1, x_2, x_3, \ldots, x_n$ perpendicular distances (either recorded directly or computed via sighting angles and observer-to-object distances).

The observed distances can be described by a frequency distribution $f(x)$, which simply describes the relative frequency at which distances x from the centerline occur in the sample data (see Chapter 5 for a refresher on frequency distributions). Figure 9.3 illustrates a typical distribution $f(x)$ of sampling distances.

Assume for the moment that we have a way to model this distribution; we show here how $f(x)$ relates to detection, and the estimation of density. First, we need to formally

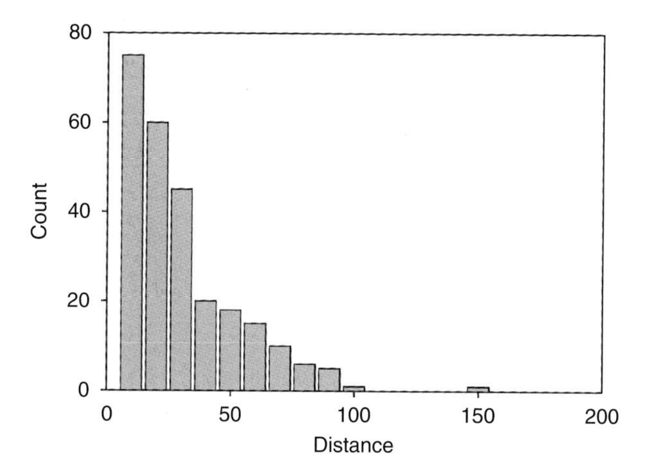

Fig. 9.3 **Distribution of distance data in a line transect study.**

define the general detection function, specific examples of which have already been introduced (Figure 9.2). We will define this function $g(x)$ as the probability of detecting an animal at distance x, given that it is present and at distance x from the centerline. Our sampling distribution $f(x)$, of course, is the reverse of this: the probability of observing distance x, given that the animal is present and detected (we obviously cannot record a distance for animals that we do not see!). The relationship between these two distributions follows from basic probability theory, given the assumption that the transect is randomly placed:

$$f(x) = \frac{g(x)}{\mu}$$

where μ is the area under the detection curve. At this point, we need to invoke the very first assumption of line transect estimation, that detection is perfect for animals present on the line. By definition this means that $g(0) = 1$, which leads to

$$f(0) = \frac{1}{\mu}$$

and

$$\hat{\mu} = \frac{1}{\hat{f}(0)}$$

This last expression shows that if we can estimate the sampling distribution $f(x)$, and therefore can evaluate the function at $x = 0$, we can then estimate the "effective half-width" (and area) of the line transect. Finally, we put it all together by substituting this relationship into Equation (9.1) to obtain:

$$\hat{D} = \frac{n\hat{f}(0)}{2L} \tag{9.2}$$

This is the general form for line transect estimation. The problem then becomes how to actually use the sample data (e.g., Figure 9.3) to estimate $f(0)$ and, ultimately, density. In this process it is especially important to select an appropriate model for $f(x)$, because the estimate of $f(0)$ is highly sensitive to the shape of the model. Buckland *et al.* (1993, 2001) approach this problem by a very flexible procedure involving combinations of "key functions" and "series adjustments" to model $f(x)$, according to general relationship, thus:

$$f(x) = key(x)[1 + series(x)] \tag{9.3}$$

The **key function** is a basic shape for the detection data that describes the way detection changes as a function of increasing distance from the centerline. Many different functions are possible, but four are in common use in line transect estimation and are implemented in the program DISTANCE (Buckland *et al.* 1993, 2001; Laake *et al.* 1993). These are uniform, half normal, negative exponential, and hazard (Figure 9.4). As you can imagine these describe the general form in which our detection moves toward zero as distance from the line increases. This is also one of the reasons that distance sampling can be so data hungry. Think about a half normal curve based on only a few observations; just a couple of outliers can completely change the detection function and thereby dramatically influence our abundance estimate. The **series adjustments** are then added to the model to improve fit to the data. Three basic series adjustments are used in DISTANCE: a cosine series and two types of polynomial series (ordinary or "simple" polynomials, and hermite polynomials). We leave the details of these series

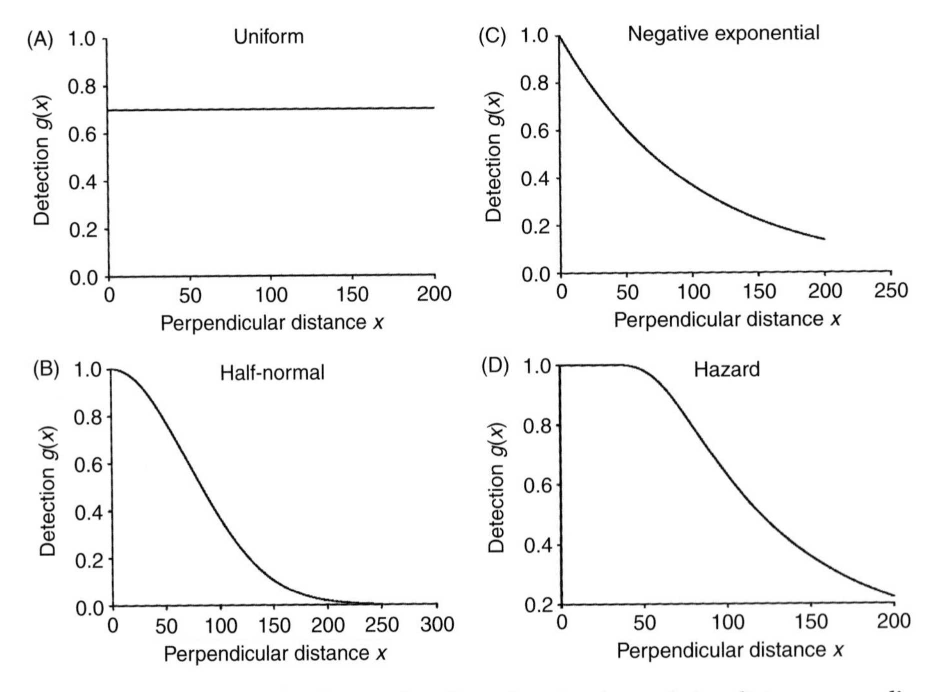

Fig. 9.4 **Major functional forms (baseline functions) used in distance sampling. (A) Uniform, (B) half-normal, (C) negative exponential, (D) hazard.**

Box 9.1 Line transect sampling.

We illustrate line transect sampling with an example of great Argus pheasants (*Argusianus argus*) studied in Sumatra (Winari 2002). Within an 800-ha study area, 144 line transects were placed, each 2220 m long. Observers walked each transect and detected Argus present, if any. During the study, birds were detected on 45 of the 144 transects. We pooled these data over transects to show the overall distribution of detection distances (Figure 9.5A). After pooling some low-frequency distance classes, a smoother distribution is obtained (Figure 9.5B), but one can anticipate some difficulties in fitting these data with detection functions. We used the distance data and transect counts to fit a series of models in the program DISTANCE. We obtained the following results for five models:

Model	No. of parameters	ΔAIC	AIC	ESW	Density	LCI	UCI	CV
Exp + cos	1	0	496.22	38.54	0.023	0.016	0.035	0.204
Hn + cos	2	3.44	499.66	42.58	0.021	0.014	0.032	0.211
Unif + cos	3	4.71	500.93	41.54	0.022	0.014	0.033	0.215
Unif + poly	3	6.96	503.18	49.48	0.018	0.012	0.027	0.199

The exponential + cosine model fit the data well (Figure 9.6) and performed considerably better as judged by AIC than the competing four models; however, all four models produced similar density estimates. Under the assumption of constant average density over the 800-ha study area, the density estimate of 0.023 Argus/ha (0.016–0.035) can be extrapolated to produce an estimate of abundance of 18.4 (12.8–28) animals.

The complete data and analysis file for this example can be found in the electronic companion to the book (see enclosed CD and website address on p. ii).

functions (and estimation in general) to sources such as Buckland *et al.* (1993, 2001) and Williams *et al.* (2002), but simply note that a large number of combinations can be formed among the four key functions and the three series functions (each of which involves choices as to numbers of series terms, including no terms at all). The program DISTANCE allows users to readily construct models via combining key functions and series adjustments, and to evaluate each for goodness of fit and parsimony. Model parsimony is evaluated by computing AIC for each model and ranking the models from lowest to highest AIC value. We illustrate this procedure with a data example (Box 9.1), which we also use to compute model-averaged estimates that take into account model uncertainty (Box 9.2).

Generalizations of line transect sampling

The above description of line transect sampling considers the most basic possible line transect study, involving continuously recorded, perpendicular distances, and a single

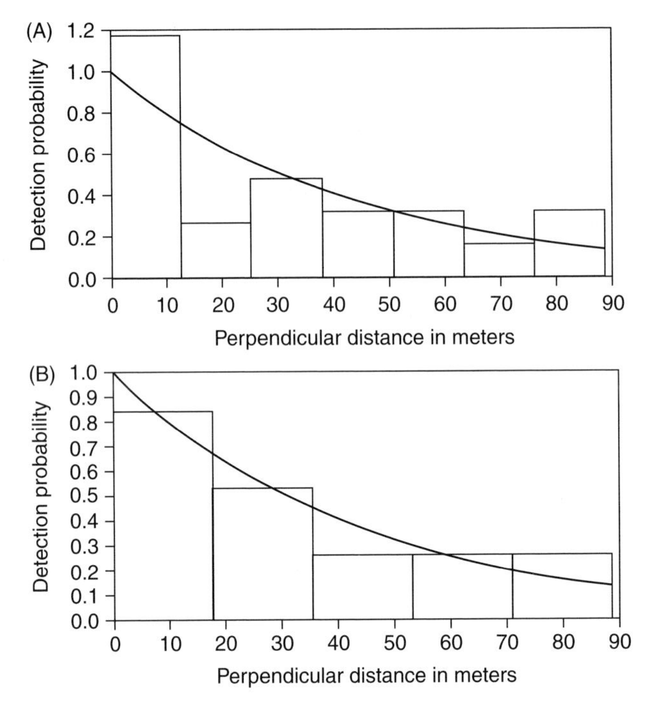

Fig. 9.5 **Fit of DISTANCE exponential + cosine adjustment model to distance data for great Argus study. (A) Unpooled perpendicular distances. (B) Data after pooling into five distance categories.**

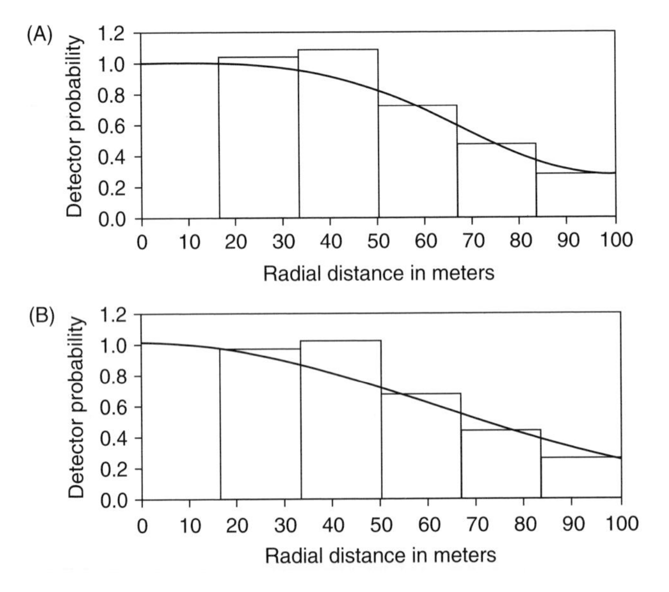

Fig. 9.6 **Fit of distance models to blue grosbeak data (see Box 9.4). (A) Exponential plus cosine adjustment. (B) Half normal plus cosine adjustment.**

Box 9.2 Incorporating model uncertainty into estimation.

As introduced in Chapter 5, we recommend using AIC for computing measures of model parsimony. This statistic can be used to select the "best" model, upon which all subsequent inference is made. However, in many situations several models will have some support (non-negligible AIC weights) and it is better to take all these models into account by computing a model-averaged estimated. This is known as **multimodel inference** (MMR; Burnham and Anderson 2002). An additional advantage of this approach is that it allows for incorporation of model uncertainty into computation of variances and confidence intervals of parameters. Ignoring this source of uncertainty leads to overly "optimistic" confidence intervals (i.e., that are narrower than they should be) and false confidence in the accuracy of the estimates.

MMR is performed automatically by some programs, but often the user will need to do a little work using as raw ingredients the output provided by programs like DISTANCE. We illustrate MMR with the Sumatra Argus example (Box 9.1). Here we had four models under consideration; each produced slightly different estimates of density. As recommended by Burnham and Anderson (2002), we used the ΔAIC values for each model to compute a weighted average for density across all four models as

$$\bar{D} = \sum_{i=1}^{4} \hat{D}_i wt_i = 0.023(0.76642) + \cdots + 0.018(0.0236) = 0.0225$$

An unconditional standard error (taking into account model uncertainty) is then computed as

$$SE_{uncond} = \sum_{i=1}^{4} wt_i \sqrt{SE(\hat{D}_i)^2 + (\hat{D}_i - \bar{D})^2}$$

$$0.76642 \times \sqrt{(0.004701)^2 + (0.023 - 0.0225)^2} + \cdots$$

$$+ 0.0236 \times \sqrt{(0.0036)^2 + (0.018 - 0.0225)^2} = 0.00475$$

This results in an approximate 95% unconditional confidence interval on D of

$$\bar{D} \pm 1.96 SE_{uncond} = (0.013, 0.032)$$

A spreadsheet providing these calculations can be found in the electronic companion to the book (see enclosed CD and website address on p. ii).

survey stratum. In practice there are several useful generalizations of line transect that allow accommodation of special situations. Details of these generalizations are found in Buckland *et al.* (1993, 2001), Laake *et al.* (1993), and Williams *et al.* (2002).

Variance estimation

Estimation of variances from the sample data is an important aspect of line transect sampling and is needed in order to construct variances and confidence intervals and otherwise account for random variation due to the sampling process (Chapter 5). In line transect sampling there are two components to the sample variance of the density estimator. First, counts vary from line to line because, just as plots are a random sample of space, so are randomly placed lines. In addition, the actual density of animals present in different portions of the study area will vary, sometimes by a great amount (if some of this variation can be accounted for by strata, the resulting estimates will be more precise). The second component of variation, which does not occur in plot sampling where detection is assumed perfect, is due to the detection model. That is, the perpendicular distances are a random sample of the underlying detection model, and so there will be statistical error in estimating this model. These relationships are summarized as

$$cv(\hat{D}) = CV(n) + CV(\hat{f}(0))$$

This expression has implications for study design, in that the precision of the density estimate can be improved both by improving the precision of the counts (usually by replicating lines or by stratification) or by improving the detectability model [usually by more effort (detection) per line]. It also has implications for variance estimation, in that $CV[\hat{f}(0)]$ is based on the detection model, which may in turn be based on distances that are either separated by line or pooled across lines or strata. Thus, this quantity can be estimated from a single, unreplicated line. The $CV(n)$ by contrast requires either replicate lines for estimation or assumptions about the mean–variance relationship of the counts. Thus, if lines are not replicated, it is typical to assume a Poisson mean–variance relationship, perhaps with a variance–inflation factor in the range of 1–3. In situations where there are plenty of data, density can be estimated for each line and an empirical estimate of variance computed (Buckland *et al.* 1993, 2001; Williams *et al.* 2002). Finally, a procedure known as the **jackknife** can be used to compute variances, in which transects are left out of the analysis one at a time and the remaining data used to predict the absent observations. The program DISTANCE (Laake *et al.* 1993) provides flexibility to users with respect to variance estimation, for instance allowing model-based, empirical, or jackknife variance estimation, depending on whether replicate lines are used.

Grouped distance data

With grouped distance data, the data occur in groups (distance intervals), either because that is how they were recorded in the field or because distance measurement is insufficiently precise so as to warrant treatment as continuous data. This is also known as heaping. For instance, in bird surveys it may be possible to estimate the distance to a singing bird in 10-m intervals, but impossible to measure the distance exactly with a tape or rangefinder (often birds can be heard but not seen). The same basic statistical theory applies to grouped samples as to continuous distance samples, with differences in some of the computational details (Buckland *et al.* 1993, 2001; Williams *et al.* 2002). Related to this is data truncation where all observations greater than some chosen distance are deleted; therefore detection does not decline all the way to zero. This is potentially useful when there are a few observations at very long distances – that is, there is a very long tail on the detections. The program DISTANCE (Laake *et al.* 1993) readily accommodates both grouped and ungrouped data and truncation, and applies the appropriate analysis depending on data type; we refer interested readers to Buckland *et al.* (1993, 2001) and Laake *et al.* (1993) for details and examples, respectively.

Objects as clusters/size-biased detection

Another frequent variant in line transect sampling occurs when the objects detected occur in clusters rather than singly. For example, many birds flush together as groups (coveys or flocks). This raises several issues from the standpoint of line transect estimation. First, clearly the individuals in the group are not independent observations; they therefore cannot be treated as such in the analysis. For example, if 10 birds flush together, there is a single perpendicular distance to the spot where they were detected (center of the group). Second, if we treat the clusters as the objects of detection, clearly what we are estimating is density of **clusters**, not density of individuals. If we desire (as we usually would) an estimate of the latter, we must also estimate mean cluster size (and its variance). Third, it should not surprise anyone that small clusters (one or two individuals) are harder to detect than larger clusters (say 10 or more): it is easier to miss a single animal, much harder to miss a large group. More generally, the sizes or other measures of conspicuousness of objects being sampled can influence detection probabilities, and needs to be taken into account in estimation.

Line transect theory (Buckland *et al.* 1993, 2001; Williams *et al.* 2002) and the program DISTANCE (Laake *et al.* 1993) take these factors into account in allowing for the inclusion of cluster size in the modeling of detection and estimation of density. First, cluster size is incorporated as a covariate potentially explaining some variation in detection rates (so that, for example, a large cluster 10 m from the centerline is potentially more detectable than a single animal). Second, group sizes are used to estimate a mean and variance for cluster sizes. Finally, the size-corrected detectability model is used to estimate density of clusters, which in turn is combined with mean cluster size to estimate density of individuals.

Stratified estimation

Two issues arise when line transect samples follow a stratified design. First, estimation can proceed under the assumption that detection rates either are the same among strata or vary, irrespective of whether true densities are different among strata. In the first case, we would model detection rates by a common model, pooling all detection distances across strata, but would still treat the stratum-specific counts separately, since these may reflect true variation in density (e.g., due to habitat preferences). In the second case, we model detection as being different among the strata. This might be expected in situations where the strata themselves have attributes that make animals more or less detectable (e.g., varying amount of vegetative cover; more noise interference from human activity in one stratum than another). Unless these differences are taken care of in the modeling process, modeling based on a common detection rate will lead to estimates of density that are of lower accuracy. The program DISTANCE allows examination of detection modeling on a stratum-specific or pooled basis, and selects a model (pooled or not) based on statistical measures such as AIC (Buckland *et al.* 1997; Burnham and Anderson 2002).

The other issue is how to combine the stratum-specific density estimates, whether these are based on a pooled detection model or stratum-specific models. This is actually a fairly straightforward problem: estimates are combined by taking the weighted averages across strata, with the weights ordinarily the relative sizes (areas) of the strata. Again, the program DISTANCE automatically performs these calculations, providing both stratum-specific and overall ("global") estimates of density.

Abundance estimation

So far we have alluded to abundance estimation, but have not shown how distance sampling can be used to estimate abundance. In principle this is an easy proposition, since by definition $D = N/A$. Thus, a straightforward estimate of abundance in an unstratified study could be described by

$$\hat{N} = \hat{D}A$$

where $\hat{D}$ is the estimate from line transect sampling. This estimate of course assumes that there is a well-defined study area of size A to which it is meaningful to apply the estimate of density. In some cases, abundance *per se* is not of interest, or there is not a well-defined study area. In these cases, we still have a reliable estimate of density, just perhaps not an area to apply it to, and it is not possible (or useful) to try to estimate abundance. In other cases, abundance is also of interest, and we do have a well-defined study area. In this case an estimate of abundance can be obtained as above, with SE obtained as

$$SE(\hat{N}) = SE(\hat{D})A$$

More generally there may be stratification, with potentially different sized strata. An estimate of overall abundance is obtained by

$$\hat{N} = \sum_{i=1}^{j} \hat{D}_i A_i$$

where $\hat{D}_i, A_i$ are the stratum-specific density estimates and areas. Again, the program DISTANCE readily accommodates abundance estimation, so long as the user can specify the global and stratum-specific areas.

Study design

Measurement accuracy

In line transect sampling it is very important that the basic field measurements of perpendicular distances (or sighting distances and angles) are accurately measured.

Depending on the exact field situation, accuracy can be greatly facilitated by the use of clearly marked, straight transects, and accurate measuring devices (measuring tapes, rangefinders, GPS units, etc.). Obviously, both the perpendicular distance x and the transect length L must be accurately measured, since both are key components of distance estimation. In addition, it is critical to ensure that animals directly on the line are always detected. Realistically, this assumption is sometimes violated, with the result that the density estimate will underestimate true density. If the assumption of perfect detection on the line cannot be reasonably approximated, then line transect sampling becomes a form of index, and requires calibration to true density by another method (see Chapter 6).

Sample placement

As emphasized in Chapter 5, proper inference about a population of interest requires an appropriate placement of sampling units. We have seen in Chapters 5 and 8 how replicate sample plots may be allocated to a study area according to simple or stratified random sampling designs. The same ideas of replication, randomization, and representative sampling apply to line transect sampling. While it is possible (and sometimes tempting) to place a single, very long transect in a study area, usually it is a much better idea to randomly assign replicate transects throughout the study area (Figure 9.7A). Randomization can be accomplished by selecting starting points at random (e.g., from a table of UTM coordinates) and then selecting a direction of the transect from a uniform distribution (e.g., over all 360 compass degrees, or just among the cardinal directions). In this way systematic biases in transect location and orientation can be avoided. We especially discourage the use of roads as "sampling units" for line transect sampling. Roads, of course, are not random representations of a target population, often either attract (e.g., for food, travel lanes) or repel (fear of hunters and poachers) animals, and create situations that artificially alter encounter rates. Of course, it is often necessary to use roads to traverse a study area, and it may only be possible to access areas within a limited distance of a road (see example in Chapter 5). In these cases, we still recommend a form of randomization, in which observers travel to randomly selected road positions and then randomly establish transect origins and directions within a logistically feasible radius. Of course, restricting the randomization to a fixed

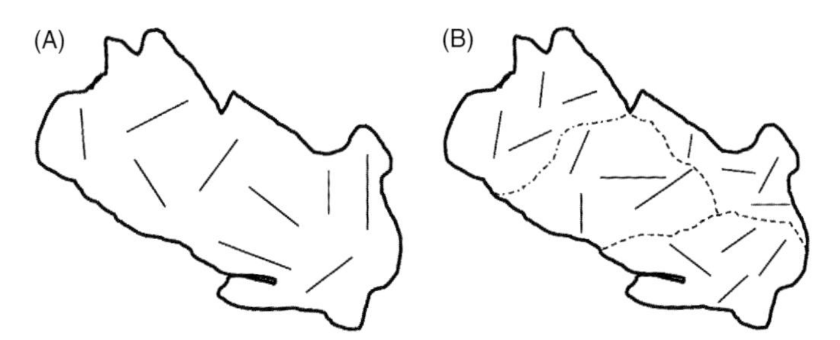

Fig. 9.7 **Sampling designs for a line transect study. (A) Simple random placement of line transects in study area. (B) Stratified random placement of line transects in study area. Note that transects may but are not required to be of equal length.**

distance from roads necessarily limits inference to the area so delineated, as discussed in Chapter 5.

As previously discussed (Chapter 5), study areas are often heterogeneous, and some type of stratification is often advantageous, for instance based on habitat types. The line transect sample can be allocated to survey strata, following the same principles as already described in Chapter 5. At a minimum, sample allocation should take into account the relative sizes of the survey strata (proportional sampling) and, if possible, differences among strata in the coefficient of variation (CV) of density and (where appropriate) sampling costs.

Sample size

There are two basic sample size formulae based on pilot study results. Either may be useful depending on circumstances. The first method assumes that sufficient data have been collected in the pilot sample to allow for a reasonable estimate of density, e.g., using the program DISTANCE. In this approach we take a pilot survey of total line length L_0 and use the resulting data to compute an estimate of density and its coefficient of variation $CV(\hat{D})$ (recall that CV is just the sample standard error divided by the estimate). We then calculate the total sampling effort L necessary to achieve a desired coefficient of variation CV_0 as

$$L = \left[\frac{CV(\hat{D})}{CV_0}\right]^2 L_0 \tag{9.4}$$

Often, however, there are insufficient detections in the pilot sample to provide sufficient data for estimates of density and CV, so an approximation formula based only on counts in the pilot sample can be used instead:

$$L = \frac{3}{[CV_0]^2}\frac{L_0}{n_0} \tag{9.5}$$

where n_0 is the number of animals detected in the pilot sample of effort L_0 (see Box 9.3).

Grouping/covariates

Finally, many situations arise where factors that may influence detection can be measured during the course of the study. In some cases, these can be anticipated in advance, and used for stratification (e.g., habitat conditions). In others, the factors cannot be anticipated in advance, but can be measured along with distance and other variables as data are collected. We have already seen one example of a factor that influences detection and can be measured during sampling: the size of detected clusters. Other attributes may be the physical size of the animal, species (in multispecies survey), or sex (for sexually dimorphic species, particularly where one sex is more conspicuous such as in antlered animals). The general use of covariates is considered to some degree by Drummer and McDonald (1987), Buckland *et al.* (1993, 2001), and more recently by Marques and Buckland (2004).

Box 9.3 Sample size estimation in line transect sampling.

We use the Argus example (Box 9.1) to illustrate sample size computation, treating the data in this analysis as a pilot study. Suppose that our goal is to estimate density with a coefficient of variation of 0.10 (10%) or less; this would result in confidence intervals roughly 0.2 times the mean density in either direction, which is good precision for many applications. Applying the first approach [Equation (9.4)] we use our pilot sample of $L_0 = 316.8$ km (144 2200-m transects) and unconditional CV of 0.21 to obtain

$$L = \left[\frac{0.21}{0.1}\right]^2 316.8 = 1397 \text{ km}$$

which is about 4.5 times the effort exerted on the pilot sample. Applying the second approach [Equation (9.5)] to the observed count of 57 animals we have

$$L = \frac{3}{[0.1]^2} \frac{316.8}{57} = 1667 \text{ km}$$

or a bit over five times the effort of the pilot sample. The second formula tends to overestimate sample size by a bit, so if a good estimate of CV is available, as in this case, we recommend using the first formula [Equation (9.4)].

Point transect sampling

In **point transect sampling**, the sampling unit is a point (or a line of zero length), placed by the investigator at a location in the study area. Points should be placed according to a study design, discussed below. The observer travels to the point and (frequently after an adjustment period) spends a specified amount of time attempting to see, hear, or otherwise detect animals in the vicinity of the point. The observer records the number of animals detected, and also records the straight-line (radial) distance from the point to the point at which the animal or other object was first detected. As with line transect sampling, the observer must count *only those objects actually detected from the point.* The necessary measurements for point transect sampling are illustrated in Figure 9.8. Ornithologists might recognize this as analogous to commonly used fixed radius point counts often used in breeding bird studies. However, the astute reader will once again recognize that a fixed radius plot is simply a quadrat in the shape of a circle. Of course, the same difficult assumption of perfect detection has often been wrongly applied to point count data.

Modeling detection in point transect sampling

As with line transect sampling, statistical modeling of point transect sampling generally requires specialized software, but the analysis is based on intuitive ideas. By analogy to line transect sampling, point transect sampling is a sort of generalization of sampling

Box 9.4 Point transect sampling.

We illustrate point transect sampling with an example of blue grosbeaks (*Guiraca caerulea*) in Georgia, USA. Points (1–2) were randomly placed in 41 agricultural fields that were being included in a longleaf pine (*Pinus palustris*) restoration program and surveyed on three occasions. For the purposes of this illustration, we treated the survey occasions as independent points; a more rigorous analysis would require taking into account the repeated nature of these surveys. Radial distances were recorded from the points to any birds detected; between one and four birds were detected per point, for a total of 108 detections. We used the distance data and point transect counts to fit a series of models in the program DISTANCE. We initially considered models in which density and detection were stratified by field, but ruled these out because of inadequate data, and instead used the pooled data (across fields) to estimate models under four different key functions; we used a cosine adjustment for each model.

Model	No. of parameters	ΔAIC	AIC	ESW	Density	LCI	UCI	CV
Uniform	2	0	966.64	76.36	0.746	0.393	1.416	0.332
Hazard	2	1.18	964.82	78.33	0.709	0.517	0.972	0.161
Half normal	1	1.99	965.62	73.58	0.804	0.607	1.065	0.143
Exponential	3	2.00	965.63	76.37	0.746	0.393	1.416	0.332

The best model (uniform key function) suggests an estimate of density of approximately 0.750 birds/ha, but with a wide confidence interval (0.39–1.46). This model seems to fit the data reasonably well, but notice that there is a wide gap in detections from 0 to 10 m (see Figure 9.6), suggesting that the assumption of perfect detection at the point was violated. Thus, the density estimates have to be considered as possibly underestimating true density, and if possible should be calibrated by independent means.

Besides possible biases because of incomplete detection at the point, the density estimates in this result are imprecise (CV = 0.33). If we wished to design a new survey to increase precision to CV = 0.10, for example, we could treat these results as a pilot survey based on 79 points and apply Equation (9.7):

$$k = \left[\frac{0.33}{0.10}\right]^2 79 = 860$$

This suggests that over 10 times the sampling effort would be required to achieve this precision (nearly 800 more points). If the goal instead was CV = 0.25, this could be achieved with $k = 138$ or 59 more points.

from circular plots. Suppose that k points are established and from these n animals are counted from the point during the course of the survey. If we assume that out to a distance w from the points detection is perfect, then a sensible estimate of density (Chapter 6) is simply the count divided by the cumulative area of the k plots defined

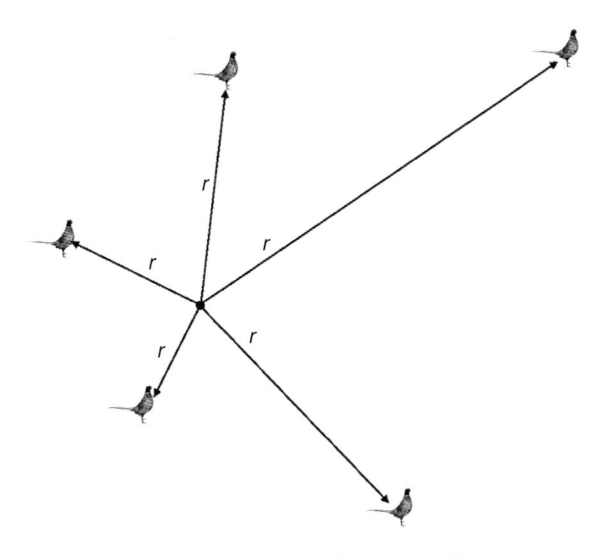

Fig. 9.8 **Example layout for point transect sampling and field measurements required.**

by w:

$$\hat{D} = \frac{n}{k\pi w^2}$$

Distance sampling takes into account that detection probabilities of less than one lead to the need to estimate an "effective area" for the counts, just as in line transect sampling. The relationship between the detection function and the observed distances is a bit more complicated for point transect sampling than for line transect sampling, but still leads to a fairly simple estimate of density as

$$\hat{D} = \frac{nf'(0)}{2k\pi} \tag{9.6}$$

where $f'(0)$ is the derivative of the function $f(r)$ of the radial distances, evaluated at $r = 0$, which in turn is based on a detection function $h(r)$. Otherwise, the basic modeling approaches described earlier for line transect sampling apply to point transect sampling, with respect to model fitting using key functions and series adjustments, variance estimation, stratification, and other issues (Box 9.4).

Assumptions of point transect sampling

The major assumptions of point transect sampling are similar to those involved in line transect sampling:

1. Animals or objects directly at the point ($r = 0$) are counted with certainty. Violation of this assumption will result in underestimation of density or abundance. This particular assumption is somewhat more critical than with line transects

because of the static versus dynamic nature of observations. In point sampling the observer is by definition standing in one spot; whereas animals flushed off the transect line can often be seen in an unbiased fashion.

2. Animals do not move prior to sampling in response to the observer. Again, some additional thought must be given to how a static observer is affecting the immediate environment.
3. Distances are measured accurately. Implications of this assumption will be discussed further under 'Study design'.
4. Points are placed randomly with respect to the animals or other objects. Ordinarily this is guaranteed by random sampling.
5. Observations (counts, distances) of animals or objects are assumed to be independent of one another. This is violated when animals occur in clusters, which can be accommodated using variable-size distance sampling and treating the cluster as the observations.

Study design

All of the major issues and approaches addressed in line transect sampling have corresponding analogs in point transect sampling. We will emphasize here areas of difference.

Measurement accuracy

As with line transect sampling, distances must be accurately measured and recorded, and animals directly at the point (e.g., overhead birds) must be detected. Accurate distance measurement can be problematic for some surveys, e.g., of singing birds, and in practice it often will be necessary to record distances in intervals. This, in turn, places limits on the realism of the resulting detection models, because if there are relatively few distance intervals (e.g., birds can only be seen out to 100 m and recorded to the nearest 25 m, resulting in four intervals) then only very simple detection models can be fit. The assumption of perfect detection at the point $[h(0) = 1)]$ may be difficult to assure, resulting in underestimation of true density. As with line transect sampling, if the assumption of perfect detection on the line cannot be reasonably approximated, then point transect sampling becomes a form of index, and requires calibration to true density by another method (see Chapter 6).

Sample placement

It may be less tempting than in line transect sampling, but if the urge arises to place a single, very intensively sampled point in the study area, it should be resisted. Again, it is a much better idea to randomly assign replicate points throughout the study area (Figure 9.9A) or to invoke a stratified randomization scheme (Figure 9.9B). This is actually simpler than for line transect sampling, as randomization is accomplished by selecting points at random (e.g., from a table of UTM coordinates). As with line

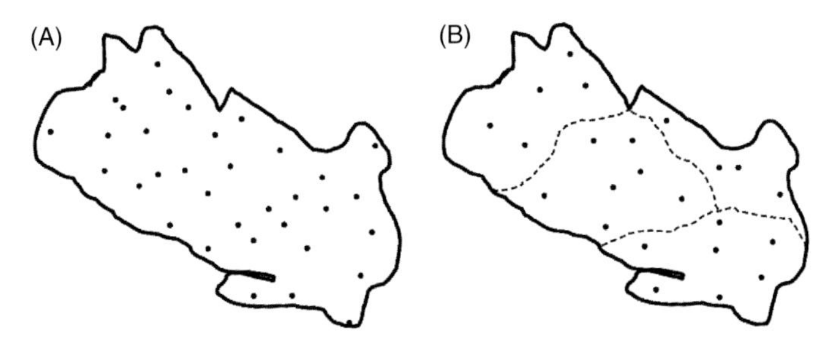

Fig. 9.9 **Sampling designs for a point transect sampling study. (A) Simple random placement of points in study area. (B) Stratified random placement of points in study area.**

transect sampling we discourage the use of roads as "sampling units" for point transect sampling.

Sample size

Sample size determination for point transect sampling is very similar to line transect sampling, the major difference being that the quantity needed is the number of replicate points, k. By direct analogy to the line transect case, k can be determined from a pilot sample of k_0 points by two approaches. If a suitable sample exists to allow estimation of density and $CV(\hat{D})$, then the total sampling effort k necessary to achieve a desired coefficient of variation CV_0 is

$$k = \left[\frac{CV(\hat{D})}{CV_0}\right]^2 k_0 \tag{9.7}$$

If there are insufficient detections in the pilot sample to provide sufficient data for estimates of density and CV, an approximation formula based only on counts in the pilot sample can be used instead:

$$k = \frac{3}{[CV_0]^2}\frac{k_0}{n_0} \tag{9.8}$$

where n_0 is the number of animals detected in the pilot sample of effort k_0.

Grouping/covariates

As with line transects, it may be possible to anticipate and record covariates in a point transect sampling study that influence detection rates, and thereby improve estimation. We refer readers to Drummer and McDonald (1987), Buckland *et al.* (1993, 2001), and Marques and Buckland (2004) for more on this topic.

Trapping webs

Point transect sampling is usually thought of as being applied to "active" counting, in which observers deliberately attempt to detect animals or other objects, often because these are emitting some type of visual or auditory "cue." In fact, both point transect and line transect sampling can be generalized to "passive" situations, in which the animals enter traps or otherwise become detected at known locations, which are arranged in some geometric manner (Lukacs *et al.* 2004). The most well known of these designs is the trapping web (Anderson *et al.* 1983), used for density estimation in capture–recapture studies. Although this is a distance estimation technique, and thus for modeling purposes belongs in this chapter, the data structure and estimation problem more closely relate to capture–recapture studies, and so will be covered in Chapter 10.

In this chapter we have extended the ideas of plot sampling (Chapter 8) for estimating abundance and density to the more general case where detection cannot be assumed perfect and distance data are used to model detection rates. The two major sampling/estimation methods considered were line transect sampling and point sampling, and each can, if assumptions are met, lead to unbiased estimation of density (and, for well-defined study areas, abundance). We showed how each method in a sense simply generalizes ordinary plot (rectangular or circular) sampling, illustrated sampling procedures and estimation, and discussed study design.

In Chapter 10 we leave methods based on observation (plot sampling and line and point transect sampling) and discuss studies that involve the capture, marking, and recapture of animals for abundance and density estimation. As we will see, these studies involve the physical capture, marking, and recapture of animals, but also cases where animals are "naturally" marked (e.g., by patterns, scars, or even DNA) or where the "marking" is via detection by independent methods.

10
Capture–mark–recapture studies for estimating abundance and density

In this chapter we describe methods that involve the capture, marking, and recapture of animals for abundance and density estimation. These studies involve the physical capture, marking, and recapture of animals, but also cases where animals are "naturally" marked (e.g., by patterns, scars, or even DNA) or where the "marking" is via detection by independent methods. Removal sampling, catch-per-unit effort, change in ratio, and trapping webs are all special cases. As with distance sampling, there has been enormous development of techniques and supportive software; therefore we do not attempt an exhaustive treatment of these methods, and readers who desire more thorough coverage are referred to Williams *et al.* (2002) and the many citations therein.

Basics of capture–mark–recapture

The basic premise of **capture–mark–recapture (CMR)** is simple, and tied to the idea that any sample of animals that is encountered by a capture is simply an incomplete count of the population. If we could somehow determine the fraction (p) of the true population (N) represented by our sample (n), we would have a means of estimating abundance from our sample thus:

$$N = \frac{n}{\hat{p}} \tag{10.1}$$

Note that this capture fraction (or **capture probability**) p is really the same thing as the generic detection rate (β) we encountered in Chapter 6 and elsewhere in other forms. For simplicity, we have not indexed p, but it may vary over time, space, or even individual animals, as we shall see. Once again, readers should note the importance of the binomial distribution (Chapter 5) in wildlife sampling.

CMR involves a couple of straightforward but important generalizations of this idea. First, "capture" and "marking" may include the actual physical capture and affixing of tags or other marks to animals, but it need not. The essential idea is that a sample of the N animals is marked somehow, and we have a list of those marks. Animals can

Quantitative Conservation of Vertebrates, 1st edition. By M.J. Conroy and J.P. Carroll. Published 2009 by Blackwell Publishing, ISBN 978-1-4051-8228-7 (pb) and 978-1-4051-9098-5 (hb).

also be tied to this list if they have individually distinctive characteristics (anything ranging from a facial mark to a genotype) and we have previously encountered this unique characteristic. For example, a tiger (*Pantheris tigris*) whose unique striping has previously been catalogued by the investigator, using say a camera trap, may be considered to have been captured (C) and marked (M). If that tiger is detected in a subsequent sample, it may be considered to have been recaptured (R), and this information is appropriate for CMR analysis (Karanth and Nichols 1998). Similarly, all animals are naturally "marked" with DNA, and the genetic signature of animals may be read by passive means such as sampling of hair or feces. Problems do arise in this type of "marking" study where marks potentially can be misread, confused with other marks, or even "invented" (i.e., marked seen but does not exist), but all of these (perhaps excepting the last) occur in conventional CMR studies involving numbered tags. Error analysis has been undertaken for some types of CMR, such as band recovery, and to a limited degree for "natural" markers (e.g., Lukacs and Burnham 2005); however, there is continued need to assess the impacts of all of the potential problems outlined above, especially when natural marks are used.

As in all cases of marking animals, the mark, whether we actively or passively mark or use some type of animal-based markers, must have a minimal impact on our "marked" sample. This includes everything from marks causing changes in animal behavior (e.g., making them more vulnerable to predation) to tag loss to biases in "unique" identifying features of an animal. We will cover some of the issues later in the chapter.

The other generalization of CMR has to do with variation in the capture probabilities (p). In the simplest (and most unrealistic) case, p is constant over time, space, and among animals, so that n is always a constant fraction (i.e., an index) of N. Common experience has shown that capture probabilities vary over time (due to weather and other factors, such as effort), space (due to habitat and other conditions), and among individual animals (both intrinsically, and related to the experience of previous capture). This is especially true when capture and physical marking are involved, but also occurs when more passive methods are used. Failure to account for this variation can lead to serious biases, if naïve estimates are used, based on constant capture rates. Fortunately, flexible and robust statistical procedures allow us to build models appropriate to the situation, as long as sufficient data are gathered according to appropriate designs.

All of the methods in this chapter, as in Chapters 8 and 9, assume that the population is closed to birth, death, and movements, so that N is unchanging over the study interval. We relax this assumption and allow for estimation of vital rates and movements with CMR data in Chapter 12.

Before embarking on particular estimation models, we will introduce some useful notational conventions:

- N is abundance (total numbers of animals) in the closed population during the study period.
- k is the number of capture/recapture occasions during the study; k must be at least 2 in order to estimate N.

- X_ω is the number of animals having unique capture history ω. The capture history ω is simply a code describing whether an animal is captured (1) or not (0) on each of the k capture occasions in the study. For example, $\omega = 101$ signifies that an animal is captured the first and third occasions of a $k = 3$ CMR study.
- n_i is the number of animals caught and marked at each capture occasion, $i = 1, \ldots, k$.
- m_i is the number of marked animals caught (recaptured) at each capture occasion, $i = 1, \ldots, k$. By definition, $m_1 = 0$ (there are no marked animals before the first period, so none can be recaptured!).
- r is the number of distinct animals captured over the course of the study.

Two-sample (Lincoln–Petersen)

The simplest possible sampling situation involves two samples: an initial marking and release sample, and a subsequent recapture sample. This approach (and statistical model) is known as **Lincoln–Petersen (L–P)**, after Frederick Lincoln and Gustav Petersen who popularized the approach in the wildlife and fisheries fields, respectively. However, the basic idea had been around a much longer time, and was used at least as far back as the 18th century by Laplace (1786) to estimate the human populations in pre-revolutionary France. (We suspect that he should not have applied methods assuming closure to mortality!)

Assumptions

There are three assumptions essential to the development of the statistical model for estimation under the Lincoln–Petersen method:

- As with all the methods in this chapter, we assume that the population is closed to birth, death, immigration, and estimation. Violation of this assumption can lead to biased estimates of abundance, although in special cases it may be possible to obtain unbiased estimates if either losses (deaths, emigration) or gains (births, immigration) between the two samples can be ruled out, so that there are gains or losses, but not both (see Williams *et al.* 2002).
- All individual animals are assumed to have the same probability of being caught in each sample, and previous capture experience does not influence subsequent probability of capture. If either of these assumptions is violated, serious biases may result in the estimates of abundance. However, capture probabilities may differ between the samples (due to effort, methods, or other reasons), and therefore there are two capture parameters (p_1 and p_2).
- It is assumed that there is no tag loss or other loss of marks (such as failure to record marks). Violations of this assumption will also bias estimates of

abundance, but potentially can be corrected for if tag loss rates can be estimated, for example by double tagging (Williams *et al.* 2002).

With the Lincoln–Petersen method, tags or marks of individuals do not need to be unique to each individual (this is called **batch marking**). Methods discussed later in the chapter, in general practice, may require that each tag be unique to the animal to allow construction of capture histories.

Data and estimation model

The data for Lincoln–Petersen are very simple to summarize. In terms of capture histories, there are only three possible histories that can be observed: captured in the first (given a 1), but not second (given a 0) sample (resulting in the data construct 10); captured in the second, but not the first (01), or caught during both occasions (11). Thus the elementary data that are collected in Lincoln–Petersen are the number of animals that fall into each category:

X_{10}, caught on the first but not second occasion;
X_{01}, caught on the second but not first occasion;
X_{11}, caught on both occasions;

for $r = X_{10} + X_{01} + X_{11}$ different animals caught over the study. Of course, there are also $N - r$ animals *never* captured. In general in CMR studies, if we could estimate this quantity we would be done, since we know r (assuming the population is closed).

We like this data description, because it makes it clear that the animals fall into four distinct categories: 10, 01, 11, and 00 (never caught). Note that the sum of these frequencies is, by definition, the total number of animals in the population. Therefore if we know the number of the first three groups and can estimate the number of animals never caught, we can estimate total abundance. This approach extends well to other CMR methods, more complicated and as we have already seen is the same type of notation used in occupancy studies. However, traditionally the basic Lincoln–Petersen data are usually summarized differently, as numbers captured or recaptured on each occasion:

- n_1 animals are captured on the first occasion; this also includes animals recaptured on the second occasion, so that $n_1 = X_{10} + X_{11}$. By definition all of these animals are unmarked ($m_1 = 0$).
- n_2 total animals are captured on the second occasion, which includes animals originally captured on the first occasion and recaptured, so that $n_1 = X_{01} + X_{11}$. Thus, n_2 includes both marked (recaptured) and unmarked (newly captured) animals.
- $m_2 = X_{11}$ marked animals are recaptured on the second occasion.

Given the above assumptions and summarized data, the statistical model for Lincoln–Petersen can be derived by intuitive or more formal means. Intuitively, once the n_1 animals are marked and released into the population, the fraction of the population that is marked is n_1/N; because we are assuming that neither gains nor losses are occurring in the population, this fraction should remain constant until the second sample. At that time, if the marked animals have become thoroughly mixed into the population and a second sample (n_2) is taken, we would expect that the proportion of marked animals in that sample would represent the same proportion in the whole population, that is:

$$\frac{n_1}{N} = \frac{m_2}{n_2}$$

Solving this relationship for N provides the basic Lincoln–Petersen estimator:

$$\hat{N} = \frac{n_1 n_2}{m_2} \tag{10.2}$$

However, this estimator is slightly biased for small capture samples, and a bias-adjusted estimator is typically used instead:

$$\tilde{N} = \frac{(n_1+1)(n_2+1)}{m_2+1} - 1 \tag{10.3}$$

The sampling variance for this estimator is computed as

$$\hat{\text{var}}(\tilde{N}) = \frac{(n_1+1)(n_2+1)(n_1-m_2)(n_2-m_2)}{(m_2+1)^2(m_2+2)} \tag{10.4}$$

which leads to approximate confidence intervals of

$$\tilde{N} \pm z_{\alpha/2}\sqrt{\hat{\text{var}}(\tilde{N})}$$

or

$$\tilde{N} \pm 1.96\sqrt{\hat{\text{var}}(\tilde{N})}$$

for a 95% confidence interval.

The Lincoln–Petersen estimator can also be derived more formally under a multinomial model (Chapter 5), where the probabilities of the capture histories are $p_1(1-p_2)$ for (1,0), $p_2(1-p_1)$ for (0,1), p_1p_2 for (1,1), and $(1-p_1)(1-p_2)$ for (00). It can be shown that maximum likelihood estimation under this model leads to the basic Lincoln–Petersen estimator [Equation (10.2)].

Study design

Meeting Lincoln–Petersen assumptions

As has been mentioned previously, all the methods in this chapter assume that the population is closed. Because births, deaths, and movements are more likely to occur over longer study intervals, this generally dictates that L–P and other closed CMR studies should be done over relatively short time periods, the exact length depending on the study organism. If trap mortality occurs, the assumption of closure is violated, and this source of mortality should be minimized, for instance by providing sufficient food in traps, checking traps early in the day to avoid heat and drought stress, and shading traps from direct sunlight. Inevitably, some mortality will occur. If it is the first sample occasion, then the animals that die should be removed from the statistic used to compute abundance, that is, revised by $n_1' = n_1 - d$, where d is the known number of trap deaths. Once $\hat{N}$ is computed, the d animals may be added back into the estimate, which is now a valid estimate of abundance before the first sampling occasion; alternatively $\hat{N}$ may be retained as an estimate of N at the second occasion. Mortalities upon capture at the second occasion do not affect estimation, other than constituting losses obvious from the population that should be accounted for (and obviously minimized). Conversely, if trapping or marking influences survival in such a way that marked animals are less likely to be recaptured (because they die differentially) at the second sample than unmarked animals, we have clearly violated the "no influence" assumption, discussed below, as well as the closure assumption.

A very common type of assumption violation that occurs in CMR studies is unequal capture probability between previously marked and unmarked animals. The problem is that marked animals are less (if **trap shy**) or more (if **trap happy**) likely to show up as recaptures than would be predicted by their fraction in the population, thus violating the key assumption that makes it possible to compute L–P. If animals are trap shy, abundance is positively biased (N is overestimated by $\hat{N}$), and if trap happy the bias is negative (N is underestimated by $\hat{N}$). The difficulty is that with only two capture samples it is impossible to account for trap response in a statistical model, and so it is critical to reduce or eliminate its effect in the study design. Trap shyness can be reduced to some extent by accustoming animals to traps by pre-baiting or otherwise allowing free entry into the traps before actual capture. Trap shyness may be reduced by minimizing handling time or by using recapture methods that do not depend on physical capture, as in the example in Box 10.1. In some studies, it is impossible to eliminate these effects, and as with individual heterogeneity (discussed below) it is better to use a study design and estimation procedure that allows for proper modeling of this variation. Alternatively, trap response can be minimized or even eliminated by using an entirely *different* method for recapture than was used for initial capture, as illustrated in the Box 10.1 example where the "recapture" is resighting and therefore no physical capture is required.

In addition to the possibility that capture affects the probability of recapture, numerous studies have documented that individual animals may differ from each other in their susceptibility to trapping. Some of this individual heterogeneity can be accounted for by age, sex, or other identifiable characteristics, and potentially be removed via a stratified design. More generally, however, individual heterogeneity cannot be predicted by individual attributes, especially when some groups of animals have very low capture probability, and thus may seldom if ever be captured. As with capture effects, the best approach may be to use a study design and estimation procedure that allows for proper

Box 10.1 Two-sample capture–mark–recapture (Lincoln–Petersen).

Our example illustrates the Lincoln–Petersen method when two different methods are used, one for the capturing and initial marking of animals, the other for detection of marks in the second sample ("recapture"). Rabbits (*Sylvilagus nuttali*) in central Oregon were captured and marked by dyeing the tails and hind legs with picric acid (batch marking) (Skalski *et al.* 1983). In the initial sample, 87 animals were captured and dyed with picric acid, and then released. In a follow-up sample, 14 rabbits were counted in a drive count, and of these seven were marked. This yields the following statistics:

$n_1 = 87$ rabbits captured on the first occasion (capture sample);
$n_2 = 14$ rabbits detected on the second occasion (drive count);
$m_2 = 7$ dyed rabbits detected on the second occasion (drive count).

These were used to compute the Lincoln–Petersen method, using the bias correction estimate of

$$\tilde{N} = \frac{(87+1)(14+1)}{7+1} - 1 = 164$$

$$\mathrm{SE}(\tilde{N}) = \sqrt{\frac{(n_1+1)(n_2+1)(n_1-m_2)(n_2-m_2)}{(m_2+1)^2(m_2+2)}} = 35.82$$

for $\mathrm{CV}(\tilde{N}) = 0.22$. This provides an approximate 95% confidence interval of 93.8 to 234.2. We can also estimate the capture probabilities by each method, which will be useful in computing sample sizes:

$$\hat{p}_1 = 87/164 = 0.53$$

$$\hat{p}_2 = 14/164 = 0.09$$

modeling of this variation; this requires several (often five or more) capture occasions and individual rather than group identification.

Sample placement

In many CMR studies, the basic unit of sampling effort will be a trap line, trap grid, mist net array, or other spatial arrangements of capture devices. Such arrangements are not strictly necessary for CMR abundance estimation, if it is reasonable to assume that animals "mix well" into the population for resampling on the second occasion. However, dispersal of traps or other devices throughout the study area may help to ensure that the initial sample is itself representative of the study area, which might not be the case if sampling were confined to one or two locations, possibly resulting in a sample with unusually high or low recapture probability (and thus contributing to heterogeneity).

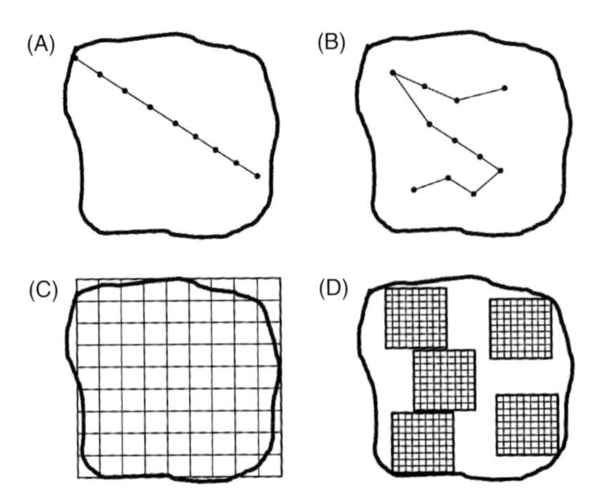

Fig. 10.1 **Possible designs for placement of trapping grids. (A) Single straight trap line, (B) single meandering trap line, (C) uniform grid placement over study area, and (D) replicated subgrids.**

Figure 10.1 provides several possible schemes for laying out capture devices in a study area. Trap lines (Figure 10.1A,B) are often convenient, but can result in poor dispersal of traps unless they are allowed to meander through the study area. Trap grids (Figure 10.1C,D) provide better dispersal, and potentially can be useful for estimating density, as we see later in this chapter. Replicated lines or grids (Figure 10.1D) potentially allow estimation of abundance on each replicate, and computation of empirical variances (similar to replicated lines in line transect; Chapter 9), if recapture sample sizes on each replicate are sufficiently high. Any of these schemes potentially can be combined with stratification (Chapter 5) which is advisable for large, diverse study areas.

Sample sizes

With distance sampling, there is a fairly straightforward relationship between "sampling effort" (line length, number of point transects, etc.) and estimator precision. Even so, the actual precision of a distance study will depend on true density (hence, the number of animals capable of being detected) and other factors (animal wariness, habitat conditions, and so on). With CMR studies, the precision of the L–P estimator will depend on two outcomes: (i) the number of animals marked at each sample (n_1, n_2) and (ii) the number of recaptures on the second occasion (m_2). Both of these will in turn be influenced to some degree by investigator effort, such as the number of traps placed. They are also influenced by factors beyond the investigator's control, such as actual abundance, and the wariness of animals to enter traps or otherwise be captured. Many studies are particularly vulnerable to low or even zero recaptures, due to low capture probabilities, or very high abundance (so that it becomes difficult to mark a substantial fraction of N). Investigators need some type of a preliminary idea in the range of abundance and capture probabilities, in order to assess if a CMR study will have a chance of providing reliable results.

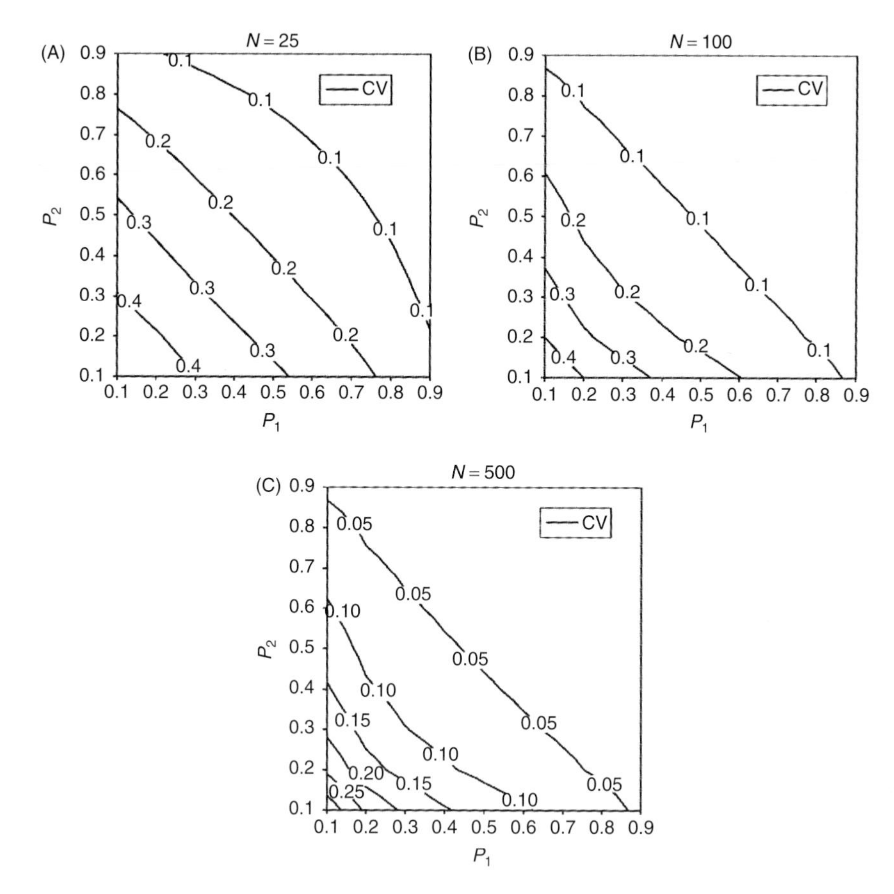

Fig. 10.2 **Relationship between capture probability at each sample occasion, abundance, and CV for a Lincoln–Petersen CMR study. (A) $N = 25$, (B) $N = 100$, (C) $N = 500$. Contour lines display contours of equal CV($\hat{N}$) for Lincoln–Petersen estimate of abundance.**

Given N, p_1, and p_2, it is straightforward to generate expected outcomes for n_1, n_2, and m_2, and treating these as data, derive estimates of N and CV($\hat{N}$) using Equations (10.3) and (10.4). These relationships can be used to produce curves showing the precision for different combinations of N, p_1, and p_2 (Figure 10.2), which can be used to guide study design (Box 10.2). As a general rule, capture probabilities must result in a large proportion of the population in the sample area being captured on one or both occasions. Because studies with low capture probabilities generally will result in estimates with low precision, it is often a good idea to conduct a pilot study to get an idea of the effort that will be needed to produce reliable estimates.

Multiple sample CMR methods (Schnabel census)

Multiple sample CMR (the so-called **Schnabel census** – we do not like this term for obvious reasons) is really just a generalization of Lincoln–Petersen to multiple samples

Box 10.2 Sample sizes for Lincoln–Petersen.

We used the example in Box 10.1 as a pilot study to design a study to give $CV(\tilde{N}) = 0.10$. We can use the graphs in Figure 10.2 to get an idea of sampling effort to achieve this result. Below is the graph for $N = 100$, which is the nearest level of abundance plotted. Following the contour line for CV $= 0.1$ gives us combinations of p_1 and p_2 that will achieve this result. For instance, suppose that we have pretty much exerted all the effort we can to increase capture rates at the first sample ($p_1 = 0.5$). The figure results show that

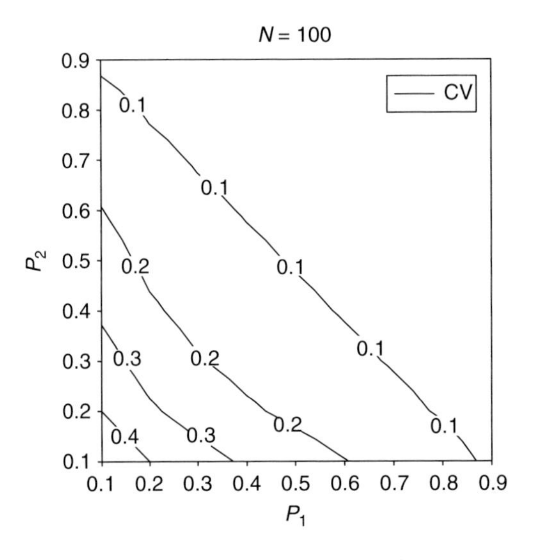

we need to boost capture rates at the second sample to about 0.5 as well, which means in excess of 80 animals at each sample (compared to 14 in our pilot study). More exact results can be obtained by using the spreadsheet provided (see enclosed CD and website address on p. ii). Doing so suggests that a CV $= 0.1$ can be achieved for $N = 164$ with capture probabilities $p_1 = 0.53$ and $p_2 = 0.3$, or sample sizes of 87 and 49 at the first and second samples, respectively. Other combinations can be explored as well, including some that may be more cost effective. For example, if it is cheaper to check for marks than it is to place marks, it may be better to decrease the first sample in favor of the second. In the present example, effort of $p_1 = 0.33$ and $p_2 = 0.53$ ($n_1 = 54$ and $n_2 = 87$) provides CV $= 0.1$, and would be favored over the previous design if, as seems likely, resampling marks is cheaper than applying them.

($k > 2$). Now, instead of a single capture–marking period, followed by a second recapture occasion, animals at the second period are also marked (if unmarked), released back into the population, and may be recaptured at a third or subsequent occasion. This design has two advantages over Lincoln–Petersen. First, because there are several (five, ten, or even more) capture occasions, more captures–recaptures accumulate as the study progresses. Thus, even if capture probabilities on a single occasion are somewhat low, the chance of capture over the study period may be higher than on

Lincoln–Petersen because of this cumulative effect over time. Second, multiple sample CMR produces a richer data structure than Lincoln–Petersen, allowing for more complex and robust modeling of capture probabilities. This in turn allows for relaxing of some of the Lincoln–Petersen assumptions, allowing for modeling of behavioral and individual animal effects on capture. This aspect is also the principal disadvantage, in that estimates can no longer be computed by relatively simple formulae, but instead require specialized computer programs. Fortunately, these are freely available and relatively easy to use.

We now need to clarify some issues relative to marking and these methods. Theoretically our discussion above means we need to modify the way animals are marked compared to L–P. Although **batch marking** can be used in a number of study designs it significantly limits the types of models that can be applied and our ability to identify possible variability in our capture histories (e.g., capture or time heterogeneity). We recommend that the starting point for any CMR study be the use of marks that allow individual animal identification. Batch marking should be viewed as a poorer alternative when individual marking is not possible.

The data resulting from a multiple sample CMR study can be summarized using notation already developed. Again, X_ω is the number of animals having unique capture history ω, but now ω is an array of ones and zeros equal in dimension to the number of capture occasions (k). For example, for $k = 5$ some possible capture histories are

01000

11111

10101

10000

00001

In general, there are $2^k - 1$ observable capture histories, so for $k = 5$ there are $2^5 - 1 = 31$ histories like those above. Not all of these capture histories will necessarily be observed in a given study. In addition, there is of course one capture history that will never be observed: the one in which animals are not captured on any occasion (e.g., 00000). The frequencies of animals with these capture histories (X_ω) are the fundamental data in multiple sample CMR. Again, several useful summary statistics are as follows:

- n_i is the number of animals caught and marked on each capture occasion, $i = 1, \ldots, k$.
- m_i is the number of marked animals caught (recaptured) on each capture occasion, $i = 1, \ldots, k$.
- r is the number of distinct animals captured over the course of the study. r in turn is simply with reference to the unique capture histories by adding the frequencies:

$$r = \sum_\omega X_\omega$$

Now thinking about this the reader should be seeing the advantages of individual identification. We can use those individual capture history patterns to assess some of the potential pitfalls of the traditional L–P method (e.g., are animals trap happy or trap shy). The following two sections discuss these issues in detail.

Assumptions

The major assumptions of closed population CMR are:

- Again, we assume that the population is closed to birth, death, immigration, and estimation.
- There is no tag loss or other loss of marks (such as failure to record marks).

We no longer assume that all individual animals necessarily have the same probability of being caught in each sample, and that previous capture experience does not influence subsequent probability of capture. Rather, these situations are handled by the modeling of capture and recapture probabilities, as described below.

Estimation models

The basic idea of modeling multiple sample CMR is that the patterns in the frequencies of capture histories X_ω will depend on underlying variation in capture probabilities over capture occasions $j = 1, \ldots, k$, depending on whether the animals have been caught previously or not, and among individual animals $i = 1, \ldots, N$. This leads us to think about capture probabilities in a very general way, in which capture may depend on time, behavior (so, previously captured or not), or the identity of the individual animal. In theory we would have capture probabilities for every occasion and animal:

$$p_{ij}, j = 1, \ldots, k; \quad i = 1, \ldots N$$

and recapture probabilities for every recapture ($k > 1$) occasion:

$$c_{ij}, j = 2, \ldots, k; \quad i = 1, \ldots N$$

Then, depending on assumptions about how capture probabilities vary, the capture histories can be modeled. For instance, if is assumed that capture probability only varies over time (sampling occasions), we would assume that $p_{ij} = p_j$ and $c_{ij} = p_j$. We would then model the probability of the capture history thus:

$$\begin{aligned} \omega &= 101011 \\ \Pr(\omega) &= p_1(1 - p_2)p_3(1 - p_4)p_5p_6 \end{aligned}$$

If instead we assumed that there were only behavioral (no time or individual) effects we would have:

$$\Pr(\omega) = p(1 - c)c(1 - c)c \quad c = p(1 - c)^2c^3$$

Finally, if we allowed for all three sources of variation we would have a very complex model:

$$\Pr(\omega) = p_{\omega 1}(1 - c_{\omega 2})c_{\omega 3}(1 - c_{\omega 4})c_{\omega 5}c_{\omega 6}$$

where both capture and recapture potentially are different for every capture history. Assuming that such models can be built, they become the basis for estimation by maximum likelihood or other approaches of capture and recapture probabilities and (of primary interest) abundance, N. Under maximum likelihood, for example, the frequencies X_ω and probabilities $\Pr(\omega)$ are used in a multinomial likelihood to obtain maximum likelihood estimates of capture and recapture probabilities, which are then used to estimate N by an extension of the ideas behind Lincoln–Petersen (basically by allowing us to estimate the probability of never capturing an animal, and thereby adjusting our sample of known captures to estimate abundance).

The detail of how estimation models are constructed is complex and beyond the scope of this book, but is covered in Otis *et al.* (1978) and Williams *et al.* (2002). Specialized computer programs (CAPTURE and MARK among others) have been written to perform these analyses and are freely available (see Appendix A). These programs are used to evaluate models under alternative assumptions about capture probabilities and compute abundance under each set of assumptions. The essential models considered (in notation similar to Otis *et al.* 1978) are as follows:

- a null model (M_0) specifying that capture and recapture rates are equal, and do not vary over time or among individuals;
- temporal variation (M_t) in capture probabilities, but no behavioral or individual heterogeneity. Lincoln–Petersen is actually a special case of this for $k = 2$;
- a behavioral (M_b) model specifying that capture and recapture probabilities differ (such as trap happy or trap shy response, but also includes removal models), but otherwise do not vary over time or among individuals;
- an individual heterogeneity (M_h) model specifying that capture probabilities vary among individuals, but not over time or in response to capture;
- combinations of the time, behavior and heterogeneity, e.g., allowing both behavioral response and heterogeneity (M_{bh}) or heterogeneity and time (M_{th}).

The central ideas of this approach are to (i) consider alternative models that fully investigate assumptions about capture probabilities, and (ii) use the study data to compare the support of the alternative models, tending toward selecting simpler (parsimonious) models that still fit the data well, but (iii) to recognize that some models (especially the null model) are not **robust** and will provide poor estimates if assumptions are violated; these should therefore be avoided unless strongly supported by the data or other evidence. We illustrate the application of CMR for multiple samples in Box 10.3.

Box 10.3 Multiple-sample capture–mark–recapture.

Our example comes from a study of meadow voles (*Microtus pennsylvanicus*) in Maryland (Nichols *et al.* 1984, from Williams *et al.* 2002). Adult female and male voles were trapped over five consecutive days in August 1981; the data here are for females only. We analyzed these data with two different programs. First, we used the web-based version of the program CAPTURE (Appendix A) to select among standard closed-population models, test for closure, and compute parameter estimates. The input for this analysis is available in the electronic companion to the book (see enclosed CD and website address on p. ii). The test of closure provides no suggestion that the closure assumption was violated ($z = -0.43$, $P = 0.33$). Model selection criteria in CAPTURE provided strong evidence ($P = 1.0$ vs. $P = 0.65$ for the next best model) that model M_h, the jackknife heterogeneity model, was the best model. The jackknife estimator was $\hat{N} = 65$, with a 95% confidence interval of (58, 81). The complete model output from CAPTURE is also available in the electronic companion to the book (see enclosed CD and website address on p. ii).

As an alternative, we also used program MARK and the Huggins heterogeneity model. MARK has the advantage that all models are presented in a maximum likelihood framework (the jackknife model, for instance, is not a likelihood model), allowing comparison via AIC. For this relatively small problem, we were able to fit only two distinct likelihood models, one allowing for time-specific capture probabilities, the other time-constant capture, and both specify a fixed probability of an animal's being in one of two capture "mixture" distributions (the approach for modeling capture heterogeneity):

Model	AICc	Delta AICc	AICc weights
{pi(.) p(t) PIM}	358.1073	0	0.99626
{pi(.) p(.) PIM}	369.2798	11.1725	0.00374

The AIC statistics provide evidence that capture probability varies over time, and provide parameter estimates as follows:

Parameter	Estimate	SE	LCI	UCI
P	0.202661	0.096895	0.072761	0.451538
P(2)	0.852698	0.097057	0.560054	0.963402
P(3)	0.304797	0.057348	0.20505	0.427001
N	62.0329	4.453235	56.91218	76.15779

Note that *N* itself is not actually a parameter under this model, but is derived from the other parameters [pi and p(t)].

The complete model input and output from MARK for this example can be found in the electronic companion to the book (see enclosed CD and website address on p. ii).

Study design

Meeting assumptions

As with Lincoln–Petersen, we must assume that the population is closed. Violation of this assumption will bias estimation. Obviously, known trap mortalities should be accounted for and removed from the release statistics prior to analysis; some programs such as MARK allow for special coding to properly handle these statistics. Again, multiple sample CMR should be done over relatively short time periods, the exact length depending on the study organism. Here we potentially run into a conflict with study design in what might be otherwise very good design (k large) if the study occurs over too long an interval. Tests for population closure are available (e.g., in the program CAPTURE), but are not completely specific for closure. If the study runs over a long period of time it will be advisable to consider open CMR methods (Chapter 12), including the Robust Design.

As noted earlier, we no longer have to assume equal capture probability between previously marked and unmarked animals or homogeneity of capture among individuals. On the other hand, if the study can be conducted in such a way as to reduce these effects, the results will be improved. As with L–P, it may be possible to reduce behavioral effects by pre-baiting or using recapture methods that do not depend on physical capture. Similarly, although some temporal effects cannot be controlled, others can be, or can be reduced in impact. The most obvious temporal effect that is controllable is capture effort: numbers of traps, amount of bait, and so forth. Effort should be kept as constant as possible over the study to reduce temporal effects. Likewise, trapping can be conducted under similar conditions, e.g., always on calm nights rather than rainy or windy nights. By such efforts it may be possible to reduce the need to model time effects, and concentrate on effects that cannot be so easily reduced, such as heterogeneity (see Box 10.3). It is important to remember that these issues can vary among research projects undertaken on the same species, depending on questions being asked or local conditions, and especially among species being studied, because of their biology. Again, planning becomes crucial to avoid pitfalls.

Sample placement

The same basic spatial design can be used for multiple CMR as for L–P. Grids or arrays have the additional advantage of allowing modeling of movements between samples. Although not of direct interest for abundance estimation, such information may be useful for the estimation of density (below).

Sample sizes

The same general procedures apply to **multiple sample CMR** as to L–P for estimation of sample size. Some notion of capture probabilities and abundance is needed, usually necessitating a pilot study (see Box 10.4). In addition, it is helpful to have some idea,

Box 10.4 Sample sizes for a k-sample capture–mark–recapture study.

We illustrate the use of capture–recapture to design a future study using the Nichols data from Box 10.3. In this study, we achieved a CV of N of about 8% ($\mathrm{SE}(\hat{N})/\hat{N} \times 100\%$), with a study with average capture probability of about 0.6. However, since capture probabilities seem to be heterogeneous, both over time and among animals, it is probably safer to assume a lower average capture probability, perhaps 0.4–0.5. We can consult the figure below ($N = 100$ is the closest graph we have created) and see that to achieve a CV of

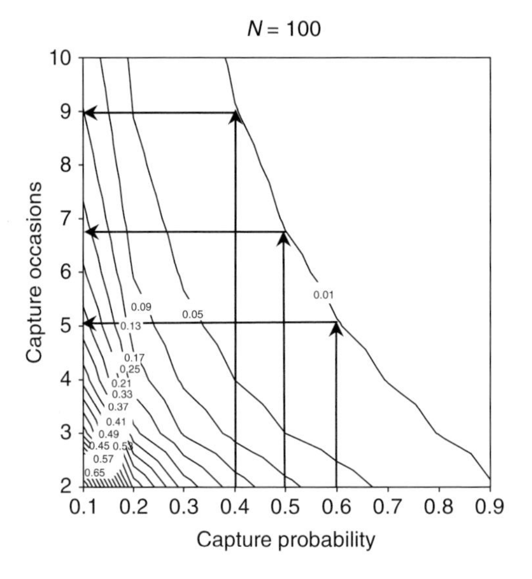

0.01 (1%), we would need in the order of seven to nine capture occasions to increase capture probability to 0.6 or higher, or both. On the other hand, if we were satisfied with a CV of 0.05 (5%), our current design, perhaps with a few more occasions, should provide a satisfactory result. Calculation of sample size estimates under the assumption of constant capture probability is performed in spreadsheets that can be found in the electronic companion to the book (see enclosed CD and website address on p. ii).

either *a priori* or from pilot data, as to sources of variation in capture and recapture probabilities likely to be encountered. The additional dimension in the sampling design is k, the number of sampling occasions. Given some anticipated sources of variation in capture and recapture (and so some candidate estimators), it is possible to come up with k-sample analogs of the sample size diagrams in Figure 10.2. We have provided a series of such diagrams in Figure 10.3, based on an assumption of constant capture probability (model M_0). In addition, Otis *et al.* (1978) provide several "rules of thumb" for multiple-sample CMR studies:

- a minimum of five sampling occasions, with $k = 7$–10 better;
- average capture probability >0.2 if $N > 200$;
- average capture probability >0.4 if $N = 50$ or lower.

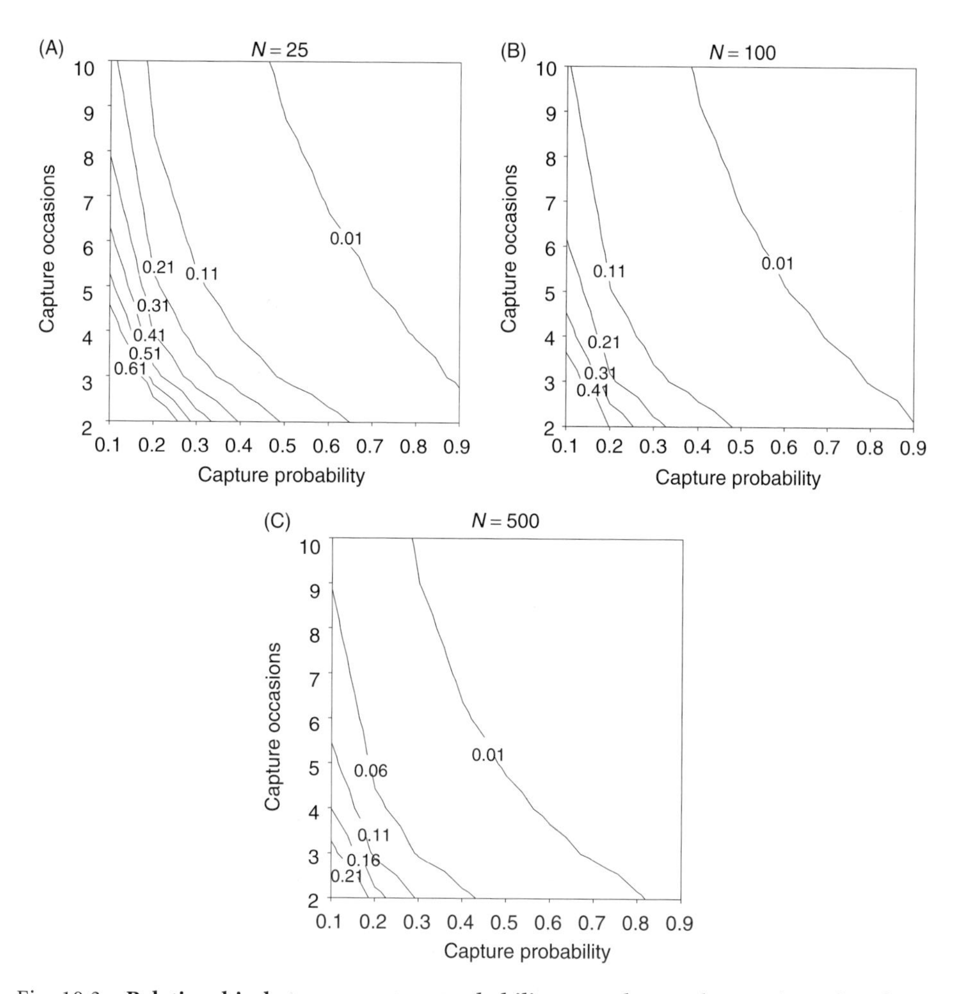

Fig. 10.3 **Relationship between capture probability at each sample occasion, abundance, and number of capture occasions for a k-sample CMR study. (A) $N = 25$, (B) $N = 100$, (C) $N = 500$. Contour lines display contours of equal $CV(\hat{N})$ for the "null" model assuming constant capture probability over time and individuals and no behavioral response.**

These are only guidelines; investigators are always encouraged to conduct pilot studies to obtain more reliable information for their particular circumstances.

Removal sampling

There are really two distinct types of **removal sampling**. The first, which we consider here, assumes that removal effort per capture occasion is constant, so that declines in the number of new, "unmarked" animals in the population occur because an increasing proportion of the population has been previously captured. The second type of removal occurs when removal effort varies over occasions, and information on this effort is used in the estimation of abundance. We discuss the first type of removal here, and the second near the end of this chapter, because in our opinion it is relatively specialized and will not be appropriate for many conservation studies (see Box 10.5).

Assumptions

The major assumptions of removal sampling are:

- the population is closed (except for the known removals);
- all removals are correctly accounted for (so no tags are missed or lost, and all physical removals are recorded);
- removal effort is constant over time.

Constant-effort removal methods can involve either true, physical removal of animals (e.g., animals are captured and killed or otherwise removed from the population) or "removal" from the unmarked population by marking. In the first case, since we are physically removing animals, we are potentially creating vacancies for new animals to move into the population. If much of this happens, we will violate the closure assumption, and our estimates will be biased. Thus, it is important to keep the study period short; often, this means five to six sampling occasions at most.

Estimation models

The basic idea behind removal estimation can be seen by considering the expected number of unmarked animals in samples under the simple case where there is a constant removal (capture) rate, p. Before the study, all N animals in the population are unmarked. Given a constant capture rate p we expect to capture:

$$pN$$

of these in the first sample, leaving $(1 - p)N$ marked animals in the population. At the second sample we can expect to capture p times this number remaining or

$$p(1 - p)N,$$

and in the third sample

$$p(1 - p)^2N$$

and so on. This leads to a model with a geometrically declining number of new (unmarked) animals, and the observed sequence is what is used to estimate N.

The astute reader may have noticed that nowhere in this discussion have we talked about modeling the *recaptures*; in fact, under the simple removal model (M_b) only the

Box 10.5 Removal sampling.

Our example is from stream insect sampling, in which five removal samples were taken for Ephemeroptera, resulting in a sequence of 181, 11, 4, 5, 3 insects captured in the successive samples. We used the web-based version of CAPTURE (Appendix A) to analyze these data via removal models. For this data structure, two variable probability removal models were fit, one by Otis *et al.* (1978) and the other by Pollock and Otto (1983). The input into CAPTURE is quite simple:

```
task read population removal
5, 'Ephemeroptera, stream insect. (data:u1,u2,u3,u4,u5)'
181,11,4,5,3
task population estimate removal
```

The output from CAPTURE provided parameter estimates and confidence intervals. For instance, the output for M_{bh} was as follows:

```
Population estimation with variable probability removal estimator.
See M(bh) or removal models of the Monograph for details.
Ephemeroptera, stream insect. (data:u1,u2,u3,u4,u5)
Occasion j = 1 2 3 4 5
Total caught M(j) = 0 181 192 196 201 204
Newly caught u(j) = 181 11 4 5 3
```

k	N-hat	SE(N)	Chi-sq.	Prob.	Estimated p-bar(j), $j = 1, \ldots, 5$				
1	204.00	0.209	70.87	0.0000	0.816	0.816	0.816	0.816	0.816
2	206.77	3.70	1.63	0.4422	0.875	0.403	0.403	0.403	0.403
3	208.43	8.37	1.07	0.3008	0.868	0.401	0.331	0.331	0.331

```
Population estimate is 207 with standard error 3.6988
Approximate 95% confidence interval 205 to 224
Profile likelihood interval 204 to 233
```

The models provided very similar estimates; we report the Otis *et al.* (1978) estimate under model M_{bh} of 207 with a profile likelihood interval of (204, 233). Because this model is robust to heterogeneity among individuals, and due to "trap response" (e.g., avoidance of insects to trapping), it should provide reliable estimates as long as (i) several samples are available, each with enough effort to deplete the remaining, uncaught individuals, and (ii) removal effort is kept relatively constant over time.

The complete model input and output from CAPTURE for this example can be found in the electronic companion to the book (see enclosed CD and website address on p. ii).

first captures (removals) are used to estimate N, and either of the removal models (M_b or M_{bh}) can be fit with only removal (first capture) data; this is what makes these models robust to "trap happy" or "trap shy" animals. However, if recapture data are available, they should be included, because this will allow computation of recapture rates, and testing of the removal models versus competitors (M_0, M_t, M_h, etc.). Naturally, if recaptures are not available, as with physical removal, these other models cannot be fit, so it becomes critical to meet the assumptions of one of the removal models.

Study design

As with "ordinary" CMR, removal studies must be designed so as to provide adequate sample sizes, and to avoid violating the major assumptions of the statistical models. Earlier we alluded to the fact that physical removal potentially results in influx into the population, so that removal studies need to be conducted over short time periods, and carefully monitored for evidence that the closure assumption is being violated. Sample size considerations for removal studies are similar to those of CMR, but with obvious focus on "first capture." Also, it is an absolute must that the number of "unmarked" animals declines from sample to sample, as expected under constant effort removal. If this does not happen, results will be unreliable, including estimates of abundance that may be negative. For model M_b, reliable results will only be obtained in a k-sample removal study with u_j removals of each sample if:

$$\sum_{j=1}^{k} (k + 1 - 2j)u_j > 0 \tag{10.5}$$

If this cannot be achieved (usually because removal is too small a fraction of the population), removal methods should not be used for estimating abundance.

Estimation of density with CMR

Often, biologists are more interested in the **density** of animals (by definition, the number per unit area) than they are in the absolute abundance of animals (N). In fact, a good argument can be made that without reference to a defined geographic area (A) abundance is a fairly meaningless parameter ($N = 100$ animals packed into 10 ha means something quite different than the same number spread over 100,000 ha). In Chapter 9, we estimated density directly via distance methods, and then (where appropriate) expanded this value to a study area of size A simply by expansion:

$$\hat{N} = \hat{D}A$$

It seems as though we ought to be able to apply the reverse logic to CMR: to estimate N using CMR and apply this estimate to a study area of size A to get an estimate of density:

$$\hat{D} = \frac{\hat{N}}{A_G} \tag{10.6}$$

The "study area" size is typically taken as the actual area A_G covered by the trapping grid or other array. The problem with this logic is that CMR sampling, unlike distance (point or line transect), depends on methods in which the capture devices (e.g., baited traps) have influence over a larger area than the grid area, either because of bait or other attractants, or because animals' home ranges may only partially overlap the grid. Thus, there arises the need to estimate an **effective grid area**:

$$A = A_G + A'$$

where A' is an additional area of influence.

Movement-based estimation

The above ideas lead to two basic approaches for estimating density using CMR data. The first is based on modeling of the animal movement, usually using information on the distance moved by individual animals between successive captures. Obviously, this approach requires a substantial number of recaptures in order to model movement. A typical approach (Williams *et al.* 2002) is to assume that half the mean maximum distance moved is a good estimate of an additional strip to add to the grid. For a square grid with sides L length this leads to:

$$\hat{A} = L^2 + 4L\hat{W} + \pi\hat{W}^2 \tag{10.7}$$

and

$$\hat{D} = \frac{\hat{N}}{\hat{A}}$$

where $\hat{W}$ is estimated from the movement data (e.g., half the mean maximum distance). Besides assuming that an arbitrary movement statistic (like half the mean maximum distance moved) is a legitimate estimate of W, the method assumes that the movement into the sampling area is not influenced by the traps themselves, and so that movement estimated represents "normal" home range activity. This assumption is probably violated in practice, although more recent modeling approaches by Efford (2004) may be more robust to this assumption.

Grid-based estimation

A second approach is based on the idea that "naïve" density estimation [as in Equation (**??**)] is more biased the greater the perimeter-to-area ratio of the grid (so, as grids become smaller). Thus, the grid is divided into nested subgrids (Figure 10.4),

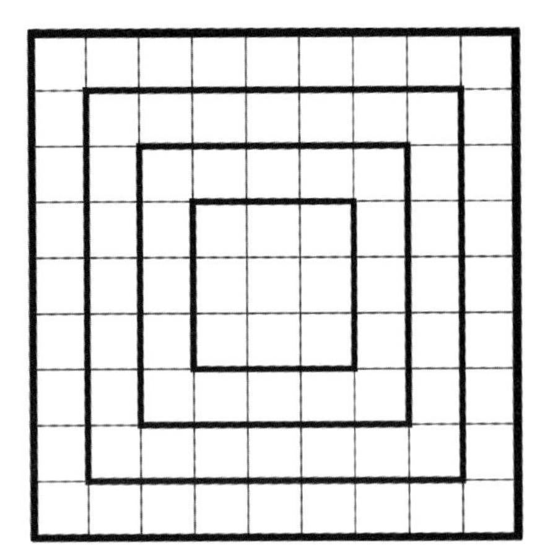

Fig. 10.4 **Layout of study design for a nested trapping grid study to estimate density. A trap is placed at the corner of each small square.**

and CMR is used to estimate abundance and naïve density on each subgrid. These are then modeled to see if there is a "flattening out" of the cumulated density versus area estimate, in order to extrapolate to an effective trap area. The method carries a number of assumptions in addition to the usual CMR assumptions, particularly that the density is uniform over the grid. Perhaps most important, the method is extremely demanding of data, since a full CMR model must be fit for every subgrid. In practice, it will often be impossible to construct a sufficient number of grids with sufficient data to make this approach work.

Trapping webs

A completely different approach to density estimation is based on applying distance estimation to the CMR data, using a **trapping web** design. This method requires the traps or other devices to be placed in a geometric configuration that tends to concentrate effort (traps per unit area) near a central point, with decreasing effort as distance from this point increases (Figure 10.5). Typically, only first captures ("removal") data are used, which are stratified by distance intervals ($i = 1, \ldots, m$) and summarized over the capture period:

$$u_i = \sum_{j=1}^{k} u_{ij}$$

These data are then used with grouped distance estimation (Chapter 9; Buckland *et al.* 1993, 2001; Williams *et al.* 2002) to estimate density by

$$\hat{D} = \frac{u\hat{f}'(0)}{2k\pi}$$

where $u = \sum_{i=1}^{m} u_i$ and $\hat{f}'(0)$ is estimated as described in Chapter 9.

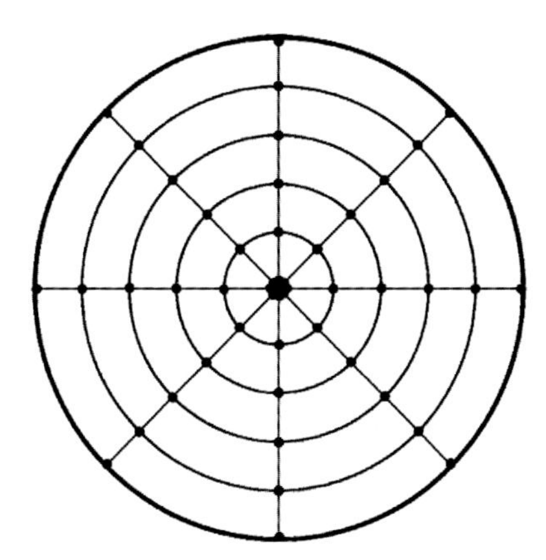

Fig. 10.5 **Layout of study design for a trapping web study. Each dot represents where a trap would be placed.**

The assumptions of the trapping web method are:

- all animals at the center of the web are captured over the course of the study (similar to the assumption of perfect detection at a sample point in point transect sampling);
- migration through the web does not occur, and distances moved during the study are "small relative to the size of the web;"
- distance from the center to each trap point is measured accurately.

The first assumption is probably violated in many cases, leading to underestimation of density. The second assumption may be reasonable, if webs are properly dimensioned so as to take into account the range of animal movements, but is also subject to violation in many studies. The last assumption is met if trap locations are accurately delimited, e.g., by recording spatial coordinates via global positioning systems (GPS).

Much more work is needed on the efficacy of trapping webs, particularly robustness to these assumptions, and considerations for optimal sampling design (e.g., see Lukacs 2001). Link and Barker (1994) used a somewhat different approach to estimate trapping web data, based on the relationship between web geometry and competition among traps, but still based on "first captures." Coming full circle, Efford (2004) advocates using both first captures and recaptures, together with inter-capture distances to model movement, although Efford's approach does not depend on a trapping web configuration for implementation. Much work continues in the area of optimal sampling and modeling approaches for density estimation with CMR data, and those contemplating estimating density via these methods are advised to keep abreast of these developments.

Other methods

We give brief mention to two other methods that fall into the general realm of CMR studies. The first is known as the **change-in-ratio** (CIR) method, and involves a combination of data on known removal of two or more types of animals (e.g., males versus females), and an independent means of estimating the shift in the proportion of these types before and after the removal. Often change-in-ratio is used in the context of harvest removals and observational surveys to detect changes in the proportions of each sex of a species (e.g., changes in the ratios of antlered deer before and after a hunting season). The method requires that a substantial fraction of the population be removed by the harvest (or other removal), and that the number removed is known exactly. The latter is usually not too difficult, but the former might easily require 30% or more removal of individuals. If these assumptions cannot be met the resulting estimates will be unreliable (e.g., because the shift in proportions cannot be detected by the observation sample). The second method is *catch-per-unit effort* (CPUE), and is a specific type of removal method based on the relationship between variable (but known) amounts of removal effort and the capture-per-unit effort. As with CIR, CPUE depends for its success on substantial and exactly quantified removals, and is perhaps most applicable in situations such as commercial fisheries. We suspect that most readers of this book will have little cause to use either CIR or CPUE, but refer those who may to Williams *et al.* (2002).

Summary

Capture–mark–recapture (CMR) methods are an important tool for estimating abundance and, potentially, density. Simple designs based on a single capture-marking sample, followed by efforts to detect marks ("recapture") can effectively estimate abundance if certain assumptions are met. Multiple-sample CMR and removal sampling provide more data, and hence better precision, and allow robust modeling of capture probabilities, important to avoid biases in estimation of abundance. It is possible to estimate density with CMR studies, but care must be taken to properly deal with the issue of "effective trap area," by means of appropriate grid-based designs, modeling of movements, or trapping webs with distance estimation. In all cases, sampling needs to take into account underlying assumptions and, in addition to meeting precision goals, meet critical assumptions where possible. In some cases it is impossible to meet all assumptions, and statistical models should be used that are robust to some deviation from assumptions. The reader must keep in mind that in terms of conservation biology research, for many species of wildlife, any type of CMR technique requires fairly substantial investment of resources. It should be obvious from some of the examples we have used and the substantial body of literature on the topic that this is very much tied to the taxa being studied. What might be a very efficient set of methods for a particular taxon might be completely inappropriate for others. This again highlights the importance of planning in designing any type of conservation research.

This is the last chapter where we assume that the population under study is closed to gains (birth, immigration) and losses (death, emigration). We go on to consider studies where the focus is on open populations. Here we may be interested in estimating abundance (which now can change over the study), but we are also interested in estimating demographic parameters: birth, death, and movement rates. In Chapter 11, we consider studies based on "known fates" of animals, nests, or other subjects, typified by radiotelemetry and nesting success studies. In Chapter 12, we reapply CMR to open population estimation, including estimation of abundance, demographic rates, and movements.

11
Estimation of survival from radiotelemetry, nesting success studies, and age distributions

In Chapters 6–10, emphasis has been on the estimation of occupancy, abundance, or density of animals. For some applications, it is sufficient to have this basic, descriptive information about populations. For other applications, it will also be important to know how populations vary over space and time; and with appropriate stratification, the methods in Chapters 6–10 can provide this information as well. Of course, populations vary over space and time for reasons, leading to our interest in building models capable of describing and predicting this variation. Thus, we now focus on models in which we assume that the population is **open** to births, deaths, emigration, and immigration. We will consider spatial variations in populations as it relates to movement of animals in Chapter 12, and as it relates to habitat use and selection in Chapter 13. In this chapter, as well as in Chapter 12, we concentrate on variation in populations over time, with special emphasis on quantifying important demographic parameters. Here we focus on methods that, for the most part, rely on the assumption that data used to quantify survival/mortality and reproduction are not biased by the issue of detection. In Chapter 12, we deal explicitly with the more general case where detection is imperfect and possibly heterogeneous, leading to more complicated data requirements and modeling.

Basic estimation problem

Let us recall the basic balance equation for population growth [Equation (3.1)]:

$$N(t+1) = N(t) + B(t) + I(t) - D(t) - E(t)$$

For the moment, let us ignore immigration (I) and emigration (E); effectively we are assuming that we have a large enough study area that movement into and out of the population is relatively small, or that I and E balance. Let us further focus on per-capita population change, $N(t+1)/N(t)$. We then have the relationship:

$$\frac{N(t+1)}{N(t)} = 1 + \frac{B(t)}{N(t)} - \frac{D(t)}{N(t)} = 1 + b(t) - d(t) = b(t) + S(t) \qquad (11.1)$$

Quantitative Conservation of Vertebrates, 1st edition. By M.J. Conroy and J.P. Carroll. Published 2009 by Blackwell Publishing, ISBN 978-1-4051-8228-7 (pb) and 978-1-4051-9098-5 (hb).

where $b(t)$ and $d(t)$ are discrete, per-capita rates of reproduction and mortality over the interval t, $t+1$ (e.g., between January 1 year 1 and January 1 year 2); $S(t)$ is (by complementarity) the per-capita discrete survival rate over this same interval. We pause here to make several observations about these quantities that will be relevant as we consider ways to estimate them from data.

The first and perhaps most obvious feature of these quantities is that given knowledge of some initial population size $N(t)$, and counts of the numbers of animals added to the population that survive to $t+1$ $[B(t)]$ and of the original $N(t)$ that are lost through mortality $D(t)$, we can obtain $b(t)$ and $S(t)$ from their definitions:

$$b(t) = B(t)/N(t)$$

$$S(t) = 1 - D(t)/N(t)$$

Thus, if we can get estimates of B, D, and N from sample data, in principle we can use these estimates to estimate the vital rates we are interested in

$$\hat{b}(t) = \hat{B}(t)/\hat{N}(t)$$

$$\hat{S}(t) = 1 - \hat{D}(t)/\hat{N}(t)$$

We do not recommend this approach, because we think that in practice study data are seldom appropriate to provide reliable results using this method. The main problem with this approach is that it depends on (i) reliable and unbiased estimation of abundance N at the beginning of the study interval, and (ii) a close match between the populations sampled to estimated N, B, and D. In some situations this can be accomplished, but we think rarely so. To begin with, as we have already seen, estimates of absolute abundance are difficult to obtain, and in many cases cannot be obtained at all (or are very unreliable). Second, even if N can be estimated reliably, it is often estimated by survey methods that operate at very different scales of resolution compared to those used to estimate reproduction and mortality, making it difficult if not impossible to form reliable quotients. For example, a survey of the abundance of white-tailed deer might be conducted over many hundreds of square kilometers, possibly using distance methods (Chapter 9), whereas reproduction might be measured on individual deer sampled over selected study areas. Even more seriously, estimates of B and D are themselves really just a form of abundance estimation, that is, they require estimation of numbers of animals (this time, falling into specific categories, namely new animals added and initial animals lost). Biases due to detectability and other factors that plague abundance estimation will carry over to these estimates, as well, and must be dealt with.

An alternative to dealing with crude reproduction and mortality statistics, and then adjusting these (if possible) to a per-capita basis, is to deal directly with data that lead to estimates of the per-capita rates we are really interested in. To see how this might work, consider the case of estimation of per-capita **survival**, $S(t)$. Suppose we have a population of unknown size, $N(t)$, for which we would like to obtain an estimate of $S(t)$. By definition,

$$S(t) = 1 - D(t)/N(t) = X(t)/N(t)$$

where $X(t)$ is the number of animals surviving from t to $t+1$. First, given a specified survival rate $S(t)$ and initial population size $N(t)$, the number $X(t)$ that survive the interval is a binomial random variable (Chapter 5). Second, given any random sample $n(t)$ of the population, the number $x(t)$ that survive the interval *also* follows the binomial model, but with sample size $n(t)$ instead of $N(t)$. This leads to a very simple (and intuitive) estimator of $\hat{S}(t)$ as

$$\hat{S}(t) = x(t)/n(t) \tag{11.2}$$

Although we do not necessarily recommend the binomial model for all situations in which estimation of survival (or, equivalently, mortality) rates is called for, it *is* the basis for important models to be considered in the next section. Furthermore, the binomial model is readily extended to the more general situations dealt with in Chapter 11, involving incomplete detection of animal fates.

A similar notion applies to the estimation of **reproduction rates**. By definition,

$$b(t) = B(t)/N(t)$$

Given a specified reproduction rate $b(t)$ and initial population size $N(t)$, the number $Z(t)$ of new animals added to the population over the interval is a random variable [we will leave its distribution unspecified for now, other than to note that it is not binomial, since $Z(t)$ can exceed $N(t)$]. Again, for any random sample $n(t)$ of the population, the number $z(t)$ that is added by reproduction over the interval follows the sample underlying model, again based on the sample size $n(t)$ instead of $N(t)$. This leads to a very simple and intuitive estimator of $\hat{b}(t)$ as

$$\hat{b}(t) = z(t)/n(t) \tag{11.3}$$

In practice, $b(t)$ often requires estimation of individual components of reproduction (such as nesting effort, nest success, and clutch size), but the above expression captures the basic idea. This expression is also the form used (with appropriate caveats and adjustments) when reproduction is estimated indirectly, as from analysis of population age ratios.

"Known fate" radiotelemetry studies

Here we deal with a situation in which a sample of n animals can be followed through time and their fates determined. The most common way to accomplish this is via radiotelemetry. This kind of data structure potentially leads to very rich inferences about animals. Among these are (i) fates (lived or died, and if died, possibly the cause of mortality), (ii) movement patterns and home range use, (iii) habitat selection, and (iv) other behavior, including in some cases inferences about reproductive success. In this chapter we discuss the use of radiotelemetry data for (i) and briefly (iv); we discuss (ii) and (iii) in Chapter 13.

Survival estimation from known fates

Binomial model

Suppose we have a sample of n animals or other subjects (e.g., nests). Assuming that this sample represents the population of N subjects (ordinarily this is met by random sampling of n from N), the known fates method assumes that at some point (e.g., the end of the study period) we can classify all the subjects into x that "succeed" (e.g., survive the defined interval of time) and $n - x$ that "fail" (e.g., die during the interval). As we will see, this ability to unambiguously classify the subjects into one of the two groups is critical; biases in estimation, and faulty interpretation, result if this assumption is seriously violated. If we have this type of data, estimation can proceed under the very simple binomial model described earlier:

$$\hat{S} = x/n \tag{11.4}$$

with estimated variance

$$\hat{\text{var}}(\hat{S}) = \hat{S}(1 - \hat{S})/n \tag{11.5}$$

Note here that we are temporarily suppressing the index t, since implicitly it is assumed that we are operating over some sampling interval $t, t + \Delta$. This estimator and its variance can be used to form a confidence interval on S, as well as to conduct simple tests of comparison of survival (e.g., between study areas or groups of individuals; see Box 11.1).

The two major assumptions of this method are (i) the fates of all the n animals are known, and (ii) fates are independent of one another. Serious violation of either means that the binomial model and estimator are inappropriate. Usually, however, we are not too concerned about the second assumption: even if fates are not independent (as when certain animals travel together, making it more likely that they are subject to similar mortality risks), the main impact is on precision estimates, not on bias. The first assumption is rather more serious, and is often likely to be violated. In radiotelemetry studies, violation occurs because some of the subjects are "censored" or disappear before the end of the study, due to radio failure, emigration from the study area, or other reasons; thus their fates at the end of the study cannot be known. Essentially this creates a third category, so that the n subjects fall into x"successes," y "failures," and n-x-y "censored." Unfortunately, this type of data does not lend itself to a binomial model, since there are three (not two) mutually exclusive outcomes. More important, it is not immediately clear how to model these data, since the n-x-y subjects may have lived or died, and so cannot be assigned to a parameter. Thus, if there is significant censoring in a radiotelemetry study, the binomial model should not be used. In addition, the binomial model is really most appropriate when all the subjects in the sample are exposed to mortality over a common study interval. This limits use of simple binomial models to some types of nesting studies or when under some circumstances animal can be captured at the same time. In addition, there is an analogous situation where there is partial success or failure of a nest. For example,

Box 11.1 Binomial estimation of survival and comparison of survival between groups.

The example is from a radiotelemetry study of mule deer (*Odocoileus hemionus*) fawns in Colorado in two areas, an oil shale development and a comparison area with no development (White and Garrott 1990). Fawns were radio-collared in both areas and followed through winter. The fates of the collared fawns are summarized below, ignoring four fawns in the oil shale area whose collars failed (and thus whose fates were unknown).

	Released	Alive	Dead
Oil area	57	19	38
No development	59	21	38
Pooled	116	40	76

These data were used with Equations (11.4) and (11.5) to estimate survival rate and a 95% confidence interval for each group and pooled. For example, the estimated survival for the shale area was

$$\hat{S} = 19/59 = 0.333$$

with SE computed as

$$\hat{SE}(\hat{S}) = \sqrt{0.333(1 - 0.333)/57} = 0.062$$

These values were then used to compute an approximate 95% confidence interval as

$$0.333 \pm 1.96 \times 0.062 = (0.211, 0.456)$$

The same procedure yields a confidence interval of (0.234, 0.478) for the comparison area, showing little difference between the areas. A χ^2 goodness-of-fit test is also performed on the frequency table, yielding a value of ($\chi^2 = 0.07$, 1 df, $P = 0.80$) under the assumption of equal survival between groups. This test thus suggests that survival is not different between the two areas, and that effectively the data may be pooled to estimate a common survival.

The data and calculations for this example are in a spreadsheet, which can be found in the electronic companion to the book (see enclosed CD and website address on p. ii).

in studies on northern bobwhite quail, one of the authors (J.P.C.) has documented fairly large numbers of nests where predators take some of the eggs, and in some cases most of the eggs, yet the hen continues to incubate and eventually hatches a smaller clutch.

In practice, many studies involve capture and release of animals staggered through time, violating this assumption. In the next section we deal with both problems.

Kaplan–Meier model

The **Kaplan–Meier** model is really a generalization of the binomial, which allows for flexibility in modeling survival from "known fates" when **censoring** (also called right censoring) occurs. It has the additional benefit of allowing for **staggered entry** (also called left censoring) into the sample, as occurs when animals are captured over a period of time (rather than all at once), or when samples depleted by mortality and censoring are replenished by new releases. The method is based on the idea of an "at risk" sample r, and tabulation of losses from mortality (d) and censoring (c) over sub-intervals of time. The idea is to estimate the cumulative probability of survival to specific points in time t over the study period, using the above data, and is best illustrated by following an initial marked sample through time. Suppose we start at time $t = 0$ with an initial sample $r_0 = 100$ released animals. The first period after release $d_0 = 3$ animals die and $c_0 = 1$ is censored. The estimate of survival is a binomial estimate of the known number of r_0 that survive the interval to time 1:

$$\hat{S}(1) = \frac{r_0 - d_0}{r_0} = \frac{100 - 3}{100} = 0.97$$

The $c_0 = 1$ censored animal is removed from the at-risk sample – since it is no longer observable (i.e., we cannot determine its fate) – as are the three dead animals, leaving a new at-risk sample of

$$r_1 = r_0 - d_0 - c_0 = 100 - 3 - 1 = 96$$

Then at the next period $d_0 = 5$ animals die, 2 are censored, but 16 more are added. In this sample, survival is based on the at-risk number going into the period (96):

$$\hat{S}(2) = \left(\frac{r_0 - d_0}{r_0}\right)\left(\frac{r_1 - d_1}{r_1}\right) = \left(\frac{100 - 3}{100}\right)\left(\frac{96 - 5}{96}\right) = 0.97 \times 0.947 = 0.919$$

with the new at-risk number for the next period taking into account losses (death and censoring) and gains (new releases):

$$r_2 = r_1 - d_1 - c_1 + n_1 = 96 - 5 - 2 + 16 = 105$$

A general expression extending to any time t over the study interval and allowing for unequal times between sample data (e.g., 1 day for some events, several days for others) is

$$\hat{S}(t) = \prod_{j|a_t<t} \left(\frac{r_j - d_j}{r_j}\right) = \prod_{j|a_t<t} \left(1 - \frac{d_j}{r_j}\right) \tag{11.6}$$

where a_j are times of deaths (the only sample points providing information). The estimated variance is

$$\hat{\text{var}}[\hat{S}(t)] = \hat{S}(t)^2 \frac{[1 - \hat{S}(t)]}{r(t)} \tag{11.7}$$

(Cox and Oakes 1984; Williams *et al.* 2002). We illustrate the calculation of the Kaplan–Meier survival estimate in Box 11.2.

It is worth noting that the Kaplan–Meier model is really just a generalization of the binomial model and collapses to that model under some idealized conditions, namely all animals are released at the same date, and all are followed until they die or the study ends at time $t = T$, i.e., there is no censoring. In that case, survival to T is estimated by

$$\hat{S}(T) = \left(\frac{r_0 - d_0}{r_0}\right)\left(\frac{r_1 - d_1}{r_1}\right)\left(\frac{r_2 - d_2}{r_2}\right)\cdots\left(\frac{r_{T-1} - d_{T-1}}{r_{T-1}}\right)\left(\frac{r_T - d_T}{r_T}\right)$$

Since there is no censoring, the number at animals at risk is always just the previous number at risk, minus any that died in the previous interval. Therefore,

$$\hat{S}(T) = \left(\frac{r_0 - d_0}{r_0}\right)\left(\frac{r_0 - (d_0 + d_1)}{r_0 - d_0}\right)\left(\frac{r_0 - (d_0 + d_1 + d_2)}{r_0 - (d_0 + d_1)}\right)$$
$$\cdots\left(\frac{r_0 - (d_0 + d_1 + d_2 + d_{T-1})}{r_0 - (d_0 + d_1 + d_{T-2})}\right)\left(\frac{r_0 - (d_0 + d_1 + d_2 + d_T)}{r_0 - (d_0 + d_1 + d_{T-1})}\right)$$

Here we notice that the numerator in each term is canceled by the denominator in the successive term, resulting in

$$\hat{S}(T) = \left(\frac{r_0 - (d_0 + d_1 + d_2 + d_T)}{r_0}\right) = \frac{x}{r_0}$$

which is simply the binomial estimator of x successes in $r_0$trials. Thus, if we have data that conform to these assumptions (admittedly rare) there is no reason to use the Kaplan–Meier model in favor of the binomial model, unless there is specific interest in investigating patterns of survival over subintervals within the study period (as opposed to simply survival to the end of the study).

The Kaplan–Meier model relaxes the assumption of "known fates" analysis that the fates of all n animals are known ($= r_0$ if all animals are released at the same time) and allows animals that are censored to be included in the computation of survival rates until censoring occurs. This makes intuitive sense and is less wasteful of data than throwing all observations out for an animal just because it disappears (e.g., on the second-to-last day of the study). The approach also should be used (via staggered entry) when animals disappear and reappear in a study (e.g., they temporarily leave the searchable area, then return), so that only animals that are actually monitored by the investigator are included in the "at risk" sample (Figure 11.1). However, the method assumes that censoring is independent of survival, so that effectively the censored individuals survive at the same rate as animals that are not censored. Since this often might not be true (such as failed radio transmitters actually failing because the predator eating your study animal chews on it), it is best if censoring is kept to a minimum. Thus, any study in which the majority of the animals wind up being censored in the early part of the study period may not provide a very realistic picture of actual mortality over the entire period.

Kaplan–Meier and related methods also allow investigation of temporal patterns of survival over the study, and the testing of group and covariate effects. Although basic

Box 11.2 Kaplan–Meier survival estimation based on failure times.

Our example is from northern bobwhites radio-tracked in North Carolina, USA, during November 1985–March 1986 (Pollock *et al.* 1989; Williams *et al.* 2002). This example illustrates both right censoring and "staggered entry" where new animals are released during the course of the study and thus become at risk at various times. The data are summarized below, by week:

Week (t)	No. at risk	No. of deaths	No. censored	New added
1	20	0	0	1
2	21	0	0	1
3	22	2	1	0
4	19	5	0	0
5	14	3	0	0
6	11	0	0	0
7	11	0	0	0
8	11	2	0	0
9	9	1	0	0
10	8	0	1	0
11	7	0	0	3
12	10	0	0	6
13	16	4	0	10
14	22	4	0	5
15	23	4	1	6
16	24	4	0	0
17	20	2	0	0

These data are used to calculate estimates of $S(t)$ and 95% confidence intervals of $S(t)$.

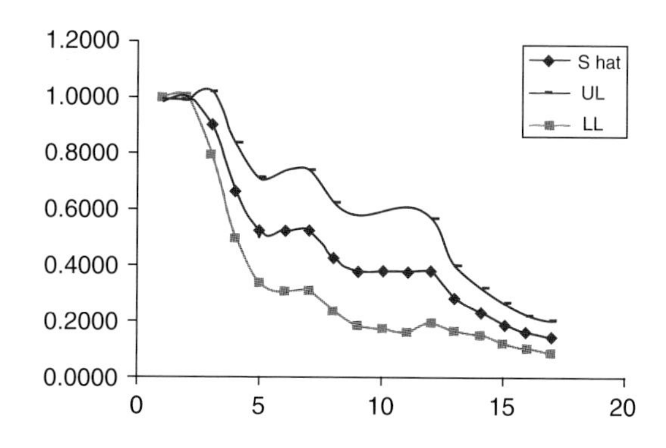

This graph suggests a relatively constant rate of decrease in survival rates, which is equivalent to assuming constant instantaneous mortality risk. A log plot confirms this, showing us that log $S(t)$ is nearly a straight line. This might be a good argument for an

Box 11.2 Continued.

analysis under a parametric model (exponential model of survival) or simply assuming constant daily survival rate (as in MARK).

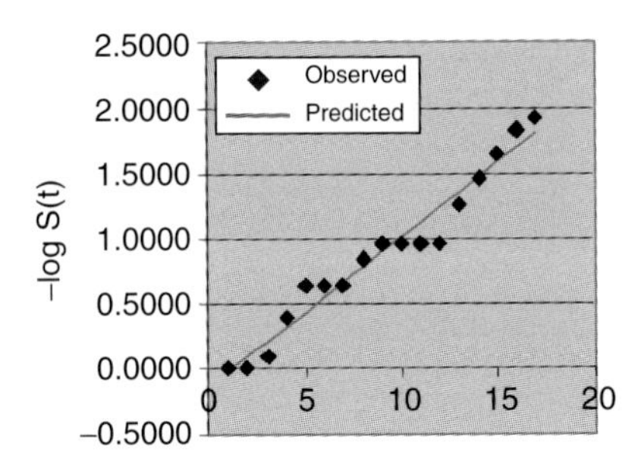

In a second example, also for northern bobwhites, survival was compared over two different 9-week periods: Autumn 1985 and the same periods one year later in Autumn 1986. A second spreadsheet was used to compute survival rates for each 9-week period, and also for the data combined across years. The plot of the 2 years at first suggests differences between years, but taking into account standard error for the estimates these are not different; this is confirmed by log-rank tests performed in the spreadsheet. Although these tests provide some ability to compare the effects of grouping and other variables, we recommend that readers instead perform such analyses using the program MARK (Box 11.3).

The data and calculations for this example are in spreadsheets, which can be found in the electronic companion to the book (see enclosed CD and website address on p. ii).

Kaplan–Meier estimates can be performed by hand or using spreadsheets, these more sophisticated analyses are best accomplished using specialized programs such as MARK (White and Burnham 1999, Appendix A). We provide a brief introduction to known fates analysis in MARK in Box 11.3.

Study design

In radiotelemetry studies, the investigator usually captures and attaches transmitters to a sample of n animals, and then follows that sample through time by surveying a study area, using towers or mobile receivers to periodically locate and infer status (alive or dead) of the individual animals. Those wishing to employ radiotelemetry are advised to consult texts specifically dealing with the technological, logistical, and statistical issues of the approach (e.g., White and Garrott 1990; Kenward 2001). Here we cover some basic points of study design as they specifically relate to survival analysis. It is important to note here that no study design or methods described in this book can overcome the poor application of radiotelemetry techniques when they influence

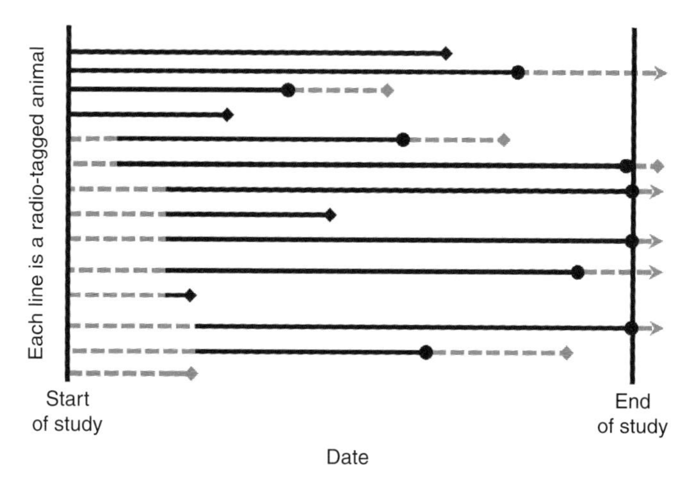

Fig. 11.1 **Example of a radiotelemetry study where a total of 13 animals are monitored. Circles represent the point where an animal is censored, diamonds are known mortality, and gray shading are periods of time when the animal was alive, but not being monitored. As with most studies, not all animals can be tagged at the beginning of the study and here those animals go from gray to black lines when they are captured and radiotagged. This is called staggered entry and we can see how failing to account for this can bias estimates. We also see that not all of the 13 animals died or survived to the end of the study; in this example, six animals were censored before the end of the study (three animals were monitored to the end of the study but are considered "censored" at that point). We show in gray the true fate of those animals, even though in a real study the researcher would not know what actually happened. Finally, this highlights the importance of accounting for exposure time in whatever method is used to estimate survival. For example, the same principles would apply to studies of nesting success.**

survival or other aspects of the biology of the study animal. Remember that all of the methods outlined here describe survival of the radiomarked population. If this turns out to be substantially different from survival of the population about which you wish to make inferences then results are problematic.

Assuming some fixed starting date, the study is then deemed to be completed after a defined time interval has elapsed; often this is determined by the expected battery life of the transmitters (e.g., 90 days), or some specific elapsing of a mortality risk of interest (e.g., a wintering period or hunting season). A basic decision that investigators must make is the number of subjects to follow in a survival study. This will largely be determined by logistics (availability and difficulty of capturing animals), cost of the radio equipment, and costs and difficulties of following n animals for T days. In some cases it may simply not be practicable to capture and radiotrack a sufficient number of animals to provide meaningful estimates of survival, and it is far better to make this determination before, rather than after, embarking on an expensive (and ultimately fruitless) project. A basic idea of sample sizes called for can be gleaned from the simple binomial model, as well as an idea of what to expect in the way of mortality over the study interval. Studies involving too few subjects will be unlikely to detect mortalities unless the mortality rate is very high. Conversely, a small starting sample

Box 11.3 Analysis of known fates using the program MARK.

We introduce readers who may be unfamiliar with MARK, or who need more familiarization beyond the closed population examples in Chapter 10, to a very simple analysis involving the same data we analyzed in Box 11.2. These data are read into MARK using a summary format containing just two columns: the numbers at risk in each period, and the numbers of mortalities each period (columns B and C of the spreadsheet in Box 11.2). The user specifies "known fates" and the number of occasions (17), then reads in the data.

The model run selection option allows the user to select between two choices: model $S(t)$ specifying time-varying interval survival, and model $S(.)$ specifying that weekly survival rate is constant (note that in MARK, S refers to survival between week t and week $t+1$, not cumulative survival from the study origin to time t, as in Kaplan–Meier). Both models are selected and run. Model $S(.)$ provides an AIC value of 194.01 and model $S(t)$ a value of 197.75, strongly suggesting that $S(.)$ is the superior model; this is the conclusion we reached graphically in Box 11.2, by the way. Examination of the estimates in model $S(t)$ in MARK reveals that these are exactly the binomial estimates of survival for each interval [e.g., $1-d(t)/r(t)$], which are in turn used to form the products for the Kaplan–Meier estimates of cumulative survival. In other words, MARK $S(t)$ and Kaplan–Meier are the same model!

A second example reveals a bit of the modeling power of MARK, where there are two groups. This example is also from the North Carolina bobwhite study of Pollock *et al.* (1989), but now for two autumn seasons, 1985 and 1986, 9 weeks each season. The data are read into MARK much the same way as the previous example, but with the two groups (years) separated. MARK then can be used to construct four models (actually more, but for illustration we stick to the four basic models): $S(.)$, $S(t)$, $S(g)$, and $S(g^*t)$, which specify weekly survival as constant over groups and time, varying by time, varying by group, and varying by group and time independently, respectively. Ranking by AIC indicates that model $S(g)$ has the best support, with weekly survival 0.991 (SE = 0.008) for 1985 and 0.944 (SE = 0.022) for 1986.

MARK summary output for the northern bobwhite example is stratified by groups.
Bobwhites fall (autumn) '85 and '86

Model	Delta AICc	AICc AICc	Model weight	Likelihood	#Par	Deviance
{$S(g)$ PIM}	62.030	0.00	0.79607	1.0000	2.0000	16.156
{$S(.)$ PIM}	64.816	2.79	0.19770	0.2483	1.0000	20.977
{$S(t)$ PIM}	71.749	9.72	0.00617	0.0078	9.0000	11.117
{$S(g^*t)$ PIM}	81.032	19.00	0.00006	0.0001	18.000	0.000

As seen in Box 11.2, these data can also be analyzed via Kaplan–Meier, but modeling of group effects becomes more difficult. We therefore strongly recommend MARK for analyzing group and other effects on survival.

We present data and calculations for both the MARK analysis and a comparable Kaplan–Meier analysis in the electronic companion to the book (see enclosed CD and website address on p. ii).

and high mortality results in few or no individuals left by the end of the study. In addition, the precision of the estimate will wind up depending on both n, the sample size, and S, the true survival rate; in Box 11.4 we explore a combination of these factors that result in estimates of desired precision. The main point here is that in some cases it will be apparent that there is really no point in conducting a survival

Box 11.4 Sample sizes for binomial survival estimation.

We can get an idea of the sample sizes needed for a survival study by using the binomial model. This can work well as a first approximation, even if we end up using a more complicated model (such as Kaplan–Meier) to do the actual estimation. The approach is based on using the binomial distribution to evaluate the survival estimate and confidence interval and confidence interval we should expect from a sample of n marked animals from a population with true survival S. For example, a sample of $n = 100$ from a population with true $S = 0.5$ would on average produce $x = 50$ animals surviving, with a 95% confidence interval of 42–58; these numbers translate into a confidence interval of 0.42–0.58 on estimated survival. The table below gives some example results for selected n and S; other values are provided in a spreadsheet, on the book website (see enclosed CD and website address on p. ii).

Survival	n	CL	CU
0.5	5	0.2	0.8
0.5	10	0.2	0.8
0.5	20	0.3	0.7
0.5	30	0.366667	0.633333
0.5	40	0.375	0.625
0.5	50	0.38	0.62
0.5	60	0.4	0.6
0.5	70	0.4	0.6
0.5	80	0.4125	0.5875
0.5	90	0.411111	0.588889
0.5	100	0.42	0.58
0.9	5	0.6	1
0.9	10	0.7	1
0.9	20	0.8	1
0.9	30	0.8	0.966667
0.9	40	0.825	0.975
0.9	50	0.82	0.96
0.9	60	0.833333	0.966667
0.9	70	0.842857	0.957143
0.9	80	0.8375	0.95
0.9	90	0.844444	0.944444
0.9	100	0.85	0.95

Box 11.4 Continued.

Often, studies are designed in order to be able to detect some anticipated difference in survival. The same basic approach can be used, but now we need to specify the survival rates for both groups, often in terms of a control (baseline) survival and an anticipated difference (higher or lower) under a treatment difference. For example, if baseline survival is 0.5 and the anticipated difference is 0.10 (so $S = 0.5$ vs. 0.6), then in a study with $n = 100$ animals per group we would get 95% confidence intervals on survival of (0.42–0.58) and (0.52–0.68). Because these overlap considerably, we would not expect to be able to detect this degree of difference with our study design. By contrast, if the anticipated difference was 0.2 (so $S = 0.5$ vs. 0.7), we would get 95% confidence intervals on survival of (0.42–0.58) and (0.62–0.77) with the same study design; since these intervals do not overlap, we would expect to be able to detect this level of difference. We provide a spreadsheet, obtainable in the electronic companion to the book (see enclosed CD and website address on p. ii), for computing anticipated results for other combinations of survival difference and sample size.

study. If too few animals are marked, it is unlikely that any results of value for survival estimation will accrue. It may still be of interest to follow these individuals for behavioral reasons (although one might well question the applicability of the conclusions to the population as a whole), but other methods will need to be used to estimate survival.

As suggested above, it is important to try to avoid censoring, even if the statistical analyses can handle censored individuals. This has implications for study design, with respect to the size of the study area, the study interval, and the frequency with which animals are relocated to determine status. Ideally, we would like to be able to relocate animals frequently (e.g., daily), so as to clearly determine fates (and avoid censoring). In some studies, as with non-migratory animals or animals with relatively low mobility, this may be logistically feasible over a relatively small and searchable area. In other studies, animals may have high mobility, and it may be impossible to search the entire area where animals could occur daily; this means that individual animals will be visited less frequently, and there may be more error in determining fates and exacts deaths and causes of mortality. On the other hand, if the area is made too small, it may be rapidly searched, and animals occupying this area will be located frequently. However, possibly the majority of animals may go outside this area at some point, resulting in much censoring. Similarly, very long study intervals may result in many animals being censored due to radio failure, but too short an interval will result in failure to detect important mortality patterns (or any mortality at all). There is thus no optimal combination of study area size, interval length, and monitoring frequency, and investigators need to take into account the goals of the study, the behavior of the animal, and the logistical means at disposal, in order to determine these factors.

Nesting success studies

Nest success is an important component of reproduction for many animals (birds, amphibians, and many reptiles). Nest success is typically defined as the probability that a nest survives from initiation (for birds, often when the first egg is laid) until at least one young is fledged. Sometimes nest success is defined over just incubation (so, until at least one offspring hatches), particularly when young are precocial (well developed and able to move and forage on their own) as soon as hatched. In either case, the typical nesting success study involves first locating nests during systematic searches, and then revisiting the located nests until either the nest has "succeeded" (either hatched or fledged) or the nest is destroyed. Early investigators estimated nest success simply as the ratio of nests succeeding (x) to total number found (n):

$$\hat{S} = \frac{x}{n}$$

which is intuitively appealing, and is in fact a legitimate binomial estimator under some situations. However, the problem with this approach is that nests usually are found at many different stages of development: some right at initiation, others just before hatching, and some at times in between. If all nests are equally counted in x in the above formula, the estimator of S winds up being positively biased: that is, nests found later in development should not count the same as those found earlier, since they have not been "at risk" as long (Mayfield 1961; Miller and Johnson 1978).

The solution to this problem is similar to that used for telemetry studies, and in fact nest success models are closely related to Kaplan–Meier and other "known fates" models. One approach, known as the **Mayfield method** (Mayfield 1961; Johnson 1979; Hensler and Nichols 1981; Bart and Robson 1982; Williams *et al.* 2002), is based on the idea of a constant "daily survival probability" given the symbol p. The method divides the data up into intervals of different length, representing the time between successive visits to nests. The data are then the number of these intervals across all nests (n_ℓ), divided into intervals over which nests survive ($n_{\ell s}$) and those over which nests fail ($n_{\ell f}$). The entire data set is then the set of these observations over all the interval lengths that occur in the study. Statistical modeling is based on an extension of the binomial model (Chapter 5), where now "success" is defined as "survival over an interval of length ℓ," with binomial probability $S = p^\ell$ (since daily survival p is assumed to be the same for all nests). Given an estimate of daily survival p from the Mayfield approach, an estimate of survival over the total nesting period of J days is

$$\hat{S} = \hat{p}^J$$

Models in the program MARK take the basic Mayfield nest success model and expand it to several situations. The first, and perhaps most obvious, allows for time-specific variation in daily survival, and is similar to the basic Kaplan–Meier model in not forcing an assumption of constant risk over the study period. Other extensions involve modeling using group or covariate effects. Using an example of nesting mourning doves (*Zenaidura macroura*), we illustrate the nest success analysis in MARK in Box 11.5.

Box 11.5 Analysis of nest success data using the program MARK.

There are a number of programs available to perform analysis of nest success data, and some analyses can even be done by hand, or using spreadsheets. However, the program MARK provides a relatively easy way to analyze these data, and since we have already introduced the program in Box 11.3, we will continue with it for nest success analysis.

The input format for MARK is similar to that for known fates, with some slight complications that take into account the unique nature of nest success data. Each row of the data input (which, like known fates, is separated by groups, for example, study areas or years) contains five columns. The first column is the day (i) the nest(s) was/were found, followed by (j) the last day the nest(s) was/were known to be present (for successful nests this should be the day the nest hatched), followed by (k) the last day that a nest(s) was/were checked or should have hatched (for successful nests this is also the day the nest hatched). Time k is important for unsuccessful nests, because it brackets the interval when the nest was destroyed. The fourth column contains an indicator for the fate of the nest(s): 0 means successful and 1 means destroyed or unsuccessful. Finally, the last (fifth) value is the number (frequency) of nests that had this history. So, for instance,

1 4 4 0 61

refers to 61 successful nests first found on day 1, last known to be present on day 4, and last hatched on day 4.

1 1 6 1 2

refers to two unsuccessful nests that were first found on day 1, last known to be present on day 1, and last checked or should have hatched on day 6; these nests were destroyed sometime between days 1 and 6.

We use an example of nesting mourning doves (*Zenaidura macroura*) from Bart and Robson (1982). These data are available in the electronic companion to the book (see enclosed CD and website address on p. ii) in two formats: the one described above, and an "encounter history" format that is more generally used for capture–recapture data and other "encounter" data. These data are used to estimate four models in MARK: allowing for group and time effects (g^*t), time effects only (t), group effects only (g), and a no effects of group or time (.). The program provides comparison of these models using:

Model	AICc	Delta AICc	AICc weights
{$S(g)$ PIM}	100.8841	0	0.6391
{$S(.)$ PIM}	102.1089	1.2248	0.34642
{$S(t)$ PIM}	108.9177	8.0336	0.01151
{$S(g^*t)$ PIM}	111.6255	10.7414	0.00297

These results suggest that the best model to use is $S(g)$, specifying group effects but no time effects, and providing an estimate of daily survival of 0.99 (SE = 0.004) for group 1 and 0.97 (SE = 0.01) for group 2.

We remind readers that in program MARK, "S" refers to daily survival, similar to the usage in Kaplan–Meier. Thus $S(t)$ models allow time-specific variation in *daily* survival probabilities.

Study design

As with any survival study, it is important to have sufficient sample sizes so that study objectives are met. For nesting success studies, the basic unit of observation is the nest, so we want to determine the number of nests, n, that meet some study goals of precision. However, this is complicated by the fact that not all nests will contribute equally to the analysis, because usually they will be followed for differing lengths of time. An approach for estimating necessary sample size for a nesting study was developed by Bart and Robson (1982) as

$$n = \left(\frac{Z_{\alpha/2} p^{\bar{\ell}/2}}{2\Delta} \right)^2 \tag{11.8}$$

where p is an advanced estimate of daily nest survival, $\Delta = \sqrt{1 - p^{*\bar{l}}} - \sqrt{1 - p^{\bar{l}}}$, p^* is the lower bound on a specified CI on p, $\bar{\ell}$ is the average interval length, and $Z_{\alpha/2}$ is the normal deviate associated with a $(1 - \alpha) \times 100\%$ confidence interval. In Box 11.6 we give an example of sample size calculation using this formula.

Box 11.6 Sample size calculation for nesting studies.

Here we treat the data in Box 11.5 as a pilot study to estimate sample sizes needed to achieve a desired level of precision in a nesting study, using Equation (11.8). Suppose we wish to design a study to estimate daily survival rate (p) with precision CV = 0.01. We need several ingredients:

1. An advanced estimate of p; we use 0.95 – somewhat lower than estimated in our study, but it is recommended by Bart and Robson (1982) that conservative (lower) estimates be used to ensure adequate sample sizes.
2. An estimate of average interval length between nest visits. From our study, we estimate this as 2.24 days.
3. A desired coefficient of variation, which we take as 0.01 (note that this is on *daily* survival rate; the resultant CV on *overall* nest survival rate will be substantially larger, as shown below).

These values are used to compute

$$p^* = p - Z_{\alpha/2} CV p = 0.95 - 1.96 \times 0.01 \times 0.95 = 0.9318$$

$$\Delta = \sqrt{1 - p^{*\bar{l}}} - \sqrt{1 - p} = 0.054$$

and

$$n = \left(\frac{Z_{\alpha/2} p^{\bar{\ell}/2}}{2\Delta} \right)^2 = 291$$

Box 11.6 Continued.

This suggests that approximately 300 nests would need to be monitored to achieve CV = 0.01 on daily survival (which would result in CV = 0.07 on overall nest survival).

To see the effects on overall nest survival, we need to specify an interval (e.g., incubation period) over which nest success is monitored (J days). Then by definition the probability of nest success over the interval is

$$S = p^J$$

For mourning doves we take $J = 10$, so that in the example we have

$$S = 0.95^{10} = 0.5987$$

We use an approximation formula (Williams *et al.* 2002, Appendix D: key to abundance and parameter estimation.) to obtain CV(S):

$$CV(S) = \frac{\sqrt{(Jp^{J-1})^2}}{p^j} = 0.04$$

By contrast, $n = 85$ nests would provide CV(p) = 0.05 and CV(S) = 0.08. This shows that, as usual, sample sizes increase rapidly with precision demands.

We provide a spreadsheet for computing sample sizes for other combinations of daily survival, interval length, and desired precision, in the electronic companion to the book (see enclosed CD and website address on p. ii).

Related to the sample (of nests) issue is how often individual nests should be revisited. Generally, more precise estimates of survival will occur if nests are monitored less frequently but more nests are included in the study. Disturbance to the nest is also a consideration, because very frequent visitation in some cases may bias results, by attracting predators to the nest that may not have encountered it otherwise. In any case, investigators must be very careful not to cue predators to the nests' locations. For example, in avian nesting studies one usually should not visibly mark the nest or nearby vegetation, particularly in open habitats or with ground-nesting species. It is better to mark a spot at some distance and then take compass or GPS bearings from that spot to the nest.

Other approaches to estimating reproduction rates

Components of reproduction

For many species, reproduction rates are difficult to estimate by direct means, such as nesting success. Even where components (such as nesting success) can be estimated with precision, these are only a portion of the total equation leading to reproduction.

For example, recruitment per adult from reproduction in birds involves at least five components:

$$b = PB \times r \times NS \times CS \times S' \tag{11.9}$$

where PB is the proportion of adults breeding, r is the number of nests per individual per season, NS is nest success, CS is average clutch size per nest, and S' is fledgling survival. For example, if $PB = 0.9$, $r = 2$, $NS = 0.6$, $CS = 7$, and $S' = 0.45$, then Equation (11.9) provides

$$b = 0.9 \times 2 \times .9 \times 10 \times 0.45 = 3.402$$

We make this point for two reasons. First, all biologists (we are no exceptions) tend to concentrate on things that are relatively easier (or even possible at all) to estimate, like nest success. However, notice that this is but one component of recruitment; if we want the "bottom line" b we need some idea of what values these other parameters assume. This relates to the second point: uncertainties in these values can overwhelm our "easy" parameter (say it is nest success). We may do an excellent job and have $NS = 0.6$ as a "spot-on" value. Notice if average clutch size is 5 instead of 7, $b = 2.4$; if birds nest only once instead of twice, $b = 1.7$; if the breeding fraction is 0.9 instead of 0.7, $b = 1.9$. Unfortunately, values such as these frequently are little more than guesses, or are based on outdated studies. Again, this is a case where the investigator must keep in view the study objectives. Nesting success studies provide valuable information about a key component of reproduction, including factors such as habitat, weather, and predators that may elevate the risk that nests fail. Identifying and where possible controlling some of these factors may be crucial to conservation. However, if it is important to be able to estimate overall recruitment from reproduction, this will generally involve many additional parameters beyond nest success. If this is the primary goal, other methods such as capture–recapture (Chapter 12) or analysis of age ratios (the next section) may be more efficient and accurate.

Analysis of age frequency data

Reproduction estimation via age ratios

In this section, we give most emphasis to the use of **age frequency data** to estimate survival rates. However, there is another very important and intuitively appealing use of age data: to estimate recruitment from reproduction. This application follows from a very simple application of a partial population model. Suppose we start off with some number N_0^a of adults alive in the population just before breeding ($t = 0$). To keep things simple, we will confine the discussion to just females or, equivalently, assume that male and females survive at the same rate. Take some later sampling period ($t = 1$), ideally just after juveniles have entered the population, but while they still can be distinguished from adults (by size, plumage, etc.). Assume for the moment that we can exactly count the N_1^a adults and juveniles N_1^y, and that the adults have survived at a rate $S_{0,1}$ and that the juveniles have been reproduced at the rate b (including survival to $t = 1$). A reasonable model for these outcomes is

$$N_1^a = N_0^a S_{0,1}$$

and

$$N_1^y = N_0^a b$$

The ratio of juveniles to adults at $t = 0$ can be rewritten as

$$A = \frac{N_1^y}{N_1^a} = \frac{N_0^a b}{N_0^a S_{0,1}} = \frac{b}{S_{0,1}}$$

Given an estimate of $S_{0,1}$, this provides an estimate of b; assuming that $S_{0,1}$ is constant over time (often not a good assumption!), this provides an index to annual variation in b. Either way, it appears that we are several steps closer to b than we were before.

Of course, this was too good to be true, so it is not. Again, it is rare to have a complete count (a so-called census) from a population, and this is no exception. This affects age ratio estimation, because often techniques used for sampling juveniles and adults have unequal probability of detecting each (the same general problem identified in Chapter 6). For example, juveniles and adults may be captured at different rates in trapping samples, because age and experience lead to trap avoidance (or trap happiness, in some cases); thus, capture samples need to be corrected for relative vulnerability to trapping. In gamebirds, juveniles are usually more vulnerable to harvest than adults, so they appear in harvest samples at higher rates. Raw age ratios based on harvest age frequencies will then be misleading as estimates of true age ratio. We can see this by examining the expected relationship of an age sample to the actual numbers of juvenile adults:

$$f_x = \beta_x N_x, x = a, y$$

where f_x is the sample frequency (e.g., from a harvest sample) and β_x is the sampling (detection) probability for each age class. An estimate of age ratio based on the sample frequencies is

$$\hat{A} = \frac{f_y}{f_x}$$

which has expected value

$$E(\hat{A}) \approx \frac{\beta_y N_y}{\beta_x N_a}$$

This only estimates true age ratio (A) when (i) detection is perfect ($\beta_x = 1, x = a, y$, or (ii) detection is the same for adults and juveniles ($\beta_y = \beta_a$). Since neither assumption is generally true (nor usually tested), the best standard practice is to collect the additional data needed to estimate β_y, β_x, or at least the ratio, $r = \beta_y/\beta_a$. This last quantity usually must be estimated by data collected independently from the age frequencies, as illustrated below.

We illustrate this with a case from harvest sampling American black ducks (*Anas rupribes*; Zimpfer and Conroy 2006). In 1990, 378 wing samples were obtained from harvested black ducks in eastern Canada: 287 juveniles (HY) and 91 adults (AHY). The unadjusted frequencies implied age proportions of 0.76 juveniles and 0.24 adults. However, from previous studies of black ducks in North America, juveniles are known to be differentially vulnerable to harvest. In order to adjust for this problem, band recovery data were used to estimate the relative vulnerability of juveniles to adults. This resulted in $r_0 = \beta_0/\beta_1 = 2.77$. What this is saying is that juveniles are 2.77 times more vulnerable to harvest than adults. That number can then be used to adjust the raw frequencies by Equation (11.10). The adjusted frequencies were then used to estimate the proportions of juveniles and adults in the population as 0.53 and 0.47. We note that in this example, age proportions were used to obtain an indirect estimate of reproduction rates, via fall age ratios, as $A = f_0/f_1$. Unadjusted for hunting vulnerability, this estimate would be 3.15; appropriately adjusted it was 1.14. Thus, failure to account for differential sampling would have resulted in a nearly three-fold bias in this important demographic estimate.

Survival estimation via age distributions

Age distribution data are some of the most popular data used for survival analysis, particularly for harvested species. Age distribution (and particularly age ratio) data also have applications in the indirect estimation of reproduction rates, as described in the previous section. For some species, ages are relatively easy to determine with reasonable accuracy, and data can be available in large quantities (e.g., aging of many harvested deer species using tooth eruption and wear at harvest check stations, or ratios of wings of game birds which can be aged to juvenile or adult). Unfortunately, age data are also some of the most commonly misused data, both because they *are* relatively available (and thus likely to be used) and, more importantly, because they are usually used with little consideration for what age data can reasonably be expected – and *not* be expected – to provide. See the recent discussion of this issue in a series of articles by Guthery and Lusk (2004), Folk *et al.* (2007), Palmer *et al.* (2007), and Terhune *et al.* (2007). We first outline the basic idea of how age data might be used to estimate survival rates, and then show some of the pitfalls of this use.

Basic idea of age data for survival analysis

The basic notion behind the use of age data for survival analysis is rather simple. Begin with a **cohort** of animals all entering the population (age $x = 0$) in the same year $t = 0$. If we let $N_x(t)$ represent the number of animals of age x in the population at time t, then the number in this cohort is $N_0(0)$, e.g., $N_0(0) = 1000$. Let $S_x(t)$ be probability (or rate) of survival rate (probability) for animals in age x at time t over 1 year, so from age x to age $x + 1$ over time t to $t + 1$. Animals in the original cohort will survive to time 1 to become age $x = 1$:

$$N_1(1) = N_0(0)S_0(0)$$

for example, if $S_0(0) = 0.25$ we would expect $1000 \times 0.25 = 250$ of the original cohort to survive to age 1. In general, the relationship over time is

$$N_{x+1}(t + 1) = N_x(t)S_x(t)$$

Of course, what we are interested in is survival, and this equation can be rearranged to provide:

$$S_x(t) = \frac{N_{x+1}(t + 1)}{N_x(t)} \tag{11.8}$$

which is the ratio of the number alive in the cohort at $t + 1$ (when all are age $x + 1$) to the number alive at t (when all are age x). Notice that this is *not* an age ratio in the usual sense of the term, which would be the ratio of ages in the population *at the same time*:

$$\frac{N_{x+1}(t)}{N_x(t)} \tag{11.9}$$

Rather, Equation (11.8) applies to the tracking of a cohort through time (known as a **cohort** or **vertical life table**). The second expression refers to the age ratio (or distribution) at a specific time (also known as a **static** or **horizontal life table**). This ratio can *only* be used to estimate survival under some very specific (and rarely tested) assumptions about population dynamics, as we further discuss. Note especially that the ratio derives from two different cohorts. For example, if we take:

$$\frac{N_3(3)}{N_2(3)}$$

we can see that the $N_3(3)$ animals were all age 0 at time 0, but the $N_2(3)$ animals entered the population 1 year later ($t = 1$). This distinction will become critical shortly.

Most analysis of age data is of the second [Equation (11.9)] rather than first [Equation (11.8)] type; that is, most age analysis is of "standing age distributions" rather than cohort fates. Furthermore, most age data do not involve either a complete age-specific count of the population to determine $N_x(t)$ or even a random, unbiased sampling to estimate relative age frequencies. Rather, age data are usually obtained from visual surveys, harvest surveys, capture, or other efforts that tend to be biased toward certain age classes. Thus, age data frequently are vulnerable to one or both of these pitfalls: (i) the data themselves do not represent the standing age distribution in an unbiased manner, and/or (ii) the standing age distribution cannot be used to estimate age-specific survival, because the population is a "moving target" (i.e., it lacks age stability, is not stationary, or both). We add a third pitfall, in which sometimes investigators use data reconstructed from population modeling to "estimate" demographic parameters. We describe each of these in much more detail below because they are critically important and are often applied in conservation biology research.

Pitfall 1 – The age data are biased

As noted above, age data often are only indirectly related to the actual age distribution of the populations. Commonly, age data are obtained via sampling processes such as hunting, trapping, or mark–recapture, which definitely may be biased toward or away from certain age classes. Consider a population of $N(t)$ with actual age distribution $N_x(t)$ ($x = 0$ to some maximum age k). Suppose we take a sample of n animals and observe f_x in each age class. As with age ratio estimation, the expected relationship of the sample frequency to the actual distribution is

$$f_x = \beta_x N_x$$

where β, are age-specific sampling probabilities, and the total sample is

$$n = \sum_{x=0}^{k} f_x = \sum_{x=0}^{k} \beta_x N_x$$

Only when $\beta_x = 1$ (all sampling is perfect), or $\beta_x = \beta$ (the sampling fraction is the same across age classes) will the sample and true age proportions be equal, that is

$$E(f_x/n) = \frac{\beta N_x}{\beta N} = \frac{N_x}{N}$$

In all other cases, f_x must be adjusted for age-specific sampling; often this can be done by estimating relative sampling rates r_x and using these to adjust the raw age frequencies:

$$f_x^{adj} = \frac{f_x}{r_x} \tag{11.10}$$

where $r_x = \beta_x/\beta^*$ and β^* is a baseline sampling rate (often for older age classes where rates are thought to have stabilized). Typically, r_x must be obtained by some independent means (i.e., not part of the harvest survey). We provided an example of this earlier for age ratios from harvest data used to estimate reproduction rates; the same basic idea applies to survival estimation.

Pitfall 2 – The population is a moving target

We know from Chapter 3 that any population that exhibits age-specific reproduction and survival rates that are constant over time will eventually achieve a **stable age distribution**. The problem is, we cannot know from any single sample in time if age stability has been achieved or, for that matter, whether vital rates are constant over time. Therefore, in most cases multiple years of data are required to assess stability/time constancy, and to provide the necessary data to fit realistic models. In addition, we generally should not assume that that population is remaining constant through time ($\lambda = 1$); even if the population is at a stable age distribution, the population can be either growing ($\lambda > 1$) or declining ($\lambda < 1$) through time (Chapter 3).

Unfortunately, *both* of these assumptions – stable age distribution and $\lambda = 1$ – are required to compute estimates of survival from a single, standing age distribution. The usual candidate for this estimation is

$$\hat{S}(t)^* = \frac{f_{x+1}^{adj}(t)}{f_x^{adj}(t)} \tag{11.11}$$

the ratio of successive age frequencies, adjusted, as needed, as per the previous section. Note that properly adjusted, this is identical to Equation (11.9), the ratio of the number in age class $x + 1$ to age class x at time t. Williams *et al.* (2002) showed that $S(t)''$ is related to true age-specific survival $S_x(t)$ by

$$S(t)'' = \frac{S_x(t-1)c_x(t-1)N(t-1)}{c_x(t)N(t)} \tag{11.12}$$

where $c_x(t) = N_x(t)/N(t)$ is the proportion of the population in age class x at time t. This means that in order for $S(t)''$ to be equal to $S(t)$, two conditions have to hold. First, the age proportions $c_x(t)$ must be constant over time, so that $c_x(t+1) = c_x(t) = c_x$; this is simply the definition of stable age distribution. Second, $N(t-1) = N(t)$ must hold; in other words, $\lambda(t) = \lambda = 1$; that is, the population is stationary (not growing or declining). If $\lambda \neq 1$ estimates are based on the standing age distribution [like Equation (11.11)], they will be biased high or low, depending on the value of λ. If the population is not at stable age distribution, the estimates will not even be consistently biased over time, but will vary in degree of bias with $c_x(t)$.

Now getting away from the mathematics and looking at it more practically, we, fortunately, do not have to make these "heroic assumptions" in order to use age data to estimate survival rates. The price we must pay here is to collect the requisite data so that the assumptions can be validated – or to estimate the "nuisance" parameters that would invalidate the results if not included. First, this will usually require the collection of several (not just one) years worth of age data. If age distributions (appropriately adjusted for sampling) indicate little change in $c_x(t)$ over several years, the stability assumption may be warranted. Second, independent estimates of λ (from population surveys or other sources) should be obtained to confirm that $\lambda = 1$. Under certain circumstances one of the above assumptions may be shown to be valid, in which case estimation is possible under "relaxed" assumptions about the other. For example, if the population is known to be at a stable age distribution, then $S(t)$ can be estimated by

$$S_x = \frac{f_{x+1}(t)\lambda}{f_x(t)}$$

for $\lambda \neq 1$ (where the value of λ is either known or estimated from data). Udevitz and Ballachey (1998) and Williams *et al.* (2002) show these and other variations involving combinations of data structures (such as ages-at-death). In Box 11.7 we present a simple analysis of age data, in which additional studies provide the evidence for the assumptions of stable or stationary ages.

Box 11.7 Analysis of age frequency data for age-specific survival rates.

Our example is based on an example of harvest data for moose (*Alces alces*) in New Brunswick, Canada (Boer 1988, presented in Williams *et al.* 2002). The original author (Boer 1988) did not present the actual raw harvest age distribution, but rather one adjusted for differential vulnerability. For illustration, we have reconstructed data under the assumption that juvenile (age $x = 0$) moose are five times more vulnerable and yearlings ($x = 1$) twice as vulnerable as adults ($x > 1$), with vulnerability unchanged after $x = 2$. The resulting table of raw and adjusted harvest age frequencies is then as follows:

Age class	Raw freq.	Vulnerability	Adjusted freq.
0	644	5	129
1	174	2	87
2	61	1	61
3	43	1	43
4	31	1	31
5	23	1	23
6	18	1	18
7	14	1	14
8	11	1	11
9	9	1	9
10	8	1	8
11	7	1	7
12	6	1	6
13	5	1	5
14	5	1	5

x	$\hat{c}$	$\hat{S}$	SE	UCI	LCI
0	0.281365	0.676137	0.093795	0.492299	0.859976
1	0.190241	0.696556	0.11648	0.468254	0.924857
2	0.132514	0.711225	0.141635	0.43362	0.988829
3	0.094247	0.727926	0.170732	0.393291	1.062561
4	0.068605	0.746259	0.203688	0.347031	1.145487
5	0.051197	0.770904	0.241334	0.297889	1.24392
6	0.039468	0.776425	0.276277	0.234923	1.317927
7	0.030644	0.801853	0.320906	0.172877	1.43083
8	0.024572	0.820444	0.364365	0.106288	1.5346
9	0.02016	0.840737	0.409473	0.03817	1.643303
10	0.016949	0.869845	0.457818	−0.02748	1.767169
11	0.014743	0.874074	0.492624	−0.09147	1.839617
12	0.012887	0.90339	0.539853	−0.15472	1.961502
13	0.011642	0.924953	0.577971	−0.20787	2.057777
14	0.010768				

Box 11.7 Continued.

In this study, the author (Boer 1988) offered supporting evidence from other surveys that the population was stationary, and at stable age distribution. However, Williams *et al.* (2002) noted that the age frequencies used were based on adjusted harvest statistics, and that biases or statistical errors in these adjustments were not accounted for in the survival estimates.

We performed these computations in a spreadsheet, which easily can be modified for other data examples, in the electronic companion to the book (see enclosed CD and website address on p. ii).

Pitfall 3 – Pretending that reconstructed data are real data

Population reconstruction refers to the calculation of the abundance and age distribution of a cohort (group of animals all born in the same year) at some initial time. Reconstruction is usually based on "ages at death," the idea being that if we can enumerate all of these, we can work backwards to the original cohort size at age $x = 0$, using the fact that that animal that is age x at time t is age $x - 1$ at time $t - 1$ (McCullough *et al.* 1990). If we were able to follow an entire cohort of animals born at $t = 0$ and determine the ages at which all the animals die, these numbers would by definition add up to the original cohort size:

$$D_0(1) + D_1(2) + \cdots + D_k(k) = N_0(0)$$

For example, suppose we have the following ages at death:

Ages (x)	Year (t)				
	0	1	2	3	4
0	50				
1		150			
2			105		
3				245	
4					

If these are *all* the deaths from this cohort, we can infer that the cohort size was $50 + 150 + 105 + 245 = 550$ at $t = 0$. We can back up the ages at death into cohort size for other cohorts in like manner, assuming that we have followed each sufficiently long.

Reconstruction is an appealingly simple idea, but has serious drawbacks. Perhaps the most obvious is the assumption that all deaths are accounted for. In practice, we think this is hardly ever the case, and violation of this assumption will lead to serious biases. For example, many investigators attempt to use reconstruction from harvest deaths, either ignoring mortality from other sources or making arbitrary assumptions about the rate of non-harvest mortality. Even worse, some investigators attempt to treat reconstructed population information as "data," entering these into modeling and estimation programs in an attempt to estimate parameters. Williams *et al.* (2002) discuss the matter of population reconstruction thoroughly, and, like them, we discourage the use of reconstruction methods, favoring more direct analysis of actual sample data.

Modeling variation in survival and reproduction rates

In this chapter we have emphasized the estimation of survival and reproduction rates from sample data. Knowledge of these rates, and of abundance or density, can be very important to conservation. In many cases, however, it is equally if not more important to understand how these rates vary among demographic or other strata over time and geographically, and how environmental or other factors influence this variation. Modeling variation in demographic rates becomes particularly important as we seek to apply demographic models to decision making (see Part III). Many of the methods used to model this variation require advanced understanding of the topics covered here, and so are beyond the scope of this book. However, we introduce the basic concepts of this modeling, using some simple examples and data structures. For illustration, we focus on binomial modeling of survival rates, but the concepts are readily extended to other examples. Philosophically, we are more inclined toward model building and estimation than we are toward hypothesis testing, so we will emphasize the former; however, the approaches can be complementary, as we will see.

Variation by groups

The basic idea here is that true survival rates S may or may not vary among groups of interest, whether these be groups of similar animals, areas being compared, experimental treatments, other groupings, or even among individual animals. For example, suppose that we wish to compare animal survival rates with forest types, where there are five categories of forest. Under the hypothesis that animal survival differs according to forest type, we have five true survival rates to estimate, S_k: $k = 1, \ldots, 5$. Under a competing model of no difference, we have a single rate, S. Let us say that we have attached radio transmitters to $n = 100$ animals in each forest type, and monitor the number surviving over 90 days x_i, and observe $\underline{x} = \{40, 50, 50, 60, 90\}$. We could construct binomial models under each hypothesis, and test the null versus the alternative; or we could use an information theory approach (such as AIC) and obtain estimates and confidence intervals for S_k. In either case, our statistical model should give us an idea of (i) what survival rate is average for all animals in the study, and (ii) how variable survival is among forest types. If some of the forest types are subjected to particular management practices, our model might give us some ability to predict the impacts of those practices on other areas, although we must be cautious if (as is often the case) there is no experimental control or randomization of treatments. Program

Box 11.8 Analysis of group effects in survival using MARK.

We take as our example the hypothetical comparison of survival in each of five forest types, where 100 animals are radio-tagged in each site and the number of survivors is observed to be $\underline{x} = \{40, 50, 50, 60, 90\}$. We enter these data into the known fates model in MARK and construct three models: $S(g)$, allowing all five types to have different survival; $S(.)$, specifying equal survival among sites; and $S(1\text{-}4,5)$, treating the first four types as a single group, compared to the last type. AIC comparison yielded the following results:

Model	AICc	ΔAICc	AICc weights
$S(g)$	621.6016	0	0.7268
$S(1\text{–}4)$ vs $S(5)$	623.5585	1.9569	0.2732
$S(.)$	682.3	60.6984	0

This provided model-weighted estimates of parameters:

Parameter	Estimate	SE	LCI	UCI
$S(1)$	0.5726801	0.061766	0.449695	0.687293
$S(2)$	0.5	0.04317	0.416185	0.583815
$S(3)$	0.5	0.04317	0.416185	0.583815
$S(4)$	0.4273199	0.061766	0.312707	0.550306
$S(5)$	0.1	0.03	0.054653	0.17597

These suggest a pronounced forest type effect, particularly for the last group, and may suggest that this type be singled out for further study. The input data and MARK files for this example are in the electronic companion to the book (see enclosed CD and website address on p. ii).

MARK, which we can use in many such cases, provides a ready means for testing groups effects, comparison of models, and computation of model-averaged estimates (Box 11.8).

Variation over time

Studies are often conducted over a number of days, weeks, months, or even years, over which study conditions can be expected to vary with time, and this may influence survival or other parameters. A number of the models we have considered allow for this variation over time. The simplest model states that survival is constant over time, that is:

$$S(t) = S, t = 0, \ldots, T$$

where 0 is the study initiation and T is the last day of the study. The opposite extreme of this model allows time to be different at every sampling occasion (potentially every day of the study). In the above case it would require estimating $T + 1$ survival rates, and is provided under some of the time-specific models we have considered (e.g., Kaplan–Meier, known fates, or nest success in MARK). Often, it is not important to know what the specific rates are for each period, but rather to estimate the average rate, and the degree of temporal variation, something that it is possible using MARK or random effects models (Link *et al.* 2002). Even better, if we can measure environmental covariates that potentially predict changes in survival or reproduction over time, we can directly include this in the estimation model (Box 11.9).

Variation in relation to covariates

As noted above, it may be possible to measure variables that are related to survival or reproduction rates, and use these in the construction of a statistical model. There are two

Box 11.9 Analysis of time covariates using MARK.

We illustrate the construction of models involving time-specific covariates by way of an example involving radiotelemetry of American black ducks (*Anas rubripes*; Conroy *et al.* 1989). Initially 48 black ducks were released with radio transmitters attached, and were followed for 8 weeks over winter. We read these data into MARK and constructed models allowing for variation in survival over each of the 8 weeks ($S(t)$) and specifying that survival was constant over time [$S(.)$]. We also created a covariate model using the design matrix feature in MARK, specifying the relationship:

$$\ln\left(\frac{S_t}{1 - S_t}\right) = \beta_0 + \beta_1 X_t$$

where X_t was a measure of winter severity (number of days from 0 to 7 per week with minimum temperature <0°C). Model comparison based on AIC provided:

Model	AICc	Delta AICc	AICc weights
Covariate	143.5428	0	0.71738
$S(.)$	145.5521	2.0093	0.26268
$S(t)$	150.7085	7.1657	0.01994

indicating strong support for the covariate model. Estimates of this model were $\hat{\beta}_0 = 5.75$ (SE = 1.69) and $\hat{\beta}_1 = -0.490$, indicating a negative relationship on the logit scale between freezing temperatures and survival. The input data and MARK files for this example are in the electronic companion to the book (see enclosed CD and website address on p. ii).

basic kinds of covariate models: those based on time-specific covariates (Box 11.9), and those based on individual attributes (either grouped measurements or characteristics, or continuous measures such as size or mass). Covariate models can be particularly useful to conservation when variables that influence survival, reproduction, or other parameters may be at least partially subject to management control. In these cases, construction of a predictive model may be a critical part of a decision model (see Part III), in which we are trying to reach decisions that are optimal with respect to some conservation outcome. We will provide further examples of covariate models in the chapters that follow.

Summary

In this chapter we have introduced several methods for the estimation of survival and reproduction rates for open populations. These include analysis of radiotelemetry data, nesting success studies, and the analysis of age data for survival and reproductive rates. In the first two of these cases, and to a large extent the third, the issue of incomplete sample detection is ignored in the statistical models. With radiotelemetry and nesting studies, this may be approximately reasonable, because the subjects (radiotagged animals or marked nests) can be revisited at will to determine their status. With age data, it often is not reasonable to make the assumption of perfect or homogenous detection, and biases must be adjusted via incorporation of independent data.

In Chapter 12 we move back into sampling methods in which sampling probabilities must be made part of the statistical model. In this chapter, we will use capture–recapture methods, this time for open populations. Our focus will be on the estimation of demographic parameters such as survival and reproduction rates, but we will also be concerned with the estimation of abundance, as well as movement rates. We will use methods that properly account for incomplete detection in capture samples, and which, under model assumptions, provide unbiased estimates of demographic parameters and functional (e.g., covariate) relationships.

12
Mark–recapture for estimating survival, recruitment, abundance, and movement rates

In Chapter 11 we considered methods such as radiotelemetry and nesting studies in which sampling probabilities typically are assumed to be perfect. In these studies, subjects (animals, nests, etc.) typically can be re-observed at will, and their fates determined. In Chapter 12 we return to sampling methods in which sampling probabilities must be made part of the statistical model. In this chapter, we use capture–recapture methods, now modified for open populations. Our focus is on the estimation of demographic parameters such as survival and reproduction rates. We will also consider sampling designs and models that allow estimation of abundance for open populations, as well as those that allow estimation of fidelity and movement rates. As always, we emphasize methods that properly account for incomplete detection in capture samples, and which, under model assumptions, provide unbiased estimates of demographic parameters and functional relationships.

Basic estimation problem

As in Chapter 11, we start out with a simplified version of the general estimation problem. We saw in that chapter that an important problem is estimating the probability that an animal survives an interval of time from t to $t + 1$. We conventionally label this period **survival rate** (S). We also know from that chapter that if we have a sample of animals n that we can monitor over t to $t + 1$ to determine the number of animal x that survive the interval, we can estimate S by

$$\hat{S} = \frac{x}{n}$$

The methods in Chapter 11 are based on this basic, binomial model, which assumes that at least over some sub-intervals of study, the fates of all animals can be determined (e.g., under Kaplan–Meier, some of the n animals may become censored and are no longer used to compute survival).

Suppose instead we have a situation where we do not expect 100% detection, even over relatively short intervals of time; this is, in fact, the situation

Quantitative Conservation of Vertebrates, 1st edition. By M.J. Conroy and J.P. Carroll. Published 2009 by Blackwell Publishing, ISBN 978-1-4051-8228-7 (pb) and 978-1-4051-9098-5 (hb).

in capture–mark–recapture (CMR) studies, just as it was for closed populations (Chapter 10). Let us suppose now that we follow a sample of tagged animals, R_i (denoting "numbers of animals released with tags") and recapture a certain number of these denoted m_i (for "marked animals in the recapture sample"). We might be tempted to use the fraction of these animals recaptured from the original sample as our estimate of S :

$$\hat{S}_i = \frac{m_{i+1}}{R_i}$$

However, a little thought will convince readers that this is *not* a good idea. Most obvious is the fact that unless detection (recapture) is perfect, some of the R_i marked animals will not occur in the recapture sample, even if alive. Using the above, naïve estimator will thus surely underestimate S, because it treats the non-detected (but still alive) animals as if they were dead. Conceptually, we can think of M_{i+1} of the original R_i as still being alive at $t+1$. If we knew M_{i+1} (as we would in a telemetry study), we could estimate S by

$$\hat{S}_i = \frac{M_{i+1}}{R_i}$$

However, we only observe m_{i+1}, which is a fraction p_{i+1} of the animals actually present:

$$E(m_i) = p_{i+1} M_{i+1}$$

Therefore, our estimation of S requires two steps. First, we must adjust m_{i+1} by an estimate of p to get an estimate of M_{i+1}, in essentially the same way we adjusted the capture sample to get an estimate of N in Chapter 10:

$$\hat{M}_{i+1} = \frac{m_{i+1}}{\hat{p}_{i+1}}$$

Then, we can use $\hat{M}_{i+1}$ to estimate S by

$$\hat{S}_i = \frac{\hat{M}_{i+1}}{R_i}$$

or, combining these steps into one expression:

$$\hat{S}_i = \frac{m_{i+1}}{\hat{p}_{i+1} R_i} \tag{12.1}$$

With elaborations, this is the basic approach we use in estimating survival rates with CR data.

Survival estimation with tag (ring, band) recovery data

There are two basic versions of open population CMR, which differ based on the type of re-encounter of marked animals. Here we consider the first type, in which re-encounters are of the "terminal" variety, that is, dead **recoveries**. These typically occur in hunting and angling situations, and for some groups of organisms (e.g., North American game birds) tag recoveries are the main source of data on survival rates. At least two periods (typically, years) and generally five or more releases followed by recoveries are needed to provide estimates under tag-recovery models. We illustrate how estimation works with the simplest possible case: 2 years of releases followed by 2 years of recoveries. The data for such a study would be

R_1	m_{11}	m_{12}
R_2		m_{22}

Here, m_{ij} denotes released in period i and recovered in period j; note that m_{21} does not exist (an animal cannot be recovered before it is released!). Conventionally, the "sampling fraction" of animals recovered that are still alive is called a **recovery rate** (***f***). Under a simple tag recovery model the expected numbers recovered are:

R_1	$R_1 f_1$	$R_1 S_1 f_2$
R_2		$R_2 f_2$

reflecting the fact that recovery involves not only survival but also the probability of recovery (f). Following the ideas that lead to Equation (12.1) we can derive a survival estimator. Again, it would be tempting to use:

$$\hat{S}_1 = \frac{m_{12}}{R_1}$$

However, as we have already seen, this does not take into account sampling (recovery) probability. Instead, we will estimate the number of marked animals still in the sample and, based on this, estimate survival:

$$\hat{S}_1 = \frac{\hat{M}_{12}}{R_1}$$

In this case, we estimate the numerator by

$$\hat{M}_{12} = \frac{m_{12}}{f_2}$$

Here we see why we need the second year of releases and recoveries to estimate f_2:

$$\hat{f}_2 = \frac{m_{22}}{R_2}$$

These steps can all be amalgamated into a single step as

$$\hat{S}_1 = \frac{m_{12} R_2}{m_{22} R_1} \tag{12.2}$$

Although this estimator is extremely simple, it represents the foundation for all the tag recovery models (Brownie *et al.* 1985; Williams *et al.* 2002). These can be generalized to allow multiple years of tagging and recovery, age-specific models, incorporation of grouping variables and covariates, and other extensions, most of which are readily enabled in the program MARK (White and Burnham 1999). We describe a few of the most common tag recovery models here and give an example in Box 12.1. Readers are referred to Williams *et al.* (2002) for a more detailed treatment of tag recovery analysis.

We note here that the interpretation of the parameter f (recovery rate) depends on the nature of the processes that give rise to recovery. In North American game bird studies, recoveries typically occur when hunters shoot, retrieve, and report banded birds. Birds that are not recovered may survive to a subsequent year; may die from causes other than hunting; or may be shot by hunters, but not retrieved or reported

Box 12.1 Tag recovery analysis for groups.

Our example is of adult female and male American black ducks banded in western, central, and eastern portions of the black duck range in Canada during 1990–2003 (Conroy *et al.* 2004). We used the program MARK and the Brownie *et al.* recovery parameterization to construct several models examining area-, sex-, and time-specific variation in survival (S) and recovery (f) rates. Some of these models were obtained by using the "preselected" models button in MARK. Others we specified by manipulation of the parameter index matrices (greatly facilitated by the graphical interface). For example, the parameter indices for $S(g)f(g)$, $S(\text{area})\,f(\text{area})$, and $S(\text{sex})\,f(\text{sex})$ are as follows:

Parameter	Area	Sex	Index group (area × sex)	Area	Sex
S	W	F	1	1	1
		M	2	1	2
	C	F	3	2	1
		M	4	2	2
	E	F	5	3	1
		M	6	3	2
f	W	F	7	4	3
		M	8	4	4
	C	F	9	5	3
		M	10	5	4
	E	F	11	6	3
		M	12	6	4

where parameters having the same index are specified as being identical in the model (implicitly here all periods within groups have the same parameter). A more detailed description of PIMs and MARK is provided by White and Burnham (1999).

Box 12.1 Continued.

We considered eight models, with results as shown below.

Model	QAICc	Delta QAICc	QAICc weights
$\{S(g)f(g)$ PIM$\}$	8389.199	0	0.99831
$\{S(.)\,f(g)$ PIM$\}$	8402.09	12.8906	0.00159
$\{S(g)f(.)$ PIM$\}$	8407.564	18.365	0.0001
$\{S(\text{sex})\,f(\text{sex})$ PIM$\}$	8419.043	29.8432	0
$\{S(\text{area})\,f(\text{area})$ PIM$\}$	8437.577	48.3781	0
$\{S(t)f(t)$ PIM$\}$	8460.274	71.0746	0
$\{S(.)\,f(.)$ PIM$\}$	8477.161	87.9612	0
$\{S(g*t)f(\underline{g}*t)$ PIM$\}$	8546.968	157.7683	0

Note that the above AIC values are adjusted both for small sample size and overdispersion (quasi-likelihood). For the latter, we used the values of $\hat{c}$ = 1.94 = deviance/df = 437.04/225, output by MARK. Model $S(g)\ f(g)$ has most of the data support (QAIC weight >0.99) and we present estimates for that model below.

Parameter	Area	Sex	Estimate	SE	LCI	UCI
S	W	F	0.649118	0.04402	0.558815	0.729872
		M	0.708682	0.021006	0.66587	0.748084
	C	F	0.545867	0.054159	0.439245	0.648441
		M	0.6092	0.034514	0.539868	0.674386
	E	F	0.548615	0.03363	0.482233	0.613312
		M	0.672929	0.022774	0.626834	0.715911
f	W	F	0.029086	0.004477	0.021485	0.039269
		M	0.050962	0.004128	0.043452	0.059688
	C	F	0.044179	0.007309	0.031874	0.060935
		M	0.05399	0.005855	0.0436	0.066684
	E	F	0.032179	0.003302	0.026299	0.03932
		M	0.034896	0.002717	0.029944	0.040632

Complete input and MARK results files for this problem are provided in the electronic companion to the book (see enclosed CD and website address on p. ii).

(Figure 12.1A). In many European ringing (banding) studies, ringed birds that can be used in these models are found dead and then reported, so that recovery involves both the probability of mortality $(1 - S)$ and the probability of finding and reporting (r) (Figure 12.1B). This distinction results in two alternative parameterizations of the

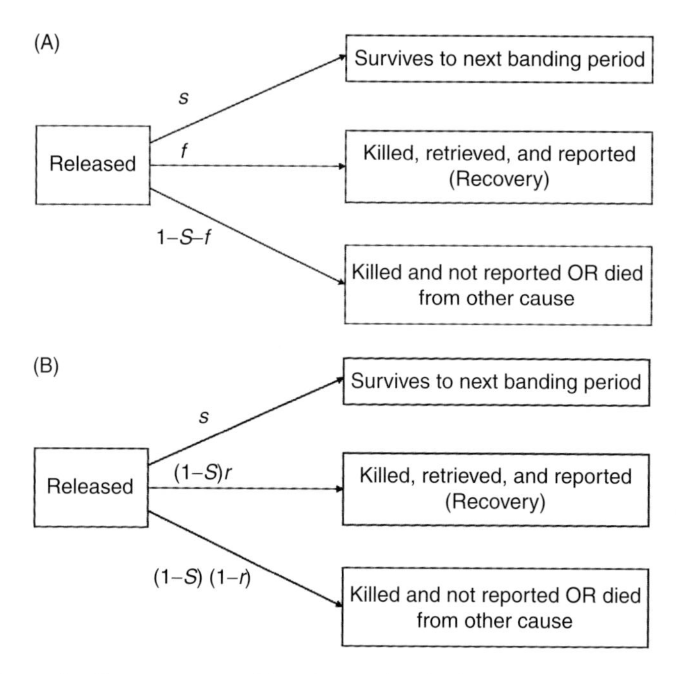

Fig. 12.1 **Events leading to capture histories under the band-recovery model: (A) harvest recoveries and (B) found-dead recoveries.**

band recovery model. In the remainder of this chapter we use the Brownie (Brownie *et al.* 1985) definition of recovery rate (f), as in Figure 12.1A. The alternative Seber (Seber 1970) parameterization (Figure 12.1B) can be obtained via the relationship:

$$f = (1 - S)r$$

so that, given one parameterization, one can always solve directly for the parameters of the other model. Program MARK (White and Burnham 1999) provides both parameterizations, and the user may select the desired form upon specifying the data input.

Single-age recovery models

We start with models in which it is assumed that all animals have a common survival and recovery rate each year (e.g., animals of the same age, sex, and a common geographic range). Because survival typically varies with age, this effectively means that we are dealing with an adult age class (or that we assume that adult and juvenile survival and recovery rates are identical). The data structure for this analysis is very simple, and is comprised of the number released each period, categorized by how many of each release cohort are recovered in each subsequent recovery period. For example, with three release and recovery periods the data structure would be as follows:

Period released	Number released	Period recovered		
		1	2	3
1	R_1	m_{11}	m_{12}	m_{13}
2	R_2		m_{22}	m_{23}
3	R_3			m_{33}

We model the outcomes $m_{11}, \ldots, m_{33}$ survival and recovery rates that are specific to each period, but otherwise the same for all animals. For instance, we model the expected number recovered in year 3 from animals released in year 2, multiplying the original number released by the survival rate from year 2 to year 3, and the recovery rate in year 3. In this way we obtain expected values for all the outcomes:

Period released	Number released	Period recovered		
		1	2	3
1	R_1	$R_1 f_1$	$R_1 S_1 f_2$	$R_1 S_1 S_2 f_3$
2	R_2		$R_2 f_2$	$R_2 S_2 f_3$
3	R_3			$R_3 f_3$

Maximum likelihood methods are used to find values of the parameter $(\mathbf{f}, \mathbf{S})$ that are best supported by the data. Once estimates are obtained, the expected values can be computed and compared to the data, to evaluate model fit (Chapter 5).

Even though we are (for now) confining analysis to a single age group, these models can accommodate different types of stratification, such as sex or geographic location, in which an animal's membership in a stratum does not change over time. An obvious type of stratification is by sex. For example, if we have females and males released and recovered in each of 3 years the data would be:

Sex	Period released	Number released	Period recovered		
			1	2	3
Female	1	R_1^f	m_{11}^f	m_{12}^f	m_{13}^f
	2	R_2^f		m_{22}^f	m_{23}^f
	3	R_3^f			m_{33}^f
Male	1	R_1^m	m_{11}^m	m_{12}^m	m_{13}^m
	2	R_2^m		m_{22}^m	m_{23}^m
	3	R_3^m			m_{33}^m

The expected numbers of recoveries, under a sex- and time-specific model, would be:

Sex	Period released	Number released	Period recovered		
			1	2	3
Female	1	R_1^f	$R_1^f f_1^f$	$R_1^f S_1^f f_2^f$	$R_1^f S_1^f S_2^f f_3^f$
	2	R_2^f		$R_2^f f_2^f$	$R_2^f S_2^f f_3^f$
	3	R_3^f			$R_3^f f_3^f$
Male	1	R_1^m	$R_1^m f_1^m$	$R_1^m S_1^m f_2^m$	$R_1^m S_1^m S_2^m f_3^m$
	2	R_2^m		$R_2^m f_2^m$	$R_2^m S_2^m f_3^m$
	3	R_3^m			$R_3^m f_3^m$

The program MARK (White and Burnham 1999) provides a very flexible means of constructing models that involve different assumptions about survival and recovery variation between strata and over time, denoted by a succinct labeling involving parameters and the symbols g, t, or other labels to indicated variation by group, time, or other dimensions. For the above example, several models are possible, including:

- $S_{g*t} f_{g*t}$ – survival and recovery varying by both group and time;
- $S_g f_g$ – survival and recovery varying by group and constant over time;
- $S_t f_t$ – survival and recovery varying by time but not group;
- $S_. f_.$ – survival and recovery constant over both group and time.

Other combinations are possible, as well (e.g., $S_g f_{g*t}$, $S_g f_t$). For each model constructed we obtain maximum likelihood estimates, evaluate goodness of fit, and compute AIC to aid with model selection. We provide an example with two groups in Box 12.1.

There are many generalizations to the one-age tag-recovery model, including covariate effects, tagging multiple times per year to estimate interval survival, and unequal intervals between tagging periods, most of them possible to construct in the program MARK. Readers wishing to construct specialized tag recovery models are urged to read Chapter 16 in Williams *et al.* (2002) and consult the examples therein.

Assumptions of band-recovery models

There are three types of assumptions common to band-recovery models, and these assumptions will also apply to the capture–capture models discussed later. Williams *et al.* (2002) distinguish these assumptions: (i) related to study design and field methods, (ii) assumptions about stochastic effects, and (iii) specific model assumptions. Under (i), it is typically assumed that marking is representative of the population of interest, that there is no tag loss, and that tags are correctly recorded during banding and reporting. Meeting the "representative" assumption is important, in that serious violation means that our statistical estimates may not apply to the population we are interested in (Chapter 5). This assumption could be violated, for example, by poor placement of traps throughout a study area, so that animals in some portions of the study area have virtually no chance of being captured. It might also be violated by trapping methods that are biased toward or against particular age, sex, or condition classes of animals. Band loss turns out to be indistinguishable from mortality in tag-recovery and CMR models, and if significant could result in serious underestimation of survival, especially for long-lived animals.

The relevant stochastic assumptions are that the fates of the tagged animals can be modeled as independent, multinomial events. This in turn allows modeling by specific maximum likelihood models requiring these assumptions. In practice, the independence assumption is probably violated, because animals travel together, e.g., in migration, or as a mated pair, family, or other social group. Deviation from this assumption does not bias estimates, but may result in some underestimation of sampling variation, with the extreme being that fates within groups of size k are perfectly correlated, resulting in n/k rather than n as the effective sample size.

Finally, assumptions are required that are specific to the particular estimation model being employed for maximum likelihood estimation. For example, under model $S_{g*t}f_{g*t}$, variation is allowed in survival and recovery rates over time, and between groups identified at time of capture, but not within a particular group in a specific year. By contrast, model $S_{.}f_{.}$ requires both survival and recovery rates to be homogeneous among groups and over time. Violation of these assumptions, given sufficient sample sizes, can be detected by failure of goodness of fit tests under the candidate model. In Box 12.1 we illustrate how goodness of fit testing can be used in conjunction with AIC for evaluating and selecting among models with differing assumptions.

Multiple-age recovery models

In many studies, animals are captured in several, identifiable ages or stages. Because survival rates and other parameters may change with age (as well as over time for other reasons), it is important to use statistical models that take this variation into account. As long as adequate numbers of *each* age class can be released *every period*, statistical models described here are appropriate. In other cases, special assumptions are required (see Williams *et al.* 2002 and Chapter 16 for more details).

In theory, any number of age classes can be specified as long as sample size criteria (see above, and below under "Study design") can be met. In practice, two-age models are most common, for a number of reasons. First, many organisms cannot reliably be identified except as juveniles (birth/hatching year) or adult (after birth/hatching year). Second, in many species mortality risk often varies little with age once adulthood is reached – until senescence; therefore simpler classification into adult and juvenile groups often suffices. Third, many organisms are relatively short lived, and therefore most animals are either juveniles or in their first or second years of life. Finally, even if many classes can be identified, it often will be difficult to capture sufficient animals in each class in order to provide recovery data for analysis. Rather than building an overly complicated model for which there is no chance of estimating parameters, it often is better to start with a simpler model for which data are available. Of course, even the "simple" two-age models we consider here are still complex, in that many parameters potentially can be estimated. Note however, we are not suggesting that when collecting data in the field, researchers should automatically default to the simpler age structures. If finer scale age classes can be assessed in the field, then it should be done and decisions about grouping age classes can be done later – the reverse is much more difficult or impossible.

To see how two-age models differ from the one-age case, consider a tagging study for three periods involving a single geographic area and one sex, but now involving captures of adults (after birth/hatching year) and juveniles (birth/hatching year) animals. Ages are now denoted by superscript letters in parentheses, i.e., (0) = juvenile, (1) = adult.

The expected numbers of recoveries under an age- and time-specific model would be:

Age at release	Period released	Number released	Period recovered		
			1	2	3
Adult	1	$R_1^{(1)}$	$R_1^{(1)} f_1^{(1)}$	$R_1^{(1)} S_1^{(1)} f_2^{(1)}$	$R_1^{(1)} S_1{}^{(1)} S_2{}^{(1)} f_3{}^{(1)}$
	2	$R_2^{(1)}$		$R_2{}^{(1)} f_2{}^{(1)}$	$R_2{}^{(1)} S_2{}^{(1)} f_3{}^{(1)}$
	3	$R_3^{(1)}$			$R_3{}^{(1)} f_3{}^{(1)}$
Juvenile	1	$R_1^{(0)}$	$R_1^{(0)} f_1^{(0)}$	$R_1^{(0)} S_1^{(0)} f_2^{(1)}$	$R_1^{(0)} S_1^{(0)} S_2^{(1)} f_2^{(1)}$
	2	$R_2^{(0))}$		$R_2^{(0)} f_2^{(0)}$	$R_2^{(0)} S_2^{(0)} f_2^{(1)}$
	3	$R_3^{(0)}$			$R_3{}^{(0)} f_3{}^{(0)}$

Here we can see that animals that are released as adults always have adult (1) survival rates; however, these rates potentially can vary over time. Juveniles always start out with juvenile (0) survival rates, but after the first period are recovered as adults and, after surviving to the next year, survive to subsequent years at adult rates. We give an example of two-age tag recovery analysis in Box 12.2.

Group and covariate effects

As seen above and in the examples, it is straightforward to include group (stratum) effects in tag recovery analysis using the program MARK. It is also possible to include time-specific covariates (such as weather effects) or individual covariates (such as body mass) that may predict survival or other parameters. Because the approach for these analyses is basically the same, we will treat them when we cover open-population CMR models, below.

Design of tag recovery studies

Data for tag recovery analysis must have several features in order to enable a valid analysis. The main features for a one-age analysis are (i) releases of tagged animals every year (or other period), usually just before a recovery period, and (ii) adequate

Box 12.2 Age- and group-specific tag recovery analysis.

Here we take the same data as in Box 12.1, but now include juvenile (hatching year) female and male releases and recoveries each year. Again, we used the program MARK and the Brownie *et al.* recovery parameterization to construct models examining area-, age-, sex-, and time-specific variations in survival (S) and recovery (f) rates. Note that these models now have the additional complication of age stratification. Although age can be identified as a group in MARK, the user must tell the program (via PIMs) exactly how the age-specific parameters change over time (e.g., when does a juvenile start surviving like an adult?). To illustrate, suppose we have a single stratum (1 area, 1 sex), with releases as adults (A) or juveniles (J), and we index the survival parameters as 1 (A) and 2 (J) in an age-specific model. The parameter indices through time will be as follows:

Age at release	Release year	Year				
		1	2	3	4	5
A	1	1	1	1	1	1
	2		1	1	1	1
	3			1	1	1
	4				1	1
	5					1
J	1	2	1	1	1	1
	2		2	1	1	1
	3			2	1	1
	4				2	1
	5					2

indicating that (i) adults always have the same survival rate (index 1), and (ii) juveniles become adults the first year after release, and survive as adults thereafter. In an age- and time-specific model we would have indices 1–5 for the adult survival rates and 6–10 for juveniles.

Age at release	Release year	Year				
		1	2	3	4	5
A	1	1	2	3	4	5
	2		2	3	4	5
	3			3	4	5
	4				4	5
	5					5
J	1	6	2	3	4	5
	2		7	3	4	5
	3			8	4	5
	4				9	5
	5					10

Box 12.2 Continued.

We ran six models with various combinations of area, age, sex, and time effects. The AIC model comparisons (after adjustment for QAIC) were:

Model	QAICc	Delta QAICc	QAICc weights	Number of parameters
{S(area * age * sex) f(area * age * sex) PIM}	38670.48	0	1	24
{S(area * age * sex * t)f(area * age * sex * t)}	38786.38	115.9032	0	323
{S(area * age)f(area * age)PIM}	38796.29	125.8079	0	12
{$S(g)f(g)$ PIM}	39100.45	429.9677	0	24
{S(area * sex)f(area * sex) PIM}	39309.19	638.7098	0	12
{$S(.)$ $f(.)$ PIM}	39604.82	934.341	0	2

indicating strong support for model S(area * age * sex) f(area * age * sex). The estimates under this model were.

Parameter	Area	Sex	Age	Estimate	SE	LCI	UCI
S	W	F	A	0.622526	0.026719	0.568914	0.673299
S			J	0.640587	0.092796	0.447181	0.797039
S		M	A	0.695148	0.015013	0.664952	0.723753
S			J	0.529321	0.042947	0.44511	0.611895
S	C	F	A	0.560515	0.039831	0.481593	0.636491
S			J	0.39114	0.078863	0.251322	0.55145
S		M	A	0.627007	0.024942	0.576974	0.674462
S			J	0.390972	0.050256	0.297987	0.492612
S	E	F	A	0.563291	0.020305	0.523169	0.602601
S			J	0.470501	0.048911	0.376852	0.566275
S		M	A	0.678892	0.013626	0.651622	0.704994
S			J	0.520498	0.038925	0.44432	0.595735
f	W	F	A	0.03082	0.00402	0.023845	0.039753
f			J	0.068978	0.004646	0.06041	0.078659
f		M	A	0.052805	0.003693	0.046018	0.06053
f			J	0.082245	0.004405	0.074013	0.091302
f	C	F	A	0.043	0.006509	0.031903	0.057727
f			J	0.113618	0.008726	0.097604	0.131876
f		M	A	0.052109	0.005115	0.042948	0.063095
f			J	0.117767	0.00671	0.105238	0.131569
f	E	F	A	0.031314	0.002815	0.026243	0.037327
f			J	0.08035	0.003037	0.074596	0.086506
f		M	A	0.034436	0.002284	0.03023	0.039203
f			J	0.085616	0.002791	0.080303	0.091246

Complete input and MARK results files for this problem are provided in the electronic companion to the book (see enclosed CD and website address on p. ii).

Box 12.3 Sample sizes for a tag recovery study.

To compute estimates of sample sizes for a tag recovery study, we use formulae developed by Brownie *et al.* (1985). These formulae are encoded in a spreadsheet provided at the book website (see enclosed CD and website address on p. ii). The formulae require the user to specify:

- the years of the study (k), that is, how many years or other periods animals will be tagged and released;
- an estimate of average annual survival rate ($\bar{S}$); this can be based on a previous study or an educated guess. For example, a long-lived species would be expected to have $\bar{S} = 0.8$ or higher, whereas a shorter-lived species might be expected to have $\bar{S} < 0.5$;
- an estimate of average tag recovery rate ($\bar{f}$), which in turn depends on harvest rates and reporting rates for game species, or mortality and tag finding rates for non-game species;
- a specified precision goal. In these examples we focus on the coefficient of variation of $\bar{S}$; $CV(\bar{S}) = 0.01$ would be considered very precise, whereas $CV(\bar{S}) > 0.1$ would provide very wide confidence intervals (and little in the way of inference about survival);
- whether this is a one-age (adults only released each year) or two-age (adults and juveniles tagged and released each year) study.

numbers of recoveries each year from the releases. If age-stratified models are used, sufficient numbers of animals in each age class much be released in each year in order to allow unique parameter estimation. In addition, all dead animals must potentially be recoverable, either by hunters or angler reports or by discovery by field investigators. These requirements tend to rule out recovery analysis for many species, either because it is infeasible to mark sufficient numbers of animals, tag recovery (e.g., harvest) rates are low, or recovery sampling is confined to the vicinity of capture sites. In these situations, we recommend against tag recovery analysis, and instead advise the use of CR (see next section). We illustrate the calculation of sample sizes for the design of one- and two-age tag recovery studies in Box 12.3.

Survival estimation with capture–recapture (CJS models)

This group of models, known as **Cormack–Jolly–Seber** (**CJS**), takes its name from three of the pioneers in CR analysis: Richard Cormack, George Jolly, and George Seber. In CJS models, unlike tag recovery models, data are from re-encounters of live animals, potentially recaptured over several occasions. Thus, the same animal may appear multiple times in the data, instead of only twice: once as a release and once as a re-encounter that we saw in tag recovery. One way that we can illustrate this type of data structure is via capture histories, which have the same meaning they did in Chapter 10, but now

Box 12.3 Continued.

As an example, consider a $k = 5$ year, one-age study, with preliminary survival and recovery estimates of $\bar{S} = 0.8$ and $\bar{f} = 0.08$. To achieve a goal of $CV(\bar{S}) = 0.05$, we would need to release $R = 535$ or more tagged animals *each year*. We can also see that if only $R = 100$ can be tagged each year, the achieved precision would be $CV(\bar{S}) = 0.12$, which may not produce results of sufficient reliability to justify continuing the study. We can also see the effects of changing recovery or survival rates. For example, with $\bar{S} = 0.8$ we can see the effects of varying $\bar{f}$ from 0.04 to 0.12, in a 5-year study designed to achieve $CV(\bar{S}) = 0.05$:

$\bar{f}$	R needed each year
0.04	1119
0.06	729
0.08	535
0.10	418
0.12	340

With $\bar{f} = 0.08$, the effects of varying $\bar{S}$ from 0.5 to 0.9 are:

$\bar{S}$	R needed each year
0.5	1081
0.6	812
0.7	645
0.8	535
0.9	461

Sample sizes for a two-age study are estimated first by estimating the number of adults needed (as above), and then by estimating the numbers of juveniles that need to be tagged and released each year. In addition to specifying k and $\bar{S}^{(1)}$ and $\bar{f}^{(1)}$ for adults, we must also specify a value for juvenile survival rates ($\bar{S}^{(0)}$). Taking values of $\bar{S}^{(1)} = 0.8$, $\bar{f}^{(1)} = 0.08$, and $\bar{S}^{(0)} = 0.5$, sample sizes to achieve $CV(\bar{S}) = 0.05$ in a 5-year study would be $R^{(1)} = 535$ adults and $R^{(0)} = 2183$ juveniles released each year of the study.

The sample size formulae described above are based on estimating the numbers needed to achieve precision goals for average survival in a k-year study. If the goal is instead to estimate *annual* survival rates with desired precision, then larger samples will be needed. Williams *et al.* (2002) present the general approach for obtaining these sample estimates, and programs are provided by Jim Hines (http://www.mbr-pwrc.usgs.gov/software.html) to perform the necessary calculations. Calculations needed to achieve precision goals for average survival are provided in spreadsheets in the electronic companion to the book (see enclosed CD and website address on p. ii).

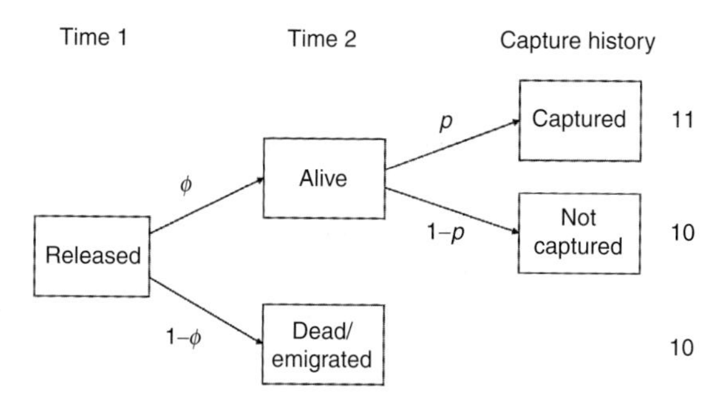

Fig. 12.2 **Events leading to capture histories under the Cormack–Jolly–Seber model.**

with an open population. For example, in a three-period CR study, "111" means captured at all three periods, "101" captured on the first and third only, "100" captured on the first only, etc.

In a closed population, we knew (by definition) that all marked animals were still in the population. Thus, "100" simply means that the animal was not captured again, but we knew (or assumed) that it was still alive and *could* be recaptured. Further, we knew that no new (unmarked) animals were being added. In open populations, both of these assumptions are violated: marked animals can leave the population (by death or emigration) and new unmarked animals can enter the population (via birth or immigration). In CJS models, we will focus on *marked* animals, that is, animals that have been caught at least once. Our capture histories will be formed by the recaptures of these marked animals, and potentially provide information about survival and other population processes. Now, if we consider a capture history, such as "101", we can say "the animal was captured at time 1, it survived to time 2 and was not recaptured, and it survived to time 3 and was recaptured." For reasons that we will discuss later, we use a slightly different symbol (ϕ_i) to represent the probability that an animal alive at occasion i survives *and does not permanently emigrate* from the population subject to capture. This is illustrated in Figure 12.2 for the even simpler case of a single capture occasion followed by a single recapture occasion, generating the histories "11" and "10." Like closed population CMR, we denote recapture probabilities at occasions $i = 2, \ldots, k$ by p_i (there is no p_1, since there are no marked animals to recapture). Using this notation, the event "101" has probability:

$$\phi_1(1 - p_2)\phi_2 p_3$$

In a three-period study, there are four possible recapture events for an animal, conditioned on it first being captured at occasion 1, and we can write out their probabilities:

Capture history	Probability
111	$\phi_1 p_2 \phi_2 p_3$
110	$\phi_1 p_2(1 - \phi_2 p_3)$
101	$\phi_1(1 - p_2)\phi_2 p_3$
100	$(1 - \phi_1) + \phi_1(1 - p_2)(1 - \phi_2 p_3)$

The histories "110" and "100" show that things can get complicated, even for a simple problem like this one. With history "110" we know that the animal lived until occasion 2 (because we recaptured it then), but we do not know what happened next: it may have died, or it may just have not been recaptured (but is still alive). All we can say is it "did not survive and get recaptured." However, the probability of this event *can* be expressed in terms of model parameters (ϕ_i, p_i). So one possible approach is to write down all the combinations of capture histories and write out the expression for each – a very large number of expressions, it turns out ($2^{k-1} - 1$, where k is the number of capture occasions).

Fortunately, one rather simple and reasonable assumption eliminates the need for this much complexity: that is, to assume that animals that are recaptured and released behave the same in terms of subsequent capture and survival as animals that are first captured. If we can make this assumption, essentially we can discard all previous history of a recapture and start over. This results in a very convenient notation based on "m_{ij}" statistics, similar to the tag recovery. For example, three periods of release with three recapture/release periods could be summarized as:

Period last released	Number released	Period next recaptured		
		2	3	4
1	R_1	m_{12}	m_{13}	m_{14}
2	R_2		m_{23}	m_{24}
3	R_3			m_{34}

Under this format, for example, R_1 are released in period 1, none of which has been previously captured (i.e., all are unmarked). Some (m_{12}) of these are recaptured at period 2, and (unless they die on capture or are sacrificed) will be released as part of the R_2 sample, along with any new (unmarked) animals. Those from R_1 and R_2 that are recaptured at period 3 ($m_{13} + m_{23}$) will be released in R_3, along with any new animals caught at that time.

This notation leads to a very simple way of representing the basic CJS model in terms of time-specific survival (ϕ) and capture (p) probabilities. For the above three-period data we have as expected values:

Period last released	Number released	Period next recaptured		
		2	3	4
1	R_1	$R_1\phi_1 p_2$	$R_1\phi_1(1 - p_2)\phi_2 p_3$	$R_1\phi_1(1 - p_2)\phi_2(1 - p_3)\phi_3 p_4$
2	R_2		$R_2\phi_2 p_3$	$R_2\phi_2(1 - p_3)\phi_3 p_4$
3	R_3			$R_3\phi_3 p_4$

Thus, for example, animals that are released in period 1 that are next recaptured in period 3 are known to have survived to time 3 ($\phi_1\phi_2$), not to have been captured at time 2 ($1 - p_2$), and, finally, were captured at time 3 (p_3). The above model is readily generalized to multiple groups (sex, area, other groupings) and ages via use of parameter index matrices (PIMs) in MARK, similar to band recovery. For the above example, several models are possible, including:

- $\phi_{g*t}p_{g*t}$ – survival and recapture probabilities varying by both group and time;
- $\phi_g p_g$ – survival and recapture probabilities varying by group and constant over time;
- $\phi_t p_t$ – survival and recovery varying by time but not group;
- $\phi_. p_.$ – survival and recovery constant over both group and time. Again, for each model we can obtain maximum likelihood estimates, evaluate goodness of fit, and compute AIC to aid with model selection. We provide an example with two groups in Box 12.4 and for age-specific data in Box 12.5. We illustrate modeling with covariates in Box 12.6.

Assumptions of CJS

The assumptions of CJS are fundamentally the same as those for tag recovery models, with respect to assumptions about study design, field methods, and stochastic effects. Additional, specific assumptions of CJS are (i) homogeneity of capture and survival probabilities for the marked animals within each sampling occasion and group, (ii) instantaneous recapture and release of animals, and (iii) all emigration from the study area is permanent. Assumption (i) can be met at least approximately if factors that influence survival and recapture (e.g., sex, area, age) can be identified and used to construct group- and time-specific models. Assumption (ii) is of course violated in practice, but can be met at least approximately if the trapping period is kept short relative to the interval between trapping occasions. For example, if one is conducting a study to estimate annual survival, trapping occasions of 2 weeks separated by 12 months would be adequate for many organisms, particularly if it is expected that mortality and movements during the trapping period would be relatively low. By comparison, if interest focused on estimating monthly survival, then 2-week trapping periods with the mid-dated separated by 4 weeks would nearly overlap, with some individuals released in the first period at risk for $>$4 weeks, and others at risk for $<$2 weeks; such a design could seriously bias estimation of survival.

Survival, abundance, and recruitment estimation with Jolly–Seber

In the previous section, we focused on estimation of survival rates using CMR data using CJS models. These models are known as "conditional" CMR models, in that

Box 12.4 CJS analysis for two groups.

This example involves a study of the European dipper (*Cinclus cinclus*), originally presented by Lebreton *et al.* (1992). Dippers were captured, and ringed during 7 years and recaptured over six subsequent years. Only adult birds were captured, but because survival was initially thought to be gender-specific, the data were stratified into releases and recaptures of males and females. We used the program MARK to fit the general model $\phi_{g*t}p_{g*t}$, allowing for time- and sex-specific survival and recapture probabilities. This model fits the data ($\chi^2 = 18.3, 21$, df, $P = 0.63$), as judged by the program RELEASE test built into MARK. However, there was some evidence of overdispersion (failure of the multinomial model to completely explain variability in the data), and we used an overdispersion factor $\hat{c} = 3.76$ (provided by MARK) to adjust likelihood scores, variances, and confidence intervals (these adjustments are provided automatically by the program, but the user must manually enter the $\hat{c}$ adjustment. This model has 24 parameters – 12 survival and 12 recapture probabilities; however, four of these parameters are confounded, namely the last survival and recovery rates for each sex, so that only the products $\phi_5 p_6$ for each group are separately estimable. We then proceeded to estimate parameters under 15 additional models, under various constraints on survival or recapture rates (parameters equal over time, across sexes, or both). The results are shown below:

Model	QAICc	Delta QAICc	QAICc weights
{Phi(.) p(.) PIM}	181.3788	0	0.51497
{Phi(.) $p(g)$ PIM}	183.236	1.8572	0.20347
{Phi(g)p(.) PIM}	183.3644	1.9856	0.19082
{Phi(g)$p(g)$ PIM}	185.263	3.8842	0.07385
{Phi(t)p(.) PIM}	189.7281	8.3493	0.00792
{Phi(.) $p(t)$ PIM}	190.9914	9.6126	0.00421
{Phi(t)$p(g)$ PIM}	191.6534	10.2746	0.00302
{Phi(g)$p(t)$ PIM}	193.022	11.6432	0.00153
{Phi(t)$p(t)$ PIM}	197.3585	15.9797	0.00017
{Phi($g * t$) p(.) PIM}	201.9476	20.5688	0.00002
{Phi(.) $p(g * t)$ PIM}	203.0141	21.6353	0.00001
{Phi($g * t$)$p(g)$ PIM}	203.9952	22.6164	0.00001
{Phi(g)$p(g * t)$ PIM}	205.1521	23.7733	0
{Phi(t)$p(g * t)$ PIM}	209.5781	28.1993	0
{Phi($g * t$)$p(t)$ PIM}	209.828	28.4492	0
{Phi($g * t$)$p(g * t)$}	220.4343	39.0555	0

These results can be used to obtained model-averaged estimates of survival and recapture probabilities, which now take into account the uncertainty of selecting among alternative models. Model-averaged estimates for survival of males are approximately 0.563 (95% CI = 0.451–0.668) and females 0.558 (0.448–0.661), and for recapture of males are 0.908 (0.701–0.976) and females 0.896 (0.685–0.972). Complete input and MARK results files for this problem are provided in the electronic companion to the book (see enclosed CD and website address on p. ii).

Box 12.5 Age-specific CJS analysis.

The example is from a study of Serins (*Serinus serinus*) ringed in Spain over ten 6-month periods during 1986–1991 (Conroy *et al.* 2002b). Male and female, adult and subadult birds were ringed and recaptured at each occasion. We read these data into the program MARK and initially used parameter index matrices (PIMS) allowing for time-, age-, and sex-specific variations in survival and recapture probabilities. We conducted 100 bootstrap simulations of this model, which provided a mean deviance of 212.91, which we compared to our sample values of 254 to obtain an estimate of variance inflation of $\hat{c} = 254/212.91 = 1.19$, subsequently used in MARK to obtain values of QAIC for model selection.

We compared eight alternative models including the general (global) model, as follows:

Model	QAICc	Delta QAICc	QAICc weights
{phi(age $*$ t)p(t)}	943.1251	0	0.97474
{phi(age $*$ sex $*$ t)p(sex $*$ t)}	950.4313	7.3062	0.02526
{phi(age $*$ sex)p(sex)}	992.9108	49.7857	0
{phi(age)p(.)}	993.3351	50.21	0
{phi(age $*$ sex)p(.)}	994.3769	51.2518	0
{phi(sex)p(sex)}	1065.49	122.3645	0
{phi(sex)p(.)}	1068.316	125.1913	0
{phi(.)p(.)}	1073.069	129.9437	0

These results suggest strong support (>0.97 weight) for a model with age $*$ time effects for survival but only time effects for recapture. The estimates under this model are as follows:

Index	Parameter	Age	Year	Period	Estimate	SE	LCI	UCI
1	Phi	Adult	1986	1	0.973817	0.091164	0.032559	0.999976
2	Phi			2	0.627637	0.090642	0.440761	0.782835
3	Phi		1987	1	0.520309	0.117531	0.30118	0.731893
4	Phi			2	0.513747	0.137616	0.264109	0.75671
5	Phi		1988	1	0.755604	0.210068	0.249576	0.966377
6	Phi			2	0.613572	0.168937	0.28208	0.865166
7	Phi		1989	1	1	3.2E-06	0.999994	1.000006
8	Phi			2	0.272991	0.113794	0.108777	0.536011
9	Phi		1990	1	0.179048	0.080355	0.069508	0.389042
10	Phi	Subadult	1986	1	0.24502	0.0774	0.125052	0.42427
11	Phi			2	0.200628	0.074216	0.092006	0.383348
12	Phi		1987	1	0.063392	0.04867	0.013392	0.252324
13	Phi			2	0.072836	0.055826	0.015304	0.284215
14	Phi		1988	1	0.045553	0.049414	0.005118	0.306898
15	Phi			2	0.151507	0.080502	0.049726	0.378612
16	Phi		1989	1	0.231353	0.126564	0.069418	0.548419
17	Phi			2	0.271085	0.160402	0.070426	0.646095

Box 12.5 Continued.

Index	Parameter	Age	Year	Period	Estimate	SE	LCI	UCI
18	Phi		1990	1	0.706553	0.087768	0.512251	0.846627
19	*p*		1986	2	0.567021	0.07738	0.413856	0.708366
20	*p*		1987	1	0.41418	0.098167	0.242375	0.609754
21	*p*			2	0.385388	0.109159	0.202618	0.607432
22	*p*		1988	1	0.303957	0.09883	0.148792	0.52175
23	*p*			2	0.340601	0.108124	0.167394	0.570274
24	*p*		1989	1	0.431114	0.091287	0.267598	0.611169
25	*p*			2	0.34401	0.144123	0.130422	0.647093
26	*p*		1990	1	0.722494	0.25034	0.183863	0.967833

Complete input and MARK results files for this problem are provided in the electronic companion to the book (see enclosed CD and website address on p. ii).

modeling is always conditional on animals that have actually been captured, marked, and released. Animals that are not captured and released (or re-released) at sample i (R_i) are not used in the statistical model and do not contribute to the estimation of survival rates or other parameters.

By contrast, the models we now consider are known as "unconditional" CMR models, in that modeling now considers both animals that have been captured and released, as well as those that have not been captured (but are in the population and may be captured at the sampling occasion). Under unconditional CMR models potentially we now can estimate, in addition to survival and capture probabilities (as under CJS), abundance and recruitment. The original and most familiar of these models is the **Jolly–Seber (JS)** model, which (along with some special cases) we emphasize here. However, we will also briefly introduce alternatives to the JS model which have important applications (Box 12.7).

The raw data used for JS modeling are identical to that for CJS: the usual matrix of capture histories with 1's representing "captured" and 0's "not captured" for each individual animals. However, a few additional summary statistics need to be computed in order to estimate abundance and recruitment. Thus, at each sample the total number of animals captured (n_i) is comprised of animals that are previously marked (m_i) as well as those that have never been captured before and are thus unmarked (u_i). Releases after sample i will then equal the number of marked and unmarked animals captured, minus any of each group that are lost due to capture mortality:

$$R_i = m_i + u_i - d_i - d_i'$$

where d_i and d_i' are the number of marked and unmarked animals, respectively, that are not released after capture (due to trap mortality, sacrifice, or other reasons). The JS model is formed as the product of two conditional binomial distributions and a

Box 12.6 CJS analysis with a covariate.

Here we return to the previous dipper analysis (Box 12.4), in which fit 16 models including various combinations of group (sex-) and time-specific variations in survival and recapture probabilities. Now we consider a very simple form of a time-specific covariate proposed by Lebreton *et al.* (1992), in which years $t = 1, \ldots, 6$ are classed as being normal ($x_i = 1$) or flood ($x_i = 0$) years. This resulted in a vector of covariates of $\underline{x} = \{1, 0, 1, 1, 1\}$. These covariates are then used in the design matrix in MARK, so that the five parameters describing variation over time are replaced by a single covariate parameter. We considered three additional models including the covariate effect: Phi(flood)p(.), Phi($g *$ flood)p(.), and Phi(flood)$p(g)$. These rank with the other 16 models as follows:

Model	QAICc	Delta QAICc	QAICc weights	Model likelihood	Number of parameter	QDeviance
{Phi(.) p(.) PIM}	181.3788	0	0.35204	1	2	22.43632
{Phi(flood) p(.)}	182.3984	1.0196	0.21144	0.6006	3	21.42744
{Phi(.) $p(g)$ PIM}	183.236	1.8572	0.13909	0.3951	3	22.26496
{Phi(g)p(.) PIM}	183.3644	1.9856	0.13045	0.3706	3	22.39338
{Phi(flood) $p(g)$}	184.4205	3.0417	0.07693	0.2185	4	21.41133
{Phi(g)$p(g)$ PIM}	185.263	3.8842	0.05048	0.1434	4	22.25391
{Phi($g *$ flood) p(.)}	186.4411	5.0623	0.02801	0.0796	5	21.38416
{Phi(t)p(.) PIM}	189.7281	8.3493	0.00541	0.0154	7	20.546
{Phi(.) $p(t)$ PIM}	190.9914	9.6126	0.00288	0.0082	7	21.80932
{Phi(t)$p(g)$ PIM}	191.6534	10.2746	0.00207	0.0059	8	20.39394
{Phi(g)$p(t)$ PIM}	193.022	11.6432	0.00104	0.003	8	21.76254
{Phi(t)$p(t)$ PIM}	197.3585	15.9797	0.00012	0.0003	11	19.80668
{Phi($g * t$)p(.) PIM}	201.9476	20.5688	0.00001	0	13	20.14995
{Phi(.) $p(g * t)$ PIM}	203.0141	21.6353	0.00001	0	13	21.21644
{Phi($g * t$)$p(g)$ PIM}	203.9952	22.6164	0	0	14	20.05917
{Phi(g)$p(g * t)$ PIM}	205.1521	23.7733	0	0	14	21.21611
{Phi(t)$p(g * t)$ PIM}	209.5781	28.1993	0	0	17	19.16394
{Phi($g * t$)$p(t)$ PIM}	209.828	28.4492	0	0	17	19.41388
{Phi($g * t$)$p(g * t)$}	220.4343	39.0555	0	0	22	19.00904

This ranking suggests that classifying years as flood or normal has some explanatory power for survival. The model Phi(flood)p(.) stipulates a linear-logistic prediction for survival as

$$\log \frac{\phi_t}{1 - \phi_t} = \beta_0 + \beta_1 x_t$$

Estimates (95% CI) under this model are $\hat{\beta}_0 = -0.146\ (-0.803, 0.512)$ and $\hat{\beta}_1 = 0.49998$ $(-0.3077, 1.307)$, suggesting a weak but positive relationship in the direction of higher survival in normal compared to flood years. The complete input and MARK results files for this problem are provided in the electronic companion to the book (see enclosed CD and website address on p. ii).

Box 12.7 Jolly–Seber analysis.

Here we analyze data from the Nichols *et al.* (1984) vole study (previously considered in Box 10.3), where now the data consist of trapping over six periods, each separated by a month. Within each of these "primary periods" voles were trapped for five sequential days, but here we ignore recaptures over the 5 days, and only count the capture history as a "1" if the animal was caught at least once during the 5-day period. We used the web-based version of the program JOLLY (Appendix A) to examine three models, perform goodness of fit, and provide estimates of survival, recapture, and recruitment. The input and output details for this analysis are available at the book website (see enclosed CD and website address on p. ii). Goodness-of-fit and likelihood model comparisons supported model $\phi(t)p(t)$, allowing for time-specific variation in both survival and capture probabilities; however, this model apparently did not fit the data very well, with goodness of fit $\chi^2 = 13.3622$, df $= 5$, $P = 0.02$. Estimates for survival rates (ϕ), abundance (N), recruitment (B), and recapture (p) under this model are:

Period	ϕ	SE(ϕ)	95% CI	Interval	N	SE(N)	95% CI	Interval
1	0.8462	0.0552	0.7381	0.9543				
2	0.5675	0.0651	0.4399	0.6951	73.38	3.82	65.89	80.88
3	0.7003	0.0726	0.5581	0.8426	59.08	5.86	47.59	70.57
4	0.5783	0.0684	0.4442	0.7125	61.94	5.68	50.81	73.07
5					54.87	5.67	43.77	65.98
Period	P	SE(p)	95% CI	Interval	B	SE(B)	95% CI	Interval
2	0.9588	0.0402	0.8801	1.0376	17.43	2.6	12.32	22.53
3	0.8222	0.0715	0.682	0.9624	20.57	2.73	15.22	25.92
4	0.911	0.0596	0.7942	1.0279	19.05	2.86	13.45	24.65
5	0.828	0.0696	0.6915	0.9645				

For comparison, we took the alternative Pradel model, based on forward–reverse temporal symmetry. There are three choices for parameterization, depending on the emphasis on "seniority," recruitment, or population growth. We chose the "recruitment" parameterization, which defines $f_i = B_i/N_i$, that is, f is the number of new adults added to the population at $t + 1$, per numbers alive at t. Several models are possible, depending on assumptions about temporal variation:

Model	AICc	Delta AICc	AICc weights
{Phi(t)p(.) f(t) PIM}	987.0727	0	0.53249
{Phi(t)p(.) f(.) PIM}	989.1215	2.0488	0.19117
{Phi(t)p(t)f(.) PIM}	989.7836	2.7109	0.13729
{Phi(t)p(t)f(t) PIM}	989.886	2.8133	0.13044
{Phi(.) p(t)f(.) PIM}	995.5147	8.442	0.00782
{Phi(.) p(t)f(t) PIM}	1000.237	13.1647	0.00074
{Phi(.) p(.) f(.) PIM}	1006.894	19.8212	0.00003
{Phi(.) p(.) f(t) PIM}	1007.17	20.097	0.00002

Box 12.7 Continued.

Most of the AIC weight was on a model assuming constant recapture rates but time variation in survival and recruitment. We used MARK to compute model-averaged estimates and unconditional confidence intervals (taking into account model uncertainty):

	Estimate	SE	LCI	UCI
$S(1)$	0.886005	0.058514	0.714035	0.960307
$S(2)$	0.567619	0.064892	0.438787	0.687912
$S(3)$	0.73368	0.069051	0.5795	0.846321
$S(4)$	0.590362	0.06893	0.45185	0.715881
$S(5)$	0.93587	8.970302	0	1
$P(2)$	0.848757	5.674052	0	1
$P(3)$	0.900227	0.04934	0.754555	0.963612
$P(4)$	0.858088	0.04984	0.730527	0.930971
$P(5)$	0.884722	0.041642	0.775156	0.944705
$P(6)$	0.855347	0.052518	0.720154	0.931446
$P(7)$	0.907537	10.18351	0	1
$f(1)$	0.35585	8.038942	0	1
$f(2)$	0.256322	0.093486	0.116457	0.47404
$f(3)$	0.375409	0.087258	0.224702	0.554856
$f(4)$	0.30834	0.081442	0.174168	0.485152
$f(5)$	0.554287	6.08132	0	1

From these, derived estimates can be obtained of population growth rate (λ); alternatively, a form of the Pradel model in MARK can be specified that includes λ as a parameter (instead of recruitment rates). The complete input and MARK results files for this problem are provided in the electronic companion to the book (see enclosed CD and website address on p. ii).

Obviously, there is no single, "correct" way to analyze these data. When emphasis focuses on demographic rates rather than abundance, we recommend using one of the Pradel models; if interest is solely on survival estimation, then CJS models (Boxes 12.4–12.6) are the best approach. Jolly–Seber may be used when abundance is also of interest, but because of concern about bias in abundance and recruitment rates under capture heterogeneity, we favor instead the Robust Design (Box 12.8).

multinomial (Chapter 5):

$$[P_1(u_i|U_i, p_i)] \times [P_2(d_i, d'_i|m_i, n_i, \eta_i, \eta'_i)] \times [P_3(m_{ij}|R_i, \phi_i, p_i)]$$

where the parameters include survival rates (ϕ_i) and capture probabilities (p_i) as under CJS, and two additional parameters, η_i and η'_i, the probabilities of release for marked and unmarked animals. The first term represents the relationship of the unmarked number of animals in the sample to that in the total population, and is used for estimating abundance. The second term accounts for the non-release (usually, trap mortality). The third term models survival and recapture of marked animals, and corresponds exactly to the CJS model; essentially, one can think of CJS as formed from JS by factoring out the first two terms.

In JS, the unknown number of unmarked (U_i), the marked (M_i), and the total number (N_i) in the population are treated as unknown variables, which can be estimated once capture and survival rates are estimated. Therefore, most modeling in JS focuses on modeling variation in ϕ_i and p_i. The original JS model (Jolly 1965; Seber 1965) allows for time (sample-to-sample) variation in both parameters, and these parameters are estimated just as they were for the CJS model. Abundance is estimated based on the same rationale as for closed population CR, except that now the number of marked animals in the population is unknown and has to be estimated. This leads to an estimator

$$\hat{N}_i = \frac{n_i}{\hat{p}_i} = \frac{n_i \hat{M}_i}{m_i}$$

which very much resembles Lincoln–Petersen (Chapter 10), and can be estimated for periods 2 through $k - 1$ if there are k sample periods. Finally, once ϕ_i, p_i, and N_i are estimated, recruitment (the number of animals entering the population between sample i and sample $i + 1$) is estimated by

$$\hat{B}_i = \hat{N}_{i+1} - \hat{\phi}_i(\hat{N}_i - n_i + R_i)$$

for periods 2 through $k - 2$.

The general JS model has many special cases. One group of these can be formed by allowing for special circumstances, such as partial closure of the populations. For example, sampling may occur at a time of year when mortality is negligible but recruitment still can occur, leading to a "births only" model ($\phi_i = 1$). Conversely, sampling may occur at a time of year when recruitment is negligible but mortality still can occur, leading to a "deaths only" model ($B_i = 1$). Estimation under both of these "partially open" models is described in more detail in Williams *et al.* (2002). Many other models are formed by modeling time variation in survival and capture probabilities under different assumptions; these can be constructed the same as under CJS. Finally, JS can be extended to multiple age classes and multistate models (e.g., for movement rates); these extensions are described in detail in Williams *et al.* (2002). We provide a JS example in Box 12.7.

Assumptions of JS

The JS model incorporates all the assumptions of CJS models, but with one critical addition with respect to the assumption of homogeneous recapture probabilities. As with CJS models, we must assume that every marked animal in the population has the same probability of recapture; now we must also assume that every animal – marked or *unmarked* – has the same probability of capture. This strong assumption is similar to what was required under the Lincoln–Petersen model for closed CR (Chapter 10), and specifically does not allow for an effect of trapping and handling on subsequent probability of recapture (in which previously captured animals would be more or less likely to be recaptured than unmarked animals). Violation of this assumption potentially results in serious biases in both abundance and recruitment estimates, although survival estimates tend to be relatively uninfluenced (robust). Fortunately, as seen in the next section, a bit of creativity in sampling design, together with appropriate statistical modeling, can overcome this problem.

Other approaches

Although readers may be most familiar with the Jolly–Seber model, there are at least two important alternative modeling approaches, both of which emphasize the estimation of recruitment. One is the approach of Schwarz and Arnason (1996) which visualizes a "superpopulation" that serves as a source for individuals in the study population. Recruitment (entry into the sampled population) is then modeled as a multinomial process over time. The Schwarz–Arnason approach is implemented in the program POPAN (Appendix A).

A second approach, which has been implemented in the program MARK (White and Burnham 1999; Appendix A), is based on the symmetry between modeling capture histories *forward* in time in order to estimate survival and *backward* in time to estimate recruitment (Pradel 1996). The Pradel (1996) model emphasizes estimation of survival, per-capita recruitment, and population growth rates, and in fact does not explicitly provide estimates of abundance. In many studies, demographic parameter estimates will suffice, and the Pradel parameterization provides a very efficient means of estimation under alternative models. However, if abundance estimates are important, then we recommend instead (or in addition) estimation under J–S, or (better yet) under the Robust Design (see below).

Combined open and closed models: the Robust Design

The **Robust Design (RD)** is a two-stage CMR design involving primary sampling periods between which the population is assumed to be demographically open, and secondary periods over which the population is assumed closed (Figure 12.3). The RD was originally developed to allow for robust modeling of capture probabilities (best done in a closed model) with estimation of survival, recruitment, and other demographic parameters. The original RD was used in conjunction with closed CMR models to estimate abundance based on the secondary periods; open (CJS) models to estimate survival; and a combination of estimates to estimate recruitment. More recently, the RD has been used in conjunction with multiple-age CMR to allow separate estimation of *in situ* reproduction from immigration, and with reverse-time modeling to allow estimation of components of recruitment from multiple sites, breeding propensity, and other parameters (e.g., Nichols *et al.* 2000). We illustrate the RD with an example in Box 12.8. Finally, in Box 12.9 we provide guidance for determining sample sizes needed to meet the goals of open population CMR in general.

Estimation of movement rates from recovery and capture–recapture data

So far we have emphasized the use of tag recovery and CR data to estimate survival, and that emphasis will be appropriate for many studies. However, in most studies the

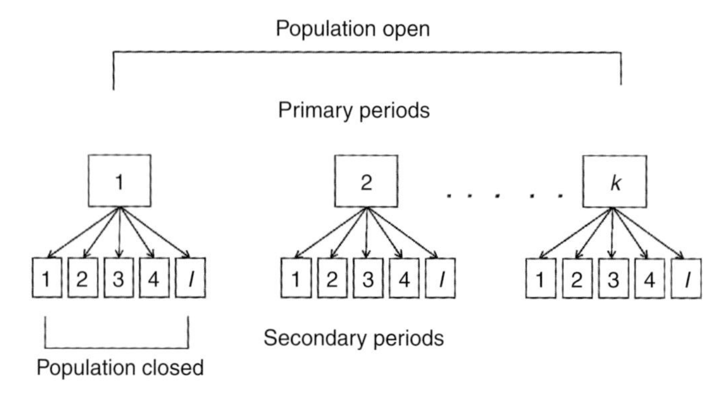

Fig. 12.3 **Pollock's Robust Design, with a combination of primary sampling periods between which population is assumed to be demographically open, and secondary periods over which population is assumed closed.**

Box 12.8 The Robust Design.

Here, we return to the Nichols *Microtus* data, but this time apply the Robust Design with heterogeneity in the program MARK. The design/data structure consists of 30 capture occasions: six primary occasions separated by 1 month, within each of which are five consecutive days of trapping. We fit these data using the full heterogeneity model of the Robust Design in MARK, specifying two mixture distributions. After adjusting for overdispersion, the model comparison results for the nine models considered are as follows:

Model	QAICc	Delta QAICc	QAICc weights
{$S(.)$gamma$''(t)$ gammat) $p(.)$ het(.)}	77.4796	0	0.81612
{$S(.)$gamma$''(t)$ gammat) $p(.)c(,)$ het(.)}	80.7174	3.2378	0.16169
{$S(t)$gamma$''(t)$ gammat) $p(.)c(,)$ het(.)}	84.6896	7.21	0.02219
{$S(t)$gamma$''(t)$ gammat) $p(t,.)c(t,.)$ het(.)}	115.2994	37.8198	0
{$S(.)$gamma$''(.)$ gamma(.) $p(t,.)c(t,.)$ het}	117.9831	40.5035	0
{$S(.))$gamma$''(t)$ gammat) $p(t,.)c(t,.)$ het}	121.4999	44.0203	0
{$S(t)$gamma$''(.)$ gamma(.) $p(t,.)c(t,.)$ het}	124.1231	46.6435	0
{$S(t)$gamma$''(t)$ gammat) $p(t,.)c(t,.)$ het}	125.6508	48.1712	0
{Global}	265.3646	187.885	0

Box 12.8 Continued.

The top-ranked model specifies constant survival, time-specific temporary immigration/emigration, and constant but heterogeneous capture probabilities (essentially equivalent to model Mh under closed CR; see Chapter 10). The estimates under this model are:

Label		Estimate	SE	LCI	UCI
S		0.89521	0.119108	0.414961	0.990375
Gamma″		2E-07	0.000317	0	0.990316
Gamma″		0.425791	0.234198	0.10188	0.828981
Gamma″		0.199031	0.259925	0.01007	0.858557
Gamma″		0.38398	0.249604	0.073037	0.831398
Gamma″		0	0	0	0.006693
Gamma′		0.00205	0	0.00205	0.00205
Gamma′		0.917306	0.255265	0.014929	0.999877
Gamma′		1	8.93E-05	0.999825	1.000175
Gamma′		0.945293	0.152732	0.050252	0.999823
pi Session 1		0.658812	0.128638	0.386114	0.855659
p Session 1	mix1	0.343228	0.076435	0.211897	0.503911
p Session 1	mix2	0.853516	0.082148	0.616483	0.954793
N Session 1		60.39561	7.415109	45.862	74.92922
N Session 2		77.79877	8.55388	61.03317	94.56438
N Session 3		52.78142	6.883607	39.28955	66.27329
N Session 4		61.48335	7.489144	46.80463	76.16207
N Session 5		49.51797	6.647814	36.48825	62.54768
N Session 6		78	0	78	78

Interestingly, over half (0.66) of the population is estimated to have low (0.34) capture probabilities, with the remainder (0.44) having high (0.85) capture probabilities. If not taken into account, this degree of capture heterogeneity could result in large biases in estimates of abundance. However, estimates of survival are relatively unaffected by capture heterogeneity, so if survival is of primary interest we recommend CJS models as a more efficient use of these data.

Complete input and MARK results files for this problem are provided in the electronic companion to the book (see enclosed CD and website address on p. ii).

spatial location of animals is determined at initial capture and subsequent recapture or recovery, and it is natural to consider the use of these data for estimating the rate and direction of movement. In fact, many of the earliest applications of banding (ringing) data, especially for birds, focused more on determining migration pathways and other aspects of movements than on estimation of demographic parameters. A full coverage of movement estimation is beyond the scope of this book, but we will briefly indicate some ways in which recovery and CMR data can be used for this purpose.

Box 12.9 Sample sizes for open CR studies.

Sample size consideration in open CR studies is complicated by the fact that there are potentially many parameters (survival, abundance, recruitment, migration) to consider. Pollock *et al.* (1990) developed a series of graphs illustrating a combination of capture probability, numbers of capture occasions, and population sizes needed to achieve various levels of precision (CV) for Jolly–Seber estimation. We have incorporated an approximation based on Pollock *et al.* (1990) but with focus on estimating survival rates [in our view, abundance estimation should be based on closed population models (Chapter 10), perhaps as incorporated into the Robust Design]. We created an Excel workbook that contains two spreadsheets: one for a 5-year study and the other for a 10-year study. The user specifies average survival rates (e.g., $\phi = 0.8$), capture probabilities ($p = 0.5$), and numbers of animals to release each year ($R = 250$); note that R is the total number of marked and unmarked animals released each year, i.e., after year 1, and contains recaptures. The program produces expected data under these conditions, and from these, calculated variances of survival rates and CV for annual survival rates out to $k - 1$ years. For these conditions, one can see that a 10-year study produces more precise (lower CV) estimates than a 5-year study; this is because survival rates are based, at least in part, on the total number of animals recaptured from each release cohort, and this number will generally be larger when longer time spans are allowed. Users can modify these programs for particular applications, or consult the graphs in Pollock *et al.* (1990).

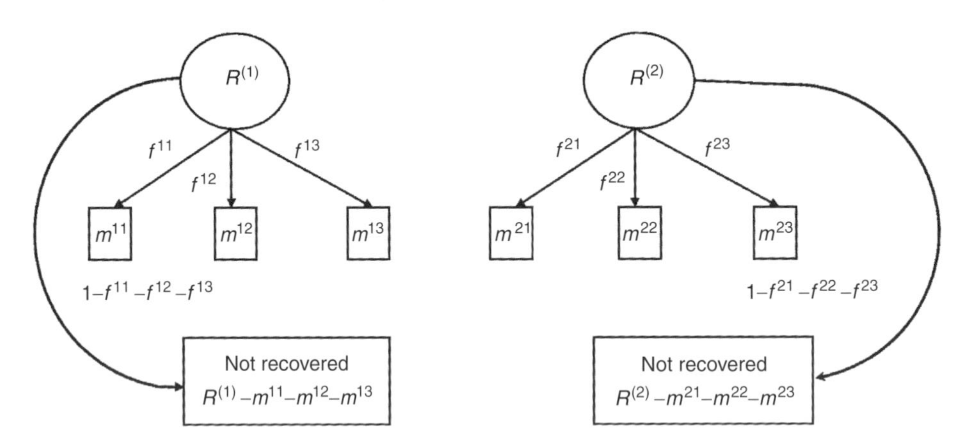

Fig. 12.4 **Post-stratified tag recovery model, in which animals are marked in two areas and move to one of two areas where some are recovered.**

Just as with estimation of demographic rates, estimation of movement needs to account for the sampling processes involved (e.g., recovery or recapture). We can illustrate this with a simple example of tag recovery, in which animals are tagged at two locations (e.g., breeding sites) and are recovered at two subsequent locations the same year (e.g., wintering sites; Figure 12.4). We wish to estimate the proportion moving from each breeding site to each wintering site based on the frequency of recoveries in each wintering site. We can use a post-stratified band recovery model (Williams *et al.* 2002)

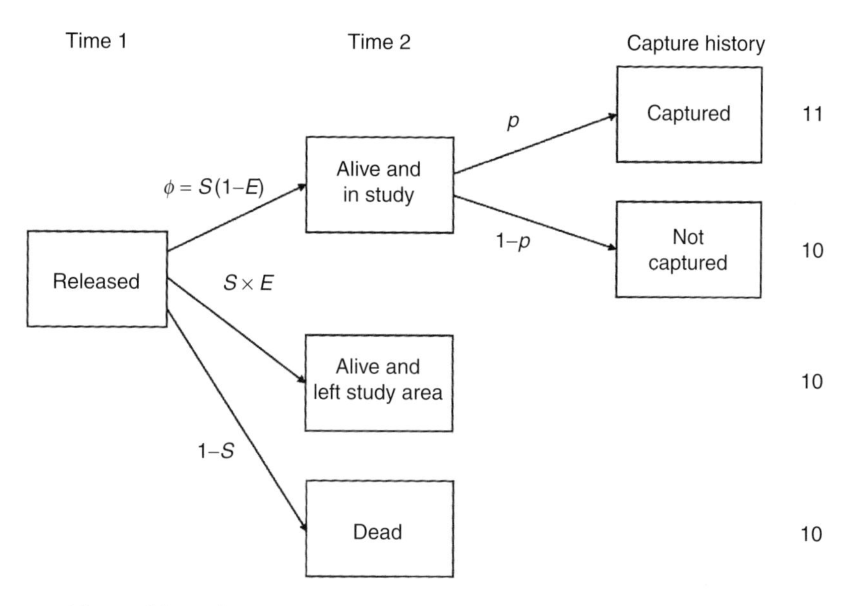

Fig. 12.5 **The problem of apparent survival under conventional CJS model. Animals alive at time 1 may be alive and present in the study area at time 2; alive but absent from the study area; or dead. Capture histories ("10") of dead, alive, and present but not captured, and alive but absent animals are indistinguishable.**

to estimate the parameters f^{ij}, the proportion of marked animals released in area i that were recovered in area j. Clearly, f^{ij} depends not only on movement, but also on the sampling intensity (e.g., rate of harvest) in each wintering area. For example, it may be reasonable to model recovery as

$$f^{ij} = \psi^{ij} h^j$$

where ψ^{ij} is the probability of movement from area i to area j, and h^j is the probability of recovery once there. Also, we note that some animals in each marking area are not recovered (Figure 12.5); these animals may be alive and simply not recovered, or they may have died. In fact, it is not possible with this simple data structure to separately estimate movement, recovery, and survival rates, and more complicated data structures and models, or simplifying assumptions, are required.

Earlier we noted that the basic CJS model, while properly separating capture and survival events, ordinarily cannot distinguish between an event that an animal died between two sampling occasions and the event that it emigrated from the study area (Figure 12.5). If emigration is permanent, there is of course no possibility of future recapture, and this event is treated identically to mortality in CJS. Temporary emigration raises the possibility of future recapture, but creates additional difficulties and requires more complex modeling, as provided under the RD.

The problem of emigration is a serious one for CMR studies, particularly for mobile species such as birds, for which it is virtually impossible to establish a spatial recapture design that would assure that all animals are subject to recapture. Burnham (1993) developed an approach for combined analysis of ring recovery and CR data that, under certain assumptions, allows for separating demographic survival and permanent emigration (confounded under CJS models) and thus enables the estimation of fidelity rates. The Burnham model depends on the critical assumption that, unlike recaptures, recoveries can potentially occur throughout the distribution of the species. This assumption is reasonable for many harvested, migratory species (e.g., North American waterfowl), where most recoveries are via hunter reports, and hunting occurs throughout the animal's distribution. It is less likely to be tenable for many European recovery situations, where the majority of recoveries are reports of birds found dead, and there is no assurance of sampling throughout the animal's range (Williams *et al.* 2002). The Burnham model is incorporated in the program MARK (White and Burnham 1999).

A more general approach involves the use of **multi-state** (multi-stratum) models, in which animals are captured, released, and recaptured in two or more "states." Again, this refers to any attribute about the individual, such as the age, physical condition, breeding status, or spatial location. These data are summarized in a manner analogous to the capture history format already seen, but where numerical or other codes now signify the state at each capture. For instance, "20310223" signifies an animal that was released in state 2 at occasion 1, recaptured in state 3 at occasion 3, state 1 at 4, state 2 at 6 and 7, state 3 at 8, and not captured at occasions 2 or 5. Multi-state models require definition of many new parameters, notably state-specific transition and recapture probabilities, and are beyond the scope of this book; interested readers are encouraged to consult Williams *et al.* (2002) for a more complete discussion of these models.

Summary

In this chapter we used recovery and recapture data for estimating abundance and demographic parameters in open populations. Our focus was on the estimation of demographic parameters such as survival and reproduction rates, but we also considered estimation of abundance, recruitment, and movement rates. We used statistical models that properly account for incomplete detection in capture samples, and which, under model assumptions, provide unbiased estimates of demographic parameters and functional (e.g., covariate) relationships.

In Chapter 13 we will change focus and deal with the important issue of quantifying resource selection. Again, however, we will carefully consider the nature of our data, and, as appropriate, include models of the sampling process to avoid confounding the comparisons of interest.

13
Analysis of habitat

In this chapter we focus on methods used to estimate habitat utilization – or as is often described in more general terms – resource use or selection by wildlife. Many terms are used in the literature to describe these methods, but they all essentially refer to the relationship between an animal and its environment (habitat). This topic is essentially derived from Hutchinson's (1957) ecological niche concept, where we attempt to describe the range of environmental characteristics encompassing those required by a particular species. Like virtually all of the other topics covered in this book we have issues of sampling, scale, and linkages to other types of data. As we have emphasized in all the topics we discuss, those basic principles outlined in Chapters 1–6 apply here.

Manly *et al.* (1993) and Thomas and Taylor (2006) provide outlines of the types of studies that might be done to assess animal resource use. They describe resource use in terms of several types of analyses depending on the sample unit being the animal or the population. Starting at the first level that they call Design I, individual animals are not marked and the availability of habitat or resources is defined at some population level. In Design II, animals are individually marked and therefore use is defined in terms of the individual, but habitat is still described at the population level. Design III includes marked animals, and habitat availability is defined for each animal. Design IV includes studies where both habitat use and availability are defined in terms of a particular point in time for a particular animal. It is quite apparent from this outline that the types of data acquisition and analytical techniques used for each of the Designs will be determined by the specific data constructs. We will review some common examples of these in the following sections. For example, radiotelemetry studies might have data constructs that fall into one or more of Designs II, III, and/or IV.

Sample units and scale

Johnson (1980) devised a hierarchy of scales for describing the habitat of animals (Figure 13.1). First-order habitat includes those environmental factors that determine the distribution of an organism. These are of interest especially in conservation of rare or poorly studied species. Second-order analysis is often the target of radiotelemetry studies and is related to assessing how habitat might affect where a particular animal might place its home range on a landscape. Third-order habitat is related to use of habitats by an animal within its home range. Fourth-order habitat is most often defined

Quantitative Conservation of Vertebrates, 1st edition. By M.J. Conroy and J.P. Carroll. Published 2009 by Blackwell Publishing, ISBN 978-1-4051-8228-7 (pb) and 978-1-4051-9098-5 (hb).

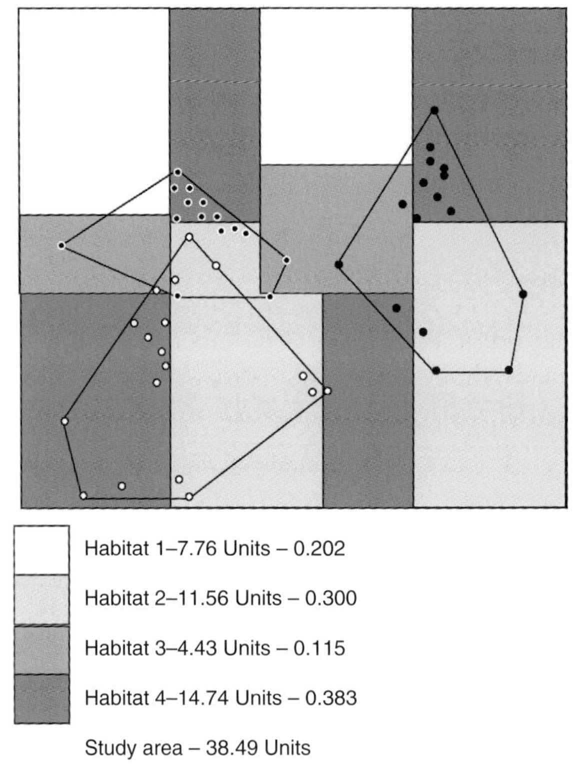

Fig. 13.1 **Hierarchical scales of resource selection. In this example we see a study area with well-defined habitats. These might represent an agricultural landscape with different crop types and other possibly natural habitats or woodlands interspersed. Overlain are a series of convex polygon home ranges of some species such as the ring-necked pheasant (*Phasianus colchicus*) often found in these landscapes. In this case we see that the home ranges, hopefully representing a random sample of the population on this landscape, are not randomly distributed (e.g. representing Johnson's second level analysis), and within those home ranges the actual observations are not randomly distributed (representing Johnson's third level analysis). The goal of most habitat analysis techniques is to identify the composition of the available habitat and how that is related to the composition of habitats within home ranges and among individual radio locations for each animal being tracked.**

as to microhabitat characteristics, such as density of vegetation or other specific details at the exact spot where the animal is found, or sometimes it is used to describe food habits of an animals. Analysis of habitat at these different scales has been traditionally dealt with as separate entities. Even when researchers take into account various scales, such as Johnson's (1980) second and third orders, which are often described using radiotagged animals, we often see them treated as independent entities (Aebischer *et al.* 1993). Although perhaps not fundamentally wrong, intuitively we can look at those scales and see that they are not independent of each other from both the perspective of the animal and in terms of how habitats are available on the landscape. More recently there have been attempts to link these various scales by using nested or hierarchical approaches in habitat assessment.

Assessing habitat from Design I studies

Occupancy studies

Linking occupancy and habitat relationships obviously has important consideration in conservation studies. As discussed in Chapter 7, we believe that presence–absence studies are a valuable tool for field research. Taking occupancy studies beyond the simple presence–absence stage is a logical extension. Many of the studies that have applied these approaches are effectively modeling occupancy based on habitat characteristics, and once again the astute reader will be aware of the importance of dealing with incomplete detection. As we outlined in Box 7.4 in the example linking longleaf pine restoration fields with occupancy by blue grosbeaks, it is easy to see how a range of independent variables can be assessed in this way.

Occupancy and habitat selection can be modeled in a variety of other ways, including commonly applied logistic regression approaches. The great change as a result of model development with occupancy data is the realization that false-negative observations (that is, the animal is present but not detected) can have a significant influence on habitat evaluation. For example, MacKenzie *et al.* (2006) reanalyzed logistic regression assessments of pronghorn antelope (*Antilocapra americana*) data that had previously been published. Accounting for habitat-specific detection probability changed the results from that distance to water was the strongest habitat factor, to one where sagebrush density was much stronger. The conclusion is that analytical techniques no matter how appropriate relative to experimental design can become flawed as a result of factors we might not consider.

Assessing habitat using radiotagged animals from Design II, III, and IV studies

Wildlife telemetry is a widely used technique which is useful for collection data often difficult to obtain using other methods. We will not go into the pros, cons, and challenges of implementing radiotelemetry studies because that is covered in detail elsewhere (Kenward 2001; Millspaugh and Marzluff 2001). As outlined above, biologists are most often describing habitat of radiotagged animals using Johnson's (1980) second and third orders of scale. In most of these cases we have a sample of radiotagged individuals in a population that are monitored over some specified period of time. Therefore our unit of measure for telemetry analysis of habitat is the radiotagged animal or that animal as a surrogate for whatever group it might belong to.

The most common way to assess habitat of radiotagged animals is to compare the use of particular habitats with availability or composition. Essentially we are using the locations (third-order) or location of an animal's home range on the landscape (second-order) as a measure of use and comparing that to the availability of those habitats – testing the question, "Is habitat use different from what is expected through random chance?" In Figure 13.1 we illustrate some example home ranges in landscapes, showing nonrandom second- and third-order habitat use.

Although this seems like an easy and straightforward question, it is fraught with difficulties. To start with we have the usual questions of experimental design and sampling. What is our target population? Are we sampling random individuals from that population? Is that sample representative? These are difficult questions because the spatial definition of our study areas is often set for us in a fairly arbitrary way. It might be a park or refuge or other land area defined by land ownership rather than chosen to represent environmental features – such as being bounded by some barriers to movements. When capturing animals to be radiotagged, researchers often are so desperate to get a sample that they think very little about how random or representative that sample might be. This is most obvious when we capture and radiotag animals living in groups. Often we capture a number of animals from the same family group or covey or whatever type of group using some trap. These animals do not represent independent samples.

Another issue is that of definition of what are the habitats of interest. For those of us who work in landscapes that are dominated by agriculture this seems to be a bit of a more straightforward question. Habitats in those landscapes are often described by sharp lines and definable units, not unlike the example in Figure 13.2. These landscapes are somewhat analogous to paint-by-numbers art – much easier for those of us who are neophyte artists. In other sorts of landscapes different habitat types look more like abstract watercolor seascapes where objects blend into each other. Those who work in primarily natural forest ecosystems will recognize problems of definition when one habitat might grade into the next over large areas. In addition, not all landscape features are definable as unit areas. Some features, such as streams or water holes, are linear or point features, which do not translate very well to often-used definitions of availability, such as amount of area. In addition, most studies do not necessarily account for distribution and size of habitat patches on the landscape. Figure 13.3 demonstrates how we can have a landscape with the same proportions of two habitats, but with different patch sizes and configurations, which adds additional challenges to our analyses.

We also have implementation issues with radiotelemetry studies. For example, researchers using telemetry to locate animals that are difficult to observe or easily influenced by the researcher's presence might want to remotely detect location. Remote detection of an animal's location, while a worthy goal, often results in a great deal of error in determining where an animal is actually located. This is often done using triangulation among two or more bearings obtained from remote locations. When the spatial error associated with the location of an animal encompasses multiple habitats, inferences about habitat use become ambiguous (Withey *et al.* 2001). A number of different methods for assessing the influence of error associated with triangulations have been presented (Springer 1979; Lenth 1981; Pace 1988; Withey *et al.* 2001). Of course location error in telemetry studies is not just a function of error associated with standard equipment limitations relative to propagation of electromagnetic radiation, but also of particular conditions associated with the environment where the study is being conducted. For those biologists working in terrestrial environments, typical problems include often unpredictable impacts of topography and habitats on direction finding. Unfortunately we still see authors often glossing over the potential substantial effects of these errors.

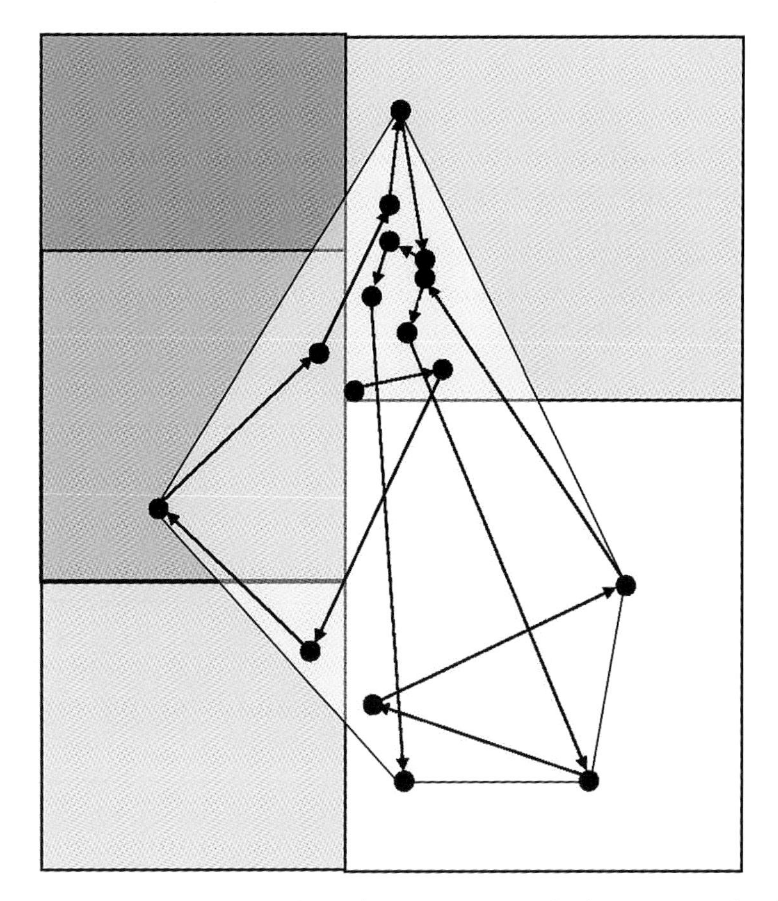

Fig. 13.2 **One of the home ranges from the previous example showing more detail of the individual radio locations. In this case we see that locations are clumped around the lower-left corner of the habitat in the upper right corner of the study area. The animal also leaves that habitat and returns a number of times. We also see that most of the locations tend to be near the edge of the habitat. This might be cover used for roosting by our hypothetical pheasant in the brushy areas near the edge of the woodland, whereas the other locations might represent foraging bouts in surrounding farm fields.**

The spatial scales most often used following Johnson (1980) create several challenges for field biologists. First, when we are looking at higher-order analyses, we often find it difficult to define what is available habitat. At this level we are usually comparing the habitats found in a home range with those found in the landscape. As in our definition of the sample population outlines above, if we assume that definition of the habitats within the home range is fairly straightforward and can be described by one of the common home range indices, then what do we actually compare it to? Biologists have used many different methods to define the "landscape" available to their study animals. In many cases this is done in terms of something completely independent of the animals, such as a predefined study area, or one defined in terms of land ownership or management patterns. Some have defined the available landscape as a conglomeration of all of the home ranges of their study animals. Others have defined it in terms of

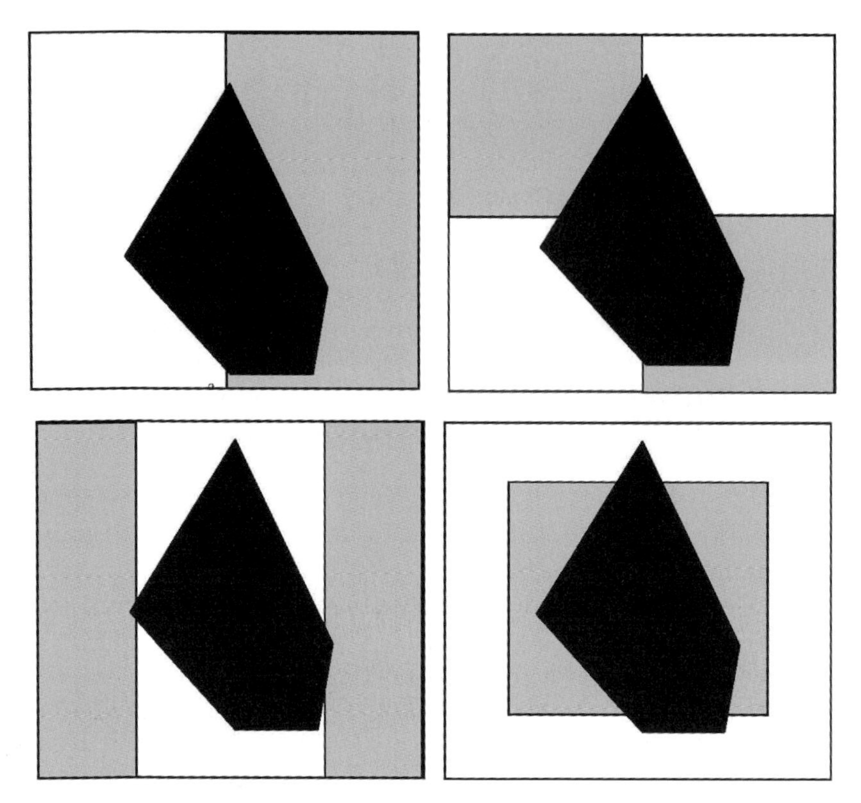

Fig. 13.3 **Hypothetical landscapes with the same proportion of two habitats, but with different patch sizes.**

home ranges with some type of buffer, and still others have looked at seasonal dispersal patterns to establish a measure of average distances an animal may move. There are some techniques such as Mahlanobis Distances and Polytomous Logistic Regression which require no measures of availability (Thomas and Taylor 2006). The difficulty with all of the above definitions is that for a particular study, the researcher could probably make pro and con arguments for any of these. The difficulty is that we are trying to define in dichotomous terms – in or out of a study area – the landscape available to individual animals – which is much more of a continuous relationship.

What is important to remember here is that although radiotelemetry is a useful technique, its implementation is not without many challenges. Researchers who plan to use telemetry need to spend time consulting the multitude of references on the topic (White and Garrott 1990; Kenward 2001; Millspaugh and Marzluff 2001).

Sampling in radiotelemetry studies

Definition of the sampling unit

Radiotelemetry studies have many issues relative to experimental design and sampling in common with other field studies (Chapter 5). However, these studies also involve repeated observations of individual radiotagged animals that pose analytical difficulties similar to behavior studies. A common error of early telemetry studies was the incorrect assignment of sample unit. It should be apparent that the sample unit is the radiotagged animal – but with an important caveat. If the animal that is radiotagged is part of a group or somehow influenced by other animals that might be part of the radiotagged sample, then these are not independent observations – an assumption of virtually all analytical techniques. This means that if we are radiotagging animals in a particular study area and we have several radiotagged animals that are members of coveys, or flocks, or herds, we must be very careful how we treat that data. For example, Carroll *et al.* (1995) radiotagged multiple members of a series of winter coveys of grey partridge (*Perdix perdix*) in North Dakota. They did not use the animal as the sample unit for habitat analysis, but instead used the radiotagged individuals as a surrogate for the covey. When they had more than one individual in a covey radiotagged they did not count locations of the multiple individuals separately, but rather as a single observation. In addition, many authors have emphasized the importance of temporal independence of individual radio locations within each tagged animal. Rather ironically, we believe that in fact there is some confusion over the independence of individual locations versus spatial representation of individual radio locations (Thomas and Taylor 2006). Sequential locations of a particular animal are always autocorrelated whether our sequential observations are over shorter or longer time periods. We believe that, by definition, individual radio locations of a particular animal cannot be independent, just less autocorrelated; however, sampling can be done to assure that the locations are representative. For example, we might be tracking an animal over a year-long study period. We do not want to go out in the field 1 day per month and obtain a series of locations on that day and claim that these represent habitat or movement of the animal in that month, or that 1 day as part of a year-long study might be representative for a year time frame. Therefore dealing with this question is actually much more complex than is implied by many authors. Various analytical techniques described in the next section attempt to overcome this issue by a variety of means.

Sample size

In telemetry studies we do not have one sample size, but two distinct and competing sample sizes. We have the sample unit which in most cases will be our target animal. A number of authors have attempted to provide guidance on sample size. Generally we see figures of more than 50 animals and sometimes sample sizes of several hundred recommended as minima – and since we are often attempting to answer questions relative to animal survival and/or home ranges and movements we also have sample size issues there. A rather sensible rule-of-thumb recommended by Aebischer *et al.* (1993) when you are analyzing habitat using Compositional Analysis is a minimum of 10 animals per habitat used in the analysis. For example, if we have two habitats, then our tracked sample should be more than 20, and if we have four habitats, then it should be more than 40. Of course if you have additional independent variables that might influence habitat use, such as sex or age, these require an increase in sample size.

We then have to decide how many times a particular animal is observed. This is important in our attempts to create representation and is also going to be rather study specific. Habitat composition that is rather coarse and simple might require smaller sample sizes than a landscape where the animal is using a variety of rare habitat patches. The difficulty researchers have is that they are often not in a position to undertake pilot studies to assess these issues. For home range studies we often see researchers use cumulative area curves to estimate necessary sample sizes. Rather interestingly, many of these analyses produce estimates somewhere around 30 observations per animal. We suspect this convergence might actually be a function of some underlying math function or simply a function of the limited sample sizes that researchers use to derive the curves in the first place. A rule-of-thumb here might again be 10 times the number of habitats available in the study.

Putting the two sample size issues together creates the ultimate problem faced by most researchers – limited resources available to study their animals. Both of these sample size issues demand financial resources in terms of equipment and personnel in the field, and maximizing both can be difficult. If a compromise is needed, we recommend radiotagging more animals, and taking fewer observations per animal. Our recommendation is, when you have to compromise – radiotag more animals.

Statistical methods for assessing habitat use from radiotagged animals

Older methods

Several methods over the years have peaked in popularity and now are used much less than in the past. Chi square (χ^2) analyses (Neu *et al.* 1974; Byers *et al.* 1984) saw significant use during the 1970s and 1980s. However, application of χ^2 statistics during that era were often incorrect, with many studies showing classical examples of pseudoreplication – generally use of individual radio locations rather than the animal as the unit of measure.

Johnson's PREFER method (Johnson 1980) is a ranking technique that overcomes many of the problems of χ^2 methods and generally saw limited use during the 1980s. Friedman's method (Freidman 1937) is a non-parametric ANOVA and is applicable to telemetry data. It never was used a great deal, but mainly in the 1970s.

Recent methods

Among recent methods, the technique that has been applied the most is Compositional Analysis (Aebischer *et al.* 1993). This method is adapted from geology and the need to compare composition of minerals from geological samples. Widely applied and easily adapted over the last 10+ years, the technique overcomes many of the problems of earlier methods through the use of a rather simple equation. The log-ratio difference equation converts individual habitat availability and use proportions into a series of habitat pairing relationships. For two habitats we see the relationship is described as follows:

$$\text{Log-ratio difference} = \ln\left(\frac{U_1/U_2}{A_1/A_2}\right)$$

where U is used for habitats 1 and 2, and A is availability for habitats 1 and 2, respectively.

It is not difficult to see that as use and availability of each habitat become close to being equal, that is, as the ratio approaches 1.0, the result of the log-ratio difference equation approaches 0.0 – and as these proportions become more different the value of the log-ratio becomes larger, either positive or negative depending on the habitat used as the denominator. When this is done for a number of animals a simple statistical test, such as a one sample paired t-test or simple presentation of the mean and 95% confidence interval, will allow the researcher to determine the probability that this value is different from 0.0. This can be extended to as many habitats as there are available, and as Aebischer *et al.* (1993) demonstrated, only a single habitat needs to be used as the denominator, allowing application of multivariate analysis of variance to test for all habitats simultaneously. Another desirable feature of this approach is that the pair-wise comparison among habitats allows the researcher to rank each habitat based on the degree of selection or avoidance. In Box 13.1 we demonstrate the application of this technique to simple examples involving use of two and three habitats.

Log-linear modeling and logistic regression

Erickson *et al.* (2001) provide background on the use of these related techniques for assessing habitat of radiotagged animals. They argue that these techniques offer some distinct advantages over other methods because they incorporate only use data and there are no implied assumptions regarding places where the animal is not found. They also argue that these methods can deal with continuous variables. These models provide a basis for analyzing habitat for a single animal. They make some basic assumptions about the independence of locations for the animal and some would argue that you cannot make these assumptions by definition. This is extended to a sample of radiotagged animals, considering the animal as the sample unit.

Future directions

Cooper and Millspaugh (1999, 2001) argue that there are still problems with the basic theory associated with how telemetry data are used in conjunction with habitat, and that these limitations have a profound effect on the inference we may draw from telemetry-based habitat studies. They argue that habitat use studies are essentially discrete choice models developed for econometrics analysis. This is similar to logistic analysis except that availability of resources may vary over time and space.

Conroy *et al.* (in prep.) have a slightly different approach that also addresses some of the difficulties in the commonly applied approaches. Their method effectively defines

Box 13.1 Sample data set demonstrating the use of Compositional Analysis (Aebischer *et al.* 1993).

Analysis 1: In this example we have two available habitats and 10 animals. From the proportional data we calculate a log ratio difference for each animal. We can then apply a 95% confidence interval or one-group t-test to determine if the mean is different from 0.0. In this case we see the 95% CI encompasses 0.0, therefore 'use' is not different from 'availability'. In looking at this table it is easy to observe that when availability is nearly equal to use then the log ratio difference value is closer to 0.0. Also, note that when use is greater than availability for Habitat 2 then the log ratio difference value is negative.

Animal	Available		Use		Log ratio difference
	Habitat 1	Habitat 2	Habitat 1	Habitat 2	
1	0.60	0.40	0.58	0.42	−0.0827
2	0.60	0.40	0.50	0.50	−0.4055
3	0.60	0.40	0.40	0.60	−0.8109
4	0.60	0.40	0.70	0.30	0.4418
5	0.60	0.40	0.55	0.45	−0.2048
6	0.60	0.40	0.90	0.10	1.7918
7	0.60	0.40	0.35	0.65	−1.0245
8	0.60	0.40	0.50	0.50	−0.4055
9	0.60	0.40	0.61	0.39	0.0418
10	0.60	0.40	0.65	0.35	0.2136
				Mean	−0.0445
				95% CI	0.4853

Analysis 2: In this example we have three available habitats and 10 animals. From the proportional data we calculate a log ratio difference for each animal. Since there are three habitats this leads to and MANOVA analysis – testing overall differences in habitat use. In this case Wilk's $\lambda = 0.115$ and $P = 0.0002$. We can apply a 95% CI or one-group t-test to determine if each mean is different from 0.0. In this case we see the 95% CI does not encompass 0.0, therefore 'use' is different from 'availability' for all three paired comparisons. Using the notation of Aebisher *et al.* (1993) we would rank the habitats from greatest to least use H3 >>> H1 >>> H2.

Animal	Available			Use		
	Habitat 1	Habitat 2	Habitat 3	Habitat 1	Habitat 2	Habitat 3
1	0.50	0.30	0.20	0.42	0.10	0.48
2	0.50	0.30	0.20	0.50	0.10	0.40
3	0.50	0.30	0.20	0.60	0.15	0.25
4	0.50	0.30	0.20	0.30	0.15	0.55
5	0.50	0.30	0.20	0.45	0.20	0.35
6	0.50	0.30	0.20	0.10	0.20	0.70
7	0.50	0.30	0.20	0.65	0.10	0.25
8	0.50	0.30	0.20	0.50	0.05	0.45
9	0.50	0.30	0.20	0.39	0.05	0.56
10	0.50	0.30	0.20	0.35	0.05	0.60

Box 13.1 Continued.

Animal	Log ratio differences		
	Habitat 1 vs. Habitat 2	Habitat 1 vs. Habitat 3	Habitat 2 vs. Habitat 3
1	−0.9242589	1.04982212	1.97408103
2	−1.0986123	0.69314718	1.79175947
3	−0.8754687	0.04082199	0.91629073
4	−0.1823216	1.52242654	1.70474809
5	−0.3001046	0.6649763	0.9650809
6	1.2039728	2.86220088	1.65822808
7	−1.3609766	−0.0392207	1.32175584
8	−1.7917595	0.81093022	2.60268969
9	−1.5432981	1.27808078	2.82137889
10	−1.4350845	1.45528723	2.89037176
Mean	−0.8307912	1.03384725	1.86463845
95% CI	0.54669604	0.51684745	0.44314977

each location of each radiotagged animal as a specific choice of a particular habitat. What is also known is that if the animal is located in that particular location it is not located anywhere else, so it becomes a binary probability exercise. They extended this idea to include hierarchical modeling, allowing multiple scales to be assessed together. This overcomes the rather artificial way Johnson's (1980) different scales are dealt with – that is, usually as completely independent decisions by the animal in question and completely independent analyses (Aebischer *et al.* 1993).

14
Estimation of species richness and other community parameters

A logical extension of studies of individual species is to study the communities of which they are members. Community ecology has been an important area of study for much of the twentieth century as biologists soon realized that individual species do not live in a vacuum, but are influenced by and themselves influence other members of the ecosystem they inhabit. In conservation biology we often identify potential degradation of ecosystems not by effects on individual species *per se*, but by overall effects on community-level attributes such as **species richness** and **diversity**. In less studied ecosystems we are often limited to fairly cursory research on all but a few charismatic species, leaving other groups within those ecosystems to be assessed as groups. This is quite common among studies of birds or amphibians in tropical forests where diversity is high and our understanding of particular species relatively low.

Although there is a long history of development of community parameters and an early recognition of some of the same problems with detection that create issues in studies of single species, we often see fairly primitive application of sampling and detection strategies to community studies. However, some biologists have recognized this parallel between studies of such biological phenomena as abundance of single species and community studies, resulting now in application of similar types of estimators (Table 14.1). For example, when sampling communities it should be apparent to readers that as in single species studies, any particular survey is not going to detect all species in the former, which is analogous to our inability to detect all individuals in the latter.

Recently, this recognition has been utilized in the development of more sophisticated techniques to estimate parameters such as species richness that allow us to take into account detection rates. Depending on the particular types of studies we are undertaking, we can base these on the general theory surrounding occupancy models as discussed in Chapter 7 or on abundance sampling as outlined in Chapter 8. Therefore in this chapter we outline the theory and metrics for assessing species richness and evenness, but also immigration and emigration, and extensions to include components of extinction and persistence, and other measures of community dynamics (Table 14.1).

Quantitative Conservation of Vertebrates, 1st edition. By M.J. Conroy and J.P. Carroll. Published 2009 by Blackwell Publishing, ISBN 978-1-4051-8228-7 (pb) and 978-1-4051-9098-5 (hb).

Table 14.1 Characterization of single species parameters and extension to communities, highlighting our ability to apply much of the theory and technique development for single species to community studies.

Single species	Community
Individual animals	Individual species
Presence–absence (occupancy)	Community occupancy
Abundance	Species richness
Survival (mortality)	Local persistence
Immigration	Colonization

Detection and communities

We make the argument here that the detection issues so critical to studies of individual populations are just as important in community analyses. We extend the logic in Chapter 6, in which we examined the effects of detection on individual species abundance estimates, to communities. First, consider a count of species C_i and the true number of species S_i. If we can detect all species, then

$$C_i = S_i$$

However, we already know that this situation is likely very rare; therefore we need to include an additional parameter p_i,the detection probability of species from S_i being included in the count statistic C_i. Our equation then becomes

$$E(C_i) = S_i p_i$$

This suggests that to obtain a reasonable estimate of species richness we first need an estimation of detection. We can then use the detection estimate, in conjunction with our count statistic, to estimate the number of species thus:

$$\hat{S}_i = C_i/\hat{p}_i$$

It should be quite apparent to the reader that these equations are exactly the same as in our introduction to abundance estimation in Chapter 6. Extension of that same basic premise will be a common thread throughout this chapter. Although we will not pursue it here, it is important to remember that there are some additional issues that can affect detection in community analyses. For example, detection rates among species may be heterogeneous and/or related to the abundance of particular species. As Williams *et al.* (2002) suggest, these variations in detection rates among species are likely to be much larger and more important than those factors that cause heterogeneity in detection within species.

Estimation of species richness

In this section we describe the sampling approaches outlined in Nichols and Conroy (1996) using quadrat sampling with spatial replication, sampling the same locality on multiple occasions (temporal replication), and sampling on a single occasion, where we include number of species encountered and individuals detected for each species developing empirical species abundance distribution (Burnham and Overton 1979).

Quadrat sampling

As we did in quadrat sampling of species abundance (Chapter 8), we can subdivide an area of interest into a number of quadrats or small sampling units. We then take a selection of a random sample of those quadrats. The investigator identifies number of species found on each selected quadrat, and the number of species shared by quadrats. In the following two-quadrat sample it is easy to see how this is analogous to a simple Lincoln–Peterson estimator [Equation (10.2)]. In this scenario, detection probability is p_i, s_i represents number of species detected in the ith quadrat, and m is the number shared among quadrats:

$$\hat{p}_1 = m/s_2$$

Therefore S or species richness can be estimated by

$$\hat{S} = s_1 s_2/m$$

or preferably by using the bias-corrected version of L–P [Equation (10.3)]. Obviously this can be extended to any number of quadrats, which a conservation biologist would be much more likely to be interested in doing. Later in this section we give some examples of these methods.

The following recommendations should be taken into account before the implementation of quadrat sampling for estimating species richness. First, species richness should only be estimated within areas for which the concept of a community makes sense. For example, if the area of interest likely has multiple community structures, such as forests associated with river bottoms and those in uplands, then limit sampling to what logically contains a "single community." Second, ensure that quadrats are selected randomly from the area of interest. Finally, use estimation methods that account for heterogeneity in detection rates.

In addition, there are several important considerations in the application of simple abundance estimators to species richness analysis. Most important is to consider the possibility that detection rates are heterogeneous among species. The simple model outlined above assumes that detection is homogeneous among species, which is often unrealistic because of inherent differences in the appearance, behavior, and relative abundance of different species. The general effect of among-species detection heterogeneity is to underestimate true species richness. Most of the estimators that have been developed to deal with this issue are based on the heterogeneity model in closed-population mark–recapture models (M_h ; Chapter 10). Application of programs, such as CAPTURE or MARK, to these problems, with specific application of M_h and M_{th} models for estimates of species richness, are quite useful (Box 14.1). We illustrate this with data for a community of grassland songbirds (Box 14.1). Here, community estimation corresponds to CMR abundance estimation, except that we are substituting observations of a particular species for our observations of a particular animal. In this example we find with CMR approaches using CAPTURE that we are very close to estimating community richness at 32 species. We will apply occupancy models and additional data to this same example below. A program called SPECRICH2, designed to run the M_h model of capture, is also available for free (Appendix A).

Box 14.1 Here we revisit part of the data from our research examples in presence–absence analysis from Chapter 7. This data set represents surveys of songbirds on former agricultural fields that were being converted to longleaf pines through a government program designed to take crop fields out of production and put them back into one of the formerly widespread ecosystems in the region. We completed three surveys (sampling periods) of each of 41 fields (quadrats) from southern Georgia during 2001. Our individual surveys on each quadrat were completed using a 250-m transect, thereby standardizing effort. In this study we detected 43 species over 2 years, most of which are classified as grassland or shrub–scrub nesters.

This table shows the data construct for all the longleaf pine fields we surveyed in southern Georgia. The columns represent each survey (or sampling period) undertaken during the nesting season of 2001. We only show the first part of the data set which included the 31 detected species.

Species	Survey number		
	Survey 1	Survey 2	Survey 3
American crow	0	0	1
American goldfinch	0	0	0
Barn swallow	1	1	1
Blue grosbeak	1	1	1
Blue jay	1	1	0
Bobolink	0	0	0
Brown thrasher	0	0	0
Brown-headed cowbird	1	1	1
Cattle egret	1	1	1
Chimney swift	1	1	1
Chipping sparrow	1	1	0
Common grackle	1	1	1

Box 14.1 Continued.

Species	Survey number		
	Survey 1	Survey 2	Survey 3
Common ground-dove	1	1	1
Common yellowthroat	0	1	0
Cooper's hawk	0	0	0
Eastern bluebird	1	1	1
Eastern kingbird	1	1	1
Eastern meadowlark	1	1	1
Eastern phoebe	0	0	0
Eastern towhee	0	0	0
Field sparrow	1	1	1
Grasshopper sparrow	1	1	1
Great egret	0	0	0
Great-crested flycatcher	1	0	1
Horned lark	1	1	0
House finch	0	1	1
Indigo bunting	1	1	1
Loggerhead shrike	0	1	1
Mourning dove	1	1	1
Northern bobwhite	1	1	1
Northern cardinal	0	1	1
Northern mockingbird	0	1	1
Northern rough-winged swallow	0	1	1
Orchard oriole	1	1	1
Painted bunting	0	1	0
Purple martin	1	1	0
Red-bellied woodpecker	0	0	0
Red-winged blackbird	1	1	1
Ruby-throated hummingbird	1	0	0
Savannah sparrow	0	0	0
Summer tanager	0	0	1
Yellow-billed cuckoo	0	0	0
Yellow-breasted chat	0	0	0

The following analysis is the data submission of the previous data using the program CAPTURE. Below is the output from this model. For this analysis we are assuming *a priori* that model M_{bh} is correct. We have truncated the output to demonstrate only the most important components.

title = 'LLP Community line 2001'
task read captures occasions = 3 × matrix
format = '(a2,1x,3f1.0)'

Box 14.1 Continued.

```
read input data
10 001
11 010
12 010
13 100
14 001
15 110
16 110
17 101
18 110
19 011
20 011
21 011
22 011
23 011
24 110
25 111
26 111
27 111
28 111
29 111
30 111
31 111
32 111
33 111
34 111
35 111
36 111
37 111
38 111
39 111
40 111
41 111

task closure test
task model selection
task population estimate ALL
task population estimate NULL JACKKNIFE REMOVAL ZIPPEN MT-CH MH-CH
MTH-CH
task population estimate APPROPRIATE
```

The following is the model selection criteria of Otis *et al.* (1978) for selecting the best model fit to the data.

Box 14.1 Continued.

Model selection criteria. Model selected has maximum value.

Model	$M(0)$	$M(h)$	$M(b)$	$M(bh)$	$M(t)$	$M(th)$	$M(tb)$	$M(tbh)$
Criteria	1.00	0.79	0.30	0.65	0.00	0.44	0.31	0.71

In this analysis we assumed *a priori* that M_{bh} would be the appropriate model, but we see that M_h is the highest ranking model after $M(0)$, which we excluded a priori as being non robust; therefore we present both below.

Model 1 M_{bh}
Population estimation with variable probability removal estimator.
See $M(bh)$ or removal models of the monograph for details.

Occasion	j	1	2	3	
Total caught	$M(j)$	0	23	30	32
Newly caught	$u(j)$	23	7	2	

k	N-hat	SE(N)	Chi-sq.	Prob.	Estimated	p-bar(j)	$j = 1, \ldots, 3$
1	32.00	0.907	0.82	0.3640	0.744	0.744	0.744

Population estimate is 32 with SE 0.9068
Approximate 95% confidence interval 32–32
Profile likelihood interval 32–35
Histogram of $u(j)$

Frequency	23	7	2
Each * equals 3 points			
24	*		
21	*		
18	*		
15	*		
12	*		
9	*		
6	*	*	
3	*	*	*

Model 2 M_h
Population estimation with variable probability of capture by animal.
See model $M(h)$ of the monograph for details.

Number of trapping occasions was 3
Number of animals captured, $M(t + 1)$, was 32
Total number of captures, n, was 76

Box 14.1 Continued.

Frequencies of capture, $f(i)$

$i =$ 1	2	3
$f(i) =$ 5	10	17

Computed jackknife coefficients

	$N(1)$	$N(2)$	$N(3)$	$N(4)$	$N(5)$
1	1.667	2.000	2.000		
2	1.000	0.833	0.833		
3	1.000	1.000	1.000		

Results of the jackknife computations

$iN(i)$	SE(i)	0.95 confidence limits	Test of $N(i+1)$ vs. $N(i)$		
0	32		Chi-square (1 d.f.)		
1	35.3	2.36	30.7	40.0	0.000
2	35.3	2.93	29.6	41.1	0.000
3	35.3	2.93	29.6	41.1	0.000

Average p-hat = 0.7677
Interpolated population estimate is 33 with SE 2.3892
Approximate 95% confidence interval 33–46
Estimate: 33.0906906 SE: 2.38921213

Histogram of $f(i)$

Frequency	5	10	17
Each * equals 2 points			
18			*
16			*
14			*
12			*
10		*	*
8		*	*
6	*	*	*
4	*	*	*
2	*	*	*

Looking back at our original data we see our naïve estimate of the total number of species is 23. Our CAPTURE models suggest two estimates of species richness: M_{bh} provides an estimate of 32 (with a range of 32–33), whereas M_h gives us an estimate of 33 (range 33–46).

Box 14.1 Continued.

It is quite apparent from the analysis that we are reasonably close to the true species richness of the study area with three surveys; however, as we will see later, this analysis includes only 1 year of data. We will see that our species richness using 2 years of data suggests some other information.

Complete input and output files for this problem are provided in the electronic companion to the book (see enclosed CD and website address on p. ii).

Sampling over multiple occasions

Here, a single area is assessed by a single investigator over time or multiple observers, rather than being divided into quadrats. Now the sampling units that form the columns of the data matrix (previously, quadrats) are either time occasions or observers.

In the case of the single investigator, the observer goes into the field for a sampling occasion and develops a matrix of species observations which will look the same as the quadrat 1 column in Table 14.2A. The observer then returns to the field at a later time to sample the study area again. This is then analogous to the second column or quadrat 2. What is likely different now is that we might assume that the observer's ability to detect species will improve through time – because once the observer has found a particular species the first time, it will be much easier to find that same species in later surveys. The most likely model to account for this type of detection is M_{bh}. This is a generalized removal model and the data that are critical here are the sampling occasion that the observer first sees the species.

The multiple observer variation treats data construct slightly differently in that the columns represent the different observers. The *a priori* model here is that there is likely heterogeneity among observers and this is best dealt with by M_{th}. This is particularly useful when a number of different techniques are used to sample the species community in question by the different observers. However, if it is possible to standardize the sampling and the observer heterogeneity can be minimized then it might be possible to use model M_h (Table 14.2B).

Empirical distributions of species abundance

A somewhat different approach is possible when the numbers of individuals encountered for each species is also recorded. This work developed by Burnham and Overton (1979) requires that we meet several assumptions. First, as we survey our study area, obtain counts of each species without repeat. We do this by marking, removing, or ensuring no double counting. This data can then be used to construct an empirical species abundance distribution (Williams *et al.* 2002). The data construct then becomes the number of species for which we observed one individual, then the number with two individuals, and so on. We also have the total number of species encountered. This

Table 14.2 Generalized survey data for entry in programs CAPTURE for generalized use and SPECRICH2 specifically for testing the M_h model when we are estimating species richness for (A) quadrats or multiple observers, and (B) single observer with multiple sampling occasions. In these tables zero indicates the species was not detected for that cell and one indicates that it was.

Species	1	2	3	4	5	6
(a) Quadrat number or observer number*						
A	0	0	1	0	0	1
B	0	1	1	1	0	1
C	1	1	0	0	0	0
D	0	0	1	0	0	0
E	1	1	1	1	1	1
(b) Sampling occasion†						
A	0	0	1			
B	0	1				
C	1					
D	0	0	1			
E	1					

* The columns here represent the survey data from each of a series of randomly selected quadrats (in this case six quadrats) in our study area or from multiple sampling occasions carried out once each by a series of observers (six observers). For this survey design, our assumptions *a priori* of the most likely models are M_h and M_{th} for quadrat sampling and M_{th} for multiple observers. This is because we would assume that detection probabilities among species would be different and for multiple observers we expect detection rates among observers to vary.

† This sampling strategy involves a single observer undertaking multiple surveys in the same study area. Each column represents a sampling occasion. We changed the table slightly to represent the data that are actually used by the model base on our *a priori* assumption that once the observer has detected the species, he/she is more likely to find it again – thereby analogous to generalized removal models (M_{bh}). In the field a researcher would more likely fill in the table as in (a) above. Therefore the data that are used in this model are the sampling occasion when the species is first detected.

type of data can be analyzed using the jackknifing procedures of Burnham and Overton (1979) using the program SPECRICH (Box 14.2).

Community richness using occupancy models

Just as the above analyses are an extension of mark–recapture analysis to community estimation, recently occupancy models have been extended to community analysis. Much of the development here has taken a slightly different approach. Here the concept of **relative species richness** becomes a key issue. This is because unlike our basic assumption in mark–recapture models, where we are making no *a priori* assumptions about the actual species richness of our study area, we instead will make assumptions about the total possible list of species that might be found. In fact, this makes sense for most studies because what we are really interested in studying is not species richness

Table 14.3 Simple demonstration of the application of a Lincoln–Peterson estimator as an example of where we observe species richness on two quadrats and assume that detection probability is the same for all species.

Number of species detected in quadrat 1 $(n_1) = 17$
Number of species detected in quadrat 2 $(n_2) = 13$
Number of species shared between n_1 and n_2 $(m) = 11$

$$\hat{p}_1 = m/n_2$$
$$= 11/13 = 0.846$$
$$\hat{N} = n_1 n_2/m$$
$$= 17 \times 13/11$$
$$= 20.09$$

The bias-adjusted version of the Lincoln–Peterson estimator is

$$\hat{N} = \frac{(n_1 + 1) \times (n_2 + 1)}{m_2 + 1} - 1$$
$$= 20.00$$

Therefore, our estimate of species richness accounting for incomplete detection is 20 species rather than our naïve estimate of 18 species. That naïve estimate is based on the 11 shared species plus the five found in quadrats 1 and two found in quadrat 2 that were not shared.

per se, but what sorts of factors might be involved in species richness at a particular location or how it has changed over time, or the influence of human factors (MacKenzie *et al.* 2006).

As with CMR models, we need to be aware of the high likelihood of heterogeneity of detection probabilities among species in our community. Fortunately, as we have already seen (Chapter 7), occupancy models can model heterogeneity in order to provide unbiased estimates. Additionally, we may be able to explain some heterogeneity with covariates (MacKenzie *et al.* 2006).

In applying occupancy models to estimate community richness we find that the data layout is similar to what we used in single species models. However, instead of the lines of data which in the single species models represent the individual sites where we conducted our surveys, they now represent the individual species (Table 14.3, Boxes 14.1 and 14.3). In the example in Box 14.3 we see that we can easily apply PRESENCE to the data. In this case we had an estimate of 43 species based on data from the complete study; however, when we used only the 2001 data we observed only 31 of the species, and taking into account detection we estimate that we missed one species that was likely present. Our data suggest in 2001 that $75.2 \pm 6.7\%$ of the avian community was present on our study sites. Our analysis in both Boxes 14.2 and 14.3 included habitat associations for each species (grassland, shrub–scrub, or other) because we thought *a priori* that there might be significant detection differences due to vegetation. As it turns out, the model including habitat ranked third with an AIC weight of only 20%, suggesting that vegetation association was not a critical factor.

Box 14.2 In this example we estimated species richness using empirical distribution of species abundance, using the same longleaf pine data from 2001 except taking advantage of our count information instead of simple presence–absence. We observed the following distribution of counts.

Number of individuals observed in three surveys	1	2	3	4	5
Number of species	5	1	2	1	4

K	N(JK)	SE(N(JK))	$T(K)$	$P(K)$
1	37.	3.1623	1.6787	0.0932
2	41.	5.4772	1.5395	0.1237
3	46.	8.3666	1.2282	0.2194
4	53.	13.0384	1.2328	0.2176
5	66.	22.0907	0.0000	1.0000

Interpolated $N = 37.0000$
SE of interpolated $N = 3.1623$
The output from SPECRICH suggested and estimated a species richness of 37 ± 3.16 SE species. Compared with our results from CAPTURE (Box 14.1) where we observed an estimated $33 + 2.39$ species with model M_h, we find that this method suggests that possibly more species should be found in this community than we observed from either the CMR or occupancy models.

Estimating parameters of community dynamics

Of course estimation of species richness should be viewed as a starting point in our assessment of species communities. There are many interesting questions that arise once we actually estimate richness. For example, we might want to look at changes in species richness, species extinction or colonization, and these lead to questions regarding turnover rates. We might also want to look at species richness questions relative to similarity among sites.

There are two general directions that have seen recent technique development. Not surprisingly they are similar to a number of topics that we covered previously. One general group is based on general mark–recapture theory. The other is based on occupancy models.

Community dynamics

In all our models above we generally made the assumption, not incorrectly, that our communities are "closed." However, when we want to examine species extinctions,

Box 14.3 Community richness estimates using occupancy models. In this example we use the same data as in Box 14.1, except that we are not estimating community richness *per se*, but relative community richness following MacKenzie *et al.* (2006). Therefore we include all species detected in the fields during the whole study. In this analysis any species not detected during the three surveys done in 2001 receives a detection history of "000". In this example we ran three models: constant detection, detection varying by survey, and with habitat association of each species as a covariate (grassland, shrub–scrub, or other). The highest ranking model was the simple constant detection model which is reported below. In this situation our model suggests that we are not dealing with important detection differences among species (i.e., if they are not being detected it is due to their not being there rather than being harder to find). We are suggesting this because our habitat association covariate was not important – something we believed *a priori* to be linked with detection.

Model	AIC	Delta AIC	AIC weight	Model likelihood	Number of parameters	(−2 * LogLike)
1 group, constant *P*	150.54	0.00	0.5503	0.3028	2	146.54
1 group, survey-specific *P*	152.14	1.60	0.2473	0.1361	4	144.14
psi(.), *p*(habitat)	152.54	2.00	0.2024	0.1114	3	146.54

Our model with 55% of the model weight was constant detection with no covariates. We present this below:

Predefined model: Detection probabilities are NOT time-specific
Number of groups = 1
Number of sites = 43
Number of sampling occasions = 2
Number of missing observations = 0

Number of parameters = 2
−2 log(likelihood) = 146.541815
AIC = 150.541815
Naïve estimate = 0.744186
Proportion of sites occupied (Psi) = 0.7518 (0.067385)
Probability of group membership (Theta) = 1.0000

Detection probabilities (p):

Group	Survey	p	SE(p)
1	1	0.783650	(0.044349)

Variance–covariance matrix

psi	p(G1)
0.0045	−0.0002
−0.0002	0.0020

Box 14.3 Continued.

The conclusions from this model are not the same as when we are analyzing occupancy. In this model the proportion of sites occupied (ψ) represents our estimate of the relative proportion of species found on our sites during a particular season (in this case 2001). We observed 31 species in 2001 and our total count of species during the study was 43; therefore our relative species richness estimate (0.7518 ± 0.067) was close to our naïve estimate of 0.744.

Complete input and output files for this problem are provided in the electronic companion to the book (see enclosed CD and website address on p. ii).

turnover, etc., we must assume that we are dealing with the situation analogous to an open population. We could apply many of the commonly used capture–recapture models for open populations (e.g., CJS, JS). However, these do not deal with the problem of heterogeneous detection probabilities, which require a more sophisticated approach based on Pollock's (1982) **Robust Design** based on mark–recapture models or extension of occupancy models as outlined in MacKenzie *et al.* (2006). We have already dealt with the basics of the Robust Design in Chapter 12, and here we will extend these ideas to community analysis. More advanced applications of these models are beyond the scope of this book, and we will limit treatment to a few examples. Interested readers should consult Williams *et al.* (2002) and MacKenzie *et al.* (2006) for more examples and a thorough treatment of these topics.

Once again we can address questions in community dynamics over space and time. We may be interested in how communities change on a single site over time or how communities vary at one time over space. An important measure of community change over time is the rate of change in species richness. This is simply a measure of how species richness changes over time; it does not account for changes in species composition. Williams *et al.* (2002) provide more detailed examples of how this is calculated and provide examples using Pollock's (1982) Robust Design. Studies employing these approaches typically occur over multiple seasons and we provide an example expanding our avian community data to 2 years (Box 14.4). Our results suggest that colonization, rather than local extinction, has provided the greatest contribution to changes in species richness. This is apparent even from a naïve and cursory view of the data, where we see most of the species found in the first year are also recorded in the second year, but with a number of additional species.

Extension of species richness

In our final examples we look at incorporating site-specific issues in our models by reorganizing the data to address a different question. In the case of our songbird community data we might also be interested in how species richness varies among sites in addition to overall estimates of species richness (Boxes 14.5 and 14.6). In Box 14.6

Box 14.4 In the following multi-season occupancy model we are investigating changes in species richness over seasons. This data set has only two seasons and therefore is somewhat limited in interpretation. Again we are expanding the community data from Box 14.3 to include years 2001–2002. Therefore we have six surveys over our sites in the 2 years with a habitat association covariate.

Open population model:

Number of sites = 43
Total number of sampling occasions = 6
Number of primary sampling periods = 2
Number of missing observations = 0

Number of parameters = 3
Number of function calls = 131
Final function value = 137.916947
−2log(likelihood) = 275.833895
AIC = 281.833895
Model has been fit using the logistic link.

Untransformed estimates of coefficients for covariates (beta's):

		Estimate (SE)
A1: occupancy	psi1	0.162241 (0.309622)
B1: colonization	gam1	2.395083 (0.587141)
D1: detection	P[1-1]	1.278250 (0.187580)

Variance–covariance matrix of untransformed estimates:

	A1	B1	D1
A1	0.095866	0.000551	−0.001878
B1	0.000551	0.344734	−0.010325
D1	−0.001878	−0.010325	0.035186

Individual site estimates of psi:

Site	Survey	psi	SE	95% confidence interval
1 1	1-1	0.5405	0.0769	0.3906–0.6833

Individual site estimates of gamma:

Site	Survey	gamma	SE	95% confidence interval
1 1	1-1	0.9165	0.0450	0.7763–0.9720

Individual site estimates of p:

Site	Survey	p	SE	95% confidence interval
1 1	1-1	0.7822	0.0320	0.7131–0.8383

Box 14.4 Continued.

Model	AIC	Delta AIC	AIC weight	Model likelihood	Number of parameters	(−2 * loglike)
psi,gamma(),eps(),p()	278.96	0.00	0.8025	1.0	4	270.96
psi(.),gam(.),eps= 1-gam,p()	281.83	2.87	0.1911	0.2381	3	275.83
psi(),gamma(),p()	288.60	9.64	0.0065	0.0081	3	282.60

What our analysis is showing us is that the model with the greatest weight includes colonization. When we consider the constructs of the data and our previous analysis of the first year of data, even a cursory examination of the data shows that the songbird community increased in number from 2001 to 2002. In this particular data set it might simply mean that 2002 was a better year than 2001, but it might also mean that the management we did, that is planting longleaf pine trees in old agricultural fields, may attract more species as we have greater development of the plant community. Unfortunately, we have only the two years of data or else we might be able to tease apart some of these important issues.

Complete input and output files for this problem are provided in the electronic companion to the book (see enclosed CD and website address on p. ii).

we see that we are detecting about nine species per site, suggesting that each of our sites is only a small representative of the whole study area and in this case species richness did not vary among sites. This might also indicate that there are many random or unmeasured factors influencing occupancy of a particular site (field) in a single year.

Species co-occurrence

Many conservation problems relate to the issue of species co-occurrence. For example, a researcher might be interested in how grassland conversion to crop agriculture might affect sympatric bird species. That is, does this conversion affect one species more than another? Again many of the capture–recapture and occupancy models outlined previously are useful in overcoming detection problems that plague traditional measures of species richness or other measures of occupancy of sites.

Using either approach, we can examine the occurrence of particular species at one location or time versus the occurrence of the same species at another time or location. In essence, we have three sets of species: those that occur at one site or time alone, those that occur at another site or time and are not shared with the first, and finally those that are shared. Hines *et al.* (1999) developed a program COMDYN for using capture–recapture models, allowing researchers to assess changes in species composition over time or among sites. For occupancy models the theory development is relatively new;

Box 14.5 Avian communities among the study sites are assessed by using the same data in the previous boxes. The first column outlines the data construct using only four of the species and 20 fields. The complete data set is presented in the second matrix. In this case a "1" represents detection for a particular species in at least one survey on a particular study plot during a breeding season.

Study site	Species				
	American crow	American goldfinch	Barn swallow	Blue grosbeak	Cont
C1	0	0	1	1	1
C2	0	0	0	1	1
F1	0	0	0	0	1
F2	0	0	0	1	
G1	0	0	1	1	
GM1	0	0	1	1	
H1	0	0	1	1	
H2	0	0	0	1	
HA1	0	0	0	1	
HA2	0	0	0	1	
HO1	0	0	0	1	
HO2	0	0	0	0	
HO3	0	0	0	0	
L1	0	0	1	1	
L2	0	0	0	1	
M1	0	0	0	1	
M2	0	0	1	1	
ME1	0	0	1	0	
MM1	0	0	0	1	
MM2	0	0	0	0	
ETC					

In this analysis we could use programs CAPTURE OR SPECRICH2. In either case we would use model M_h as the appropriate model analysis for our data which assumes capture heterogeneity to estimate species richness for all of our sample quadrats. The sample data set with 41 survey sites and 33 species is outlined for program CAPTURE as follows:

```
title = 'llp line 2001 by site'
task read captures occasions = 41 × matrix
format = '(a2,1x,41f1.0)'
```

Box 14.5 Continued.

```
read input data
10 00000000000000000000000000000000000010000
11 00000000010000000000000000000000000000000
12 00000000000000000000000010000000000000000
13 00000000000001000000000000000000000000000
14 00000010000000000000000000000000000000000
15 00000000000000000000001000000000000000000
16 00000000010000000000000000000000000000000
17 00000000000000000000000000000000000000010
18 00000000000010000100000000000000000000000
19 00100000100000000000000000000000000000000
20 00001100000001000000000000000000000000000
21 00000100010000000000000000000010000000000
22 00010000000000000000000000000010000011000
23 00000000100000000000000000100000110000000
24 00000000000000001111000000000000001000000
25 00000010000000000000000000001011000011000
26 00010111000100000000000000000000000000001
27 00001100000001001001000000000000101000000
28 01001110001000010000000000100100010000000
29 00001110010000101100000001000000100000000
30 00000000011100000011000100000000111010000
31 00001000001000000100000001101001000001110
32 10001110000001001100011000001000100001000
33 10000110000100010100110000010000001010100
34 10001110110000110001100000000110000000001
35 01100010101100100000000010001110001000110
36 01011100110000010000000001100111010000010
37 01010110101010101110000001100110111010010
38 00001101110100101101111111100001000000101
39 00110000011100110100011111111110000110101
40 10101111001010110110111111100110011000111
41 11011111111100111101011111111101110011111
task closure test
task model selection
task population estimate JACKKNIFE
```

Population estimation with variable probability of capture by animal.
See model $M(h)$ of the monograph for details.

Number of trapping occasions was 41
Number of animals captured, $M(t + 1)$, was 32
Total number of captures, n, was 275

Box 14.5 Continued.

Frequencies of capture, $f(i)$

i = 1 2 3 4 5 6 7 8 9 10 11 12 13 14 15 16 17 18 19 20 21 22 23 24 25 26 27 28 29 30 31 32 33 34 35 36 37 38 39 40 41
$f(i)$ = 8 2 2 2 1 2 1 0 2 2 0 2 1 2 0 0 0 0 0 2 0 0 1 0 0 1 0 0 0 0 0 0 1 0 0 0 0 0 0 0 0

Computed jackknife coefficients

	$N(1)$	$N(2)$	$N(3)$	$N(4)$	$N(5)$
1	2.000	3.000	−4.000	5.000	6.000
2	1.000	0.000	−2.000	−5.000	−9.000
3	1.000	1.000	2.000	5.000	11.000
4	1.000	1.000	1.000	0.000	−4.000
5	1.000	1.000	1.000	1.000	2.000

The results of the jackknife computations

i	$N(i)$	SE(i)	0.95 confidence limits	Test of $N(i+1)$ vs. $N(i)$	
0	32			Chi-square (1 d.f.)	
1	40.0	4.00	32.2	47.8	3.930
2	46.0	6.93	32.4	59.6	2.067
3	52.0	10.58	31.3	72.7	0.777
4	58.0	16.12	26.4	89.6	0.168
5	63.0	26.12	11.8	114.2	0.000

Average p-hat = 0.1677
Interpolated population estimate is 40 with SE 6.9820
Approximate 95% confidence interval 34–66
Estimate: 40.2885056 SE: 6.98204231
Histogram of $f(i)$

Frequency	8	2	2	2	1	2	1	0	2	2	0	2	1
8	*												
7	*												
6	*												
5	*												
4	*												
3	*												
2	*	*	*	*		*				*	*	*	
1	*	*	*	*	*	*	*			*	*	*	*

This model suggests that there is an estimated 40 (34–66 95% CI) species on our study sites.

Complete input and output files for this problem are provided in the electronic companion to the book (see enclosed CD and website address on p. ii).

Box 14.6 Occupancy analysis using the same data as in Box 14.5. However, in this example we included all species detected during the study and therefore estimates here are of relative species richness. We ran three models including constant detection, variable detection (in this case by site), and constant detection with a habitat covariable for each species. Our model table output from PRESENCE 2.0 resulted in the following.

Model	AIC	Delta AIC	AIC weight	Model likelihood	Number of parameters	(−2 * LogLike)
1 group, constant *P*	1400.14	0.00	0.7311	0.5344	2	1396.141405
psi(.), *p*(habitat)	1402.14	2.00	0.2689	0.1966	3	1396.1414
1 group, survey-specific *P*	1433.93	33.79	0.0000	0.0000	42	1349.928371

We now provide the output from the model with the lowest AIC to demonstrate the results and interpretation.
Predefined model: detection probabilities are NOT time-specific

Number of groups = 1
Number of sites = 43
Number of sampling occasions = 41
Number of missing observations = 0

Number of parameters = 2
−2log(likelihood) = 1396.141405
AIC = 1400.141405
Naïve estimate = 0.744186
Proportion of sites occupied (Psi) = 0.7442 (0.066549)
Probability of group membership (Theta) = 1.0000

Detection probabilities (p):

Group	Survey	p	SE(p)
1	1	0.209590	(0.011524)

Variance–covariance matrix

psi	p(G1)
0.0044	−0.0000
−0.0000	0.0001

The output here provides us with two estimates. The first is what is described as detection probability. In this analysis it actually represents the number of species found on each survey site – in this case 0.210 ± 0.012 or about nine species on any particular site. Our model of survey-specific detection (in this case specific to survey site) ranked last and had a model weight of 0.0, therefore suggesting that species richness did not vary among sites. Our naïve estimate of relative species richness was 0.744, which is not much different from our predicted estimate of relative species richness of 0.744 ± 0.067. These results suggest that over 41 study sites used in this analysis, we are likely observing all of the species that were present on the site in 2001, which represents about 74.4% of the species richness we observed in the study.

therefore programs such as PRESENCE do not allow more than two-species models to be assessed. MacKenzie *et al.* (2006) suggest that more than four species interactions with these methodologies become very difficult.

Summary

Traditional approaches to estimating community parameters are fraught with the same types of detection issues that have affected indices and other uncorrected counts for abundance estimation. In addition, many interesting questions relative to the relationships and dynamics of communities need more analysis than simple indices of richness or evenness can provide. Fortunately many of the same methods for developing detection estimates in abundance estimation extrapolate to community estimation. Basic community richness estimates are now available using capture–recapture models and occupancy models. Extension of these models for assessing community parameters, such as extinction, colonization, turnover, and species interactions, is receiving a great deal of attention. Model development will progress very quickly over the next few years as research solves many of the community analysis issues. This rapidly developing research area will require readers to delve into the latest ecological and wildlife literature in order to assess the latest available techniques.

Part III

Integrating modeling and monitoring for conservation

15
Elements of conservation decision making

In Parts I and II, we developed the basic tools for quantitative analysis of conservation problems. Previously, a conservation decision-making context was generally implied, but perhaps not made explicit. In Part III we make this connection explicitly, introducing the elements of quantitative decision making for conservation problems. We show how fairly complicated resource problems typically can be broken down into smaller components that are more easily understood (and communicated). Once in this "modular" form, decision problems can be approached using a variety of tools, ranging from simple graphical analysis, to spreadsheets, to complex models calling for dynamic optimization or other sophisticated tools.

In this chapter, we will assume that the major aspects of the decision problem are well understood, and thus that the outcomes of the conservation decision problem can be predicted with certainty. In other words, we are going to "suspend disbelief" about uncertainty. In later chapters we will tackle the issue of uncertainty head on, and show how uncertainty can (and must) be dealt with in decision making, and in some cases reduced, leading to improved decision making.

Before proceeding, we recognize that some readers may be both unfamiliar with and perhaps skeptical of the idea of approaching conservation in such a structured, formal way. They may, for instance, argue that conservation requires the synthesis of biological (and in many cases, socio-political) knowledge, experience, and intuition that cannot be easily captured in a model. Without denying the importance of these elements to conservation (or any decision making), we argue that conservation biologists must be able to explain, justify, and, in most cases, replicate their problem-solving. This in turn requires a certain degree of objectivity and rigor in the process itself. Furthermore, by considering the decision problem in a structured, organized manner, conservation biologists sometimes can see aspects of the problem that they would not have otherwise noticed.

Finally, we note that there is not a single way of approaching decision-making problems. We favor a proactive approach, in which the decision maker identifies objectives and a range of possible actions (decisions) and then structures the decision problem in order to meet the objectives (e.g., Lindley 1986; Clemen 1996). However, others approach the decision problem from the opposite (reactive) point-of-view, first identifying the decision situation and then identifying objectives that can be met. Although both views are valid, we favor a proactive approach because it leads to "getting out ahead

Quantitative Conservation of Vertebrates, 1st edition. By M.J. Conroy and J.P. Carroll. Published 2009 by Blackwell Publishing, ISBN 978-1-4051-8228-7 (pb) and 978-1-4051-9098-5 (hb).

of" (anticipating) problems, instead of continually reacting (and striving to catch up to) situations. Unfortunately, conservation biology often tends more toward the latter than the former.

Elements of decision making

All conservation decision problems – indeed, all problems requiring decisions – share several elements. These include, at a minimum, values, a decision context, objectives, and decision alternatives. We define these terms below.

Values express what matters to the decision maker (and, by proxy, stakeholders whom are represented by the decision maker). In some cases values are represented by familiar measures such as money, time, and other outcomes, whereas in other cases values are more difficult to measure objectively, but can still be expressed in relative terms. As an example values with familiar measures, suppose we are managing a reserve for bird conservation, and want to do so in the most cost-effective matter. Assuming that our conservation objectives can be otherwise met, those decisions that lead to lower costs would be more valuable than those with higher costs, and our value measure might simply be dollars or some other currency. As an example of values that are more difficult to measure, some decisions might lead to high rates of local extinction, and presumably these would lower the value of the decision compared with decisions that lead to persistence.

Objectives are statements of what the decision maker would like to achieve, and therefore incorporate the decision maker's values. For instance, the objective might be to maximize a species' persistence at the lowest possible cost. As implied by this example, objectives often, perhaps usually, incorporate tradeoffs: it might be possible to maximize species persistence, but for unrealistically high costs, something we believe most conservation biologists can readily visualize. However, another common but frequently neglected situation involves decisions that are beneficial for one species, but may be detrimental to another. To the extent that both species have value to the decision maker, the objective needs to take into account the tradeoff in value under any proposed action. In addition, it is often useful to distinguish between what might be termed "fundamental objectives" and "means objectives." **Fundamental objectives** express what the decision maker wants to accomplish, based on his or her values, whereas **means objectives** are some intermediate objective that must be accomplished along the way. For example, the fundamental objective may be to assure the persistence of some important group of species. The implementation of habitat management beneficial to the species is the means objective to arrive at that goal, but the habitat management is not in and of itself of value.

Decision alternatives are simply the actions that the decision maker has at his or her disposal in trying to reach the objective. These can include positive actions, such as construction of reserves and manipulation of habitats, and regulatory actions, such as setting of harvest quotas and import restrictions. By implication, "no action" is also a decision and has consequences (see below) that should be taken into account. This last point is important because it emphasizes that the decision to defray an action – temporarily or permanently – should be a measured choice, and not a consequence of one's inability to decide.

Consequences are the outcomes that follow from decision making. These are, by definition, directly related to the objectives of the decision maker, and are influenced at least in part by the decisions that are made. Also, when there are multiple objectives (or decisions), there will be multiple consequences: building a reserve leads both to some biological consequences (persistence or not of species) and to economic consequences (expenditure of more or less money). Finally, in most cases the outcomes of decision making are subject to uncertainty: for example, we cannot know with certainty that a particular group of species will persist if we do build the reserve. Uncertainty in decision making is the subject of Chapter 16.

All decisions have a **decision context**, which is the setting in which the decision occurs. The context determines the objectives that need to be considered, and, in many situations, how decisions affect one another. This last point becomes important because many conservation problems involve actions that are sequentially dependent through time, with earlier decisions influencing the outcomes that may result from later decisions. The decision context also relates to the *time horizon* over which decision making must be considered. In some cases, short time horizons are appropriate, but for many conservation problems, the fundamental objectives (e.g., species persistence or recovery) are only realizable (or meaningful) over a long time horizon.

Steps in decision making

With the ideas of the previous section in mind, we here lay out a sequence of steps that can be taken to formally describe and model a decision problem (Figure 15.1). As a first step, we should define the objectives and the context of the decision-making problem. Here we would also, if necessary, distinguish between means and fundamental objectives, and determine the time horizon over which decision making is operating. Once we have identified the objectives and the decision context, we can consider the alternatives that are at our disposal, and then proceed to develop a model that describes how the decision alternatives potentially will affect consequences, which in turn will affect the degree to which each decision alternative will move us toward (or away) from our objective. At this point, we should be able to use our model to select the decision alternative that appears to most likely lead to our desired objective, which we refer to as the **optimal** decision. Finally, once we have selected the apparent optimal decision, the decision is implemented. However, in many situations we will want to conduct additional analyses at this point (Figure 15.1B), particularly given that our model of the decisions outcomes may be subject to uncertainty, the topic of Chapter 16. These analyses may lead to a modification of the **decision model**, or in some cases to consideration of additional decision alternatives, or even modification of the objectives (as when, for example, no decisions that can be made will lead to the desired objective!).

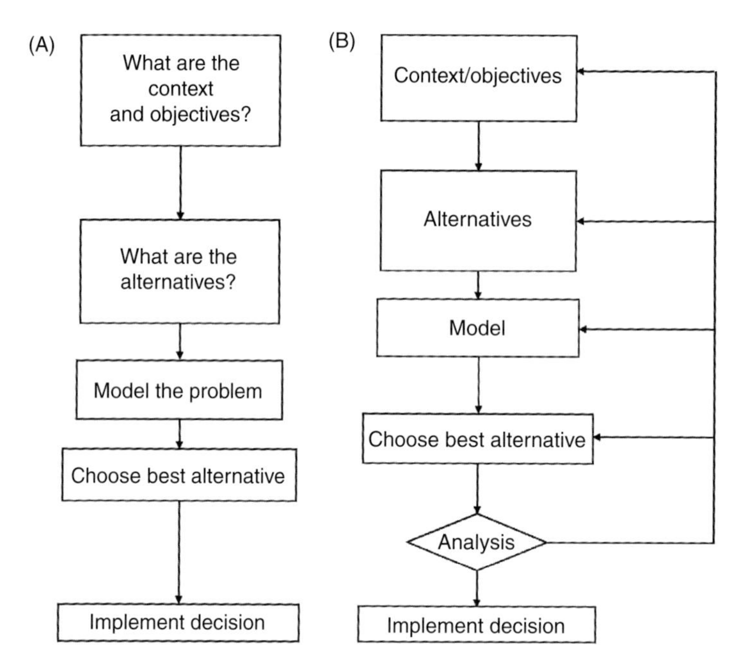

Fig. 15.1 **(A) Flow diagram of steps in developing a decision model. (B) Decision-model flow diagram with feedback from statistical and sensitivity analyses.**

This is a very skeletal outline and leaves out many important details, such as specifically how to model the decision outcomes, and how to select among the competing decision alternatives. However, it emphasizes the main point we are trying to make here, which is that the decision model needs to incorporate all but *only* those aspects of the problem that are relevant to making an optimal decision (which we define as "that alternative best fulfilling the objective"). Therefore, for instance, we are interested in *all* decision alternatives that are available to us, but we are *not* interested in those that are not.

Likewise, we are interested in outcomes that may occur following our decision, but not those that cannot occur, or that are not in any way related to our decision (although a knowledge of factors beyond our control is important, because it influences the decision context).

Example – reserve construction

Our first example is a very simple conservation decision. The context is that we are faced with the potential loss of an endangered species, which is known to occur at the time of our decision, but is critically imperiled. Our objective is to maintain the species if possible, but we must take into account the costs of our efforts (which might include the fact that resources we expend will be unavailable for other purposes). We have two decision alternatives available to us: the design and management of a 100-km^2 reserve,

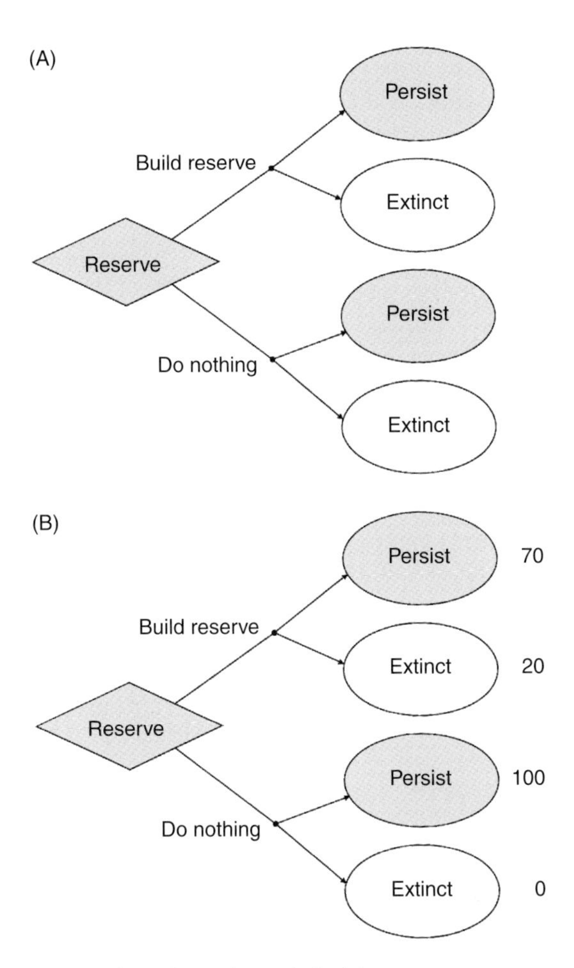

Fig. 15.2 **Decision model for a hypothetical decision to construct or not to construct a reserve designed to protect species. (A) Decision-outcome possibilities. (B) Utilities under alternative decision-outcome scenarios.**

and a "do-nothing" alternative (Figure 15.2A). Given either of the alternative decisions, there are two possible outcomes: the population persists and possibly increases in abundance ("persists"), or the population declines to local extinction ("extinct"). As part of the decision context, we will assume for this illustration that (i) this is a one-time decision (i.e., it will not be revisited in the future), and (ii) that the consequences of the decision will be immediately known. Although such assumptions are not realistic, they serve to keep the problem simple, so that we can illustrate the main points.

Each combination of a decision and outcome has associated potential costs (e.g., reserve construction) and benefits (e.g., species persistence), which are incorporated into a utility function **U** that depends on both the decision and its outcome (Figure 15.2B). From the point-of-view of endangered species management, population persistence is always preferable to extinction, and the best situation might involve persistence along with no action. Conversely, the worst situation might involve no action and extinction, because of the ramifications (e.g., lawsuits, negative publicity) of inaction followed by extinction. The specific values for each decision-outcome combination will vary depending on the decision maker's perspective. We have assigned values to this problem as follows:

	Utility	
	Persist	Extinct
Reserve	**70**	20
Nothing	100	**0**

where the entries may be dollars, or simply the relative value of the outcome on a 0–100 scale (where 0 = worst, 100 = best).

In the event that decision-specific outcomes are certain (i.e., the consequences of conservation and inaction are known), a determination of the optimal decision becomes a straightforward comparison of the corresponding utilities. For now, we are assuming that the management is certain to result in population persistence, whereas inaction is certain to lead to extinction. Thus, our model of decision-outcome combinations is simply:

	Probability	
	Persist	Extinct
Reserve	1	0
Nothing	0	1

Since the respective utilities are 70 and 0 respectively (in bold in the first table), the optimal decision clearly is to build and maintain the reserve.

As noted, this is a very simplified and unrealistic portrayal of a reserve design problem, but nonetheless conveys the main points, and is a useful jumping off point for more realistic models. We will revisit this problem in Chapter 16, when we take into account uncertainty in decision making.

Example – habitat management for two species

As a second example, we consider a problem in which the decisions involve the manipulation of habitats in order to enhance carrying capacity for a species of concern. This example was motivated by work (Moore and Conroy 2006) on the conservation of the threatened red-cockaded woodpecker (*Picoides borealis*) in Georgia, USA. This species requires older pine (*Pinus* spp.) trees for nest cavities, with a sparse, savannah-like understory. Such conditions can be created through forestry practices including thinning to low tree density and prescribed fire. However, these conditions also may remove important foraging and nesting substrate for other species of concern, including the

Neotropical migrant wood thrush (*Hylostichla mustelina*). In this situation, the objective of management is to enhance habitats for woodpeckers while still maintaining habitats for wood thrushes. Actually, these could be viewed as the means objectives, with the fundamental objectives being the conservation of population of both species, which in turn may depend on many other factors (mostly beyond the control of managers). This example is useful because it forcefully illustrates the issue of conflicting values, a common theme in resource conservation (Box 15.1).

Box 15.1 Habitat management for two species.

In this example, the decision alternatives range from no action (0% burning) to very aggressive habitat manipulation (100% burning and other removal of understory and midstory vegetation). The anticipated response to this range of actions is graphically captured in Figure 15.3 (recall that a graphical model is still a model!). For the moment, we will take this model at face value; that is, we will not consider the possibility of other (weaker, stronger, differently shaped) responses to management. In Chapter 16 we will consider the possibility that the response may take multiple forms, under different biological hypotheses.

Given this conjecture model, it is obvious that what is "good" for woodpeckers is not equally good for thrushes. How do we reconcile this conflict? One approach is to assign value to each species, and select the decision that optimizes some combined value. For instance, we might take as our objective to maximize O, the weighted sum of numerical response (habitat suitability) across the two species:

$$O = v_1 S_1 + v_2 S_2$$

Clearly, the value for O will depend on the specific values v_1 and v_2. For instance, we might equally value both woodpeckers and thrushes, so that our overall objective value is simply

$$O = S_{wood} + S_{thrush}$$

This would lead to a decision that is intermediate (approximately 50% burning level), essentially splitting the difference between no management (favoring thrushes) and very aggressive management (favoring woodpeckers; Figure 15.3B). Higher values for one species would skew decision making in the direction favoring that species. For example, giving woodpeckers higher values (2) relative to thrush (1.5) would result in the objective function

$$O = 2S_{wood} + 1.5S_{thrush}$$

leading to management more aggressively oriented toward woodpeckers (i.e., more burning; Figure 15.3C). The spreadsheet for this example is available in the electronic companion of the book (see enclosed CD and website address on p. ii).

Of course, it may not be possible or desirable to assign values to competing resource objectives. Instead, one approach is to select one resource as the primary objective, but to constrain decision making so as to maintain the other resource within acceptable bounds. For example, red-cockaded woodpeckers are classified as endangered by the US Government, and thus legal protection is mandated, particularly on lands managed by the Government. However, it may still be possible to maintain highly suitable habitat for woodpeckers, while not completely eliminating suitable habitats for thrushes, particularly given the diminishing rate of habitat improvement as burning intensity increases (Figure 15.3A,D). Alternatively, one could dictate minimal habitat conditions for woodpeckers, and select from these conditions that are best suited for thrushes. Similar types of tradeoffs exist between conservation and cost objectives, in which the first objective can be set as limiting, while optimizing for the second.

Before moving on, we will say a bit about how one might derive the specific mathematical model describing this relationship between the conservation decision and the outcomes following that decision. In this particular example, the model is specified by the mathematical relationship between the inputs (burning levels, X) and some output in terms of habitat suitability for woodpeckers and thrushes (Y_1, Y_2). The relationships illustrated graphically (Figure 15.3) indicate a generally increasing (but eventually decreasing) relationship for woodpeckers, and a linearly decreasing one for thrushes. The former could be described by a quadratic equation:

$$Y_1 = a + bX - cX^2$$

while the latter is described by a linear equation:

$$Y_2 = d - eX$$

If possible, the coefficients (a–e) of this model would be both motivated by biological understanding and supported by empirical studies, using the principles in Part I.

Therefore, a series of studies may have been conducted on both species, over a range of burning intensities, in order to measure response (Y_1, Y_2). The data generated by these studies could then be used (e.g., via linear regression methods) to estimate the coefficients for the response models. Of course, predictions under these models would have to take into account how well the models fit the data (statistical uncertainty), as well as other forms of uncertainty (Chapter 16).

Example – sustainable harvest

Neither of the previous examples involved decision making through time or explicit consideration of how current decision making potentially affects future conservation outcomes. However, sequential, dynamic decision making is more the rule than the exception in conservation, and is very well illustrated by the problem of sustainable yield harvest (SY). At this point we remind readers, who might never be faced with legal sustainable harvest questions, that these ideas are readily extended to a variety of

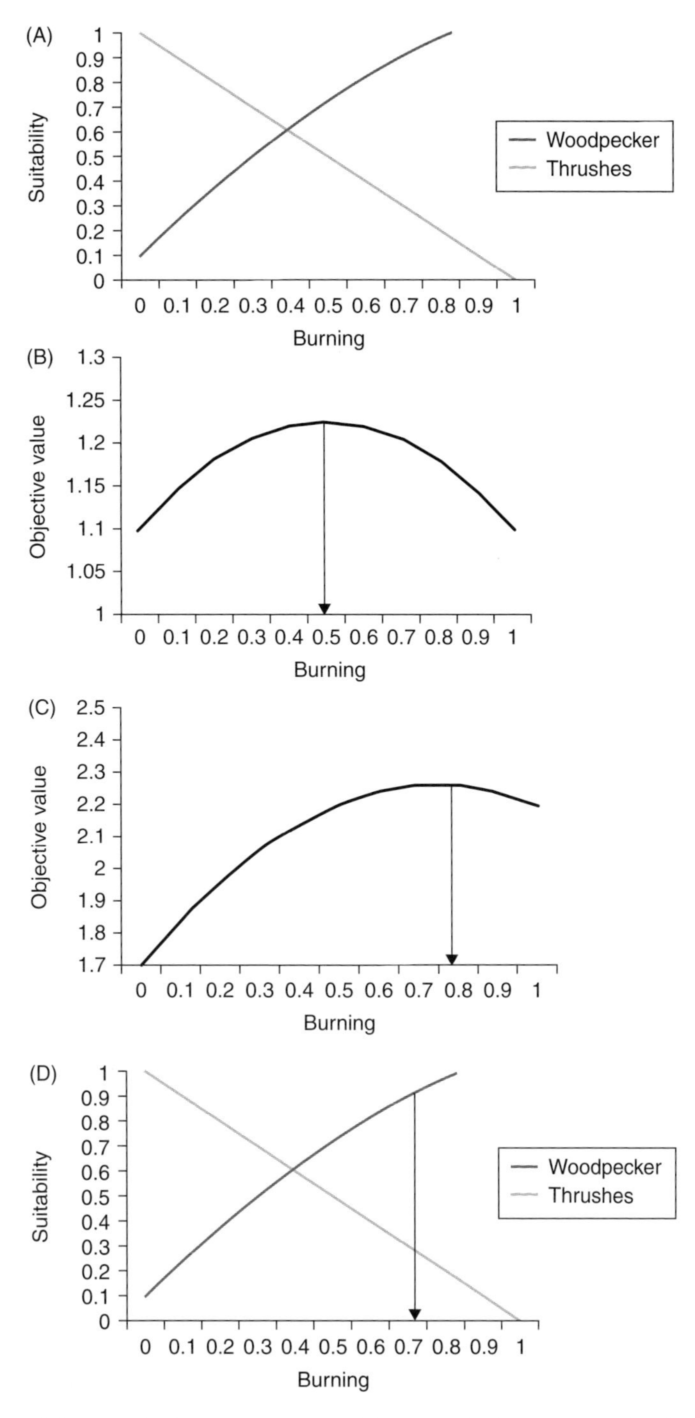

Fig. 15.3 **Decision model for response of habitat suitability to prescribed burning levels for red-cockaded woodpeckers and wood thrushes. (A) Habitat suitability response model. (B) Objective function giving equal values to woodpeckers and thrushes. (C) Objective value giving woodpeckers value = 2.0 and thrushes value = 1.5. (D) Habitat suitability response for woodpeckers constrained by minimum suitability of thrushes = 0.3.**

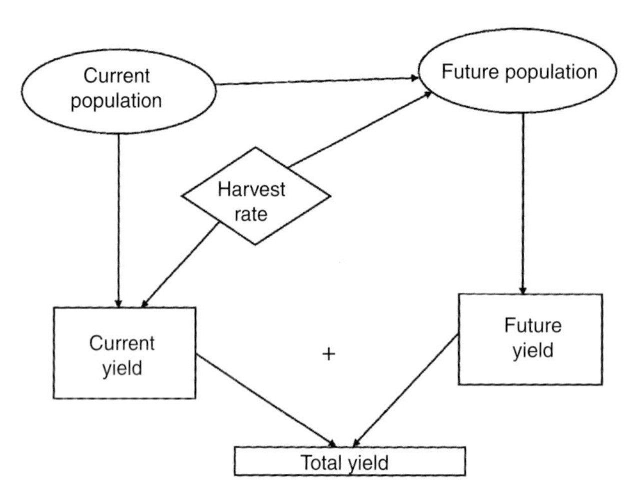

Fig. 15.4 **Dynamic decision model for optimal sustainable harvest. Objective of total yield is the sum of current harvest yield and future yield. Future harvest yield is affected by current population conditions and harvest in current year. Optimal strategy balances short-term harvest gain with long-term harvest potential.**

conservation problems. In SY, even when the objective is strictly in terms of the yield (numbers, biomass, dollars) that can be obtained by exploiting a resource, conservation decisions can be **sustainable** so long as future harvest opportunities matter. Note that this definition of sustainability is different from one sometimes invoked by economists, which treats the resource as a monetary investment. In that view, the **sustainable yield** refers to return on the investment, not biological yield, and can result in situations where the "optimal" decision is to liquidate the resource and invest the money elsewhere (Hardin 1968).

To illustrate the idea of a sustainable harvest, consider a simple harvest problem, where the decision is what percentage of the current stock of a population to harvest (Figure 15.4). Obviously, this year's harvest of the population results in a yield that has immediate value. However, if we define the objective in terms of the *total* yield, current and future, it is obvious that we cannot maximize our objective if we harvest the entire population this year. In general, our current harvest, while providing us some immediate gratification, will also influence the rate at which the population grows (or declines) through time, which will in turn affect the future potential for exploitation. The actual influence will depend on a number of factors, including the size and natural growth rates of the population, and the relationship of harvest to population dynamics, and will be considered in more detail in the next chapter. The main idea is that maximizing total yield always involves a tradeoff between the present and the future, but (given a sufficiently long time horizon) the only way to maximize total yield is to maintain healthy populations – the essence of "sustainability." See Box 15.2 for specific example of the tradeoff between current and future "reward" from harvesting a population.

In general, we can expect that conservation decisions we make today influence our opportunities to make decisions tomorrow. Positively, enhancements of habitats

Box 15.2 Tradeoff of current and future harvest reward for a population growing according to the MSY model.

Here we consider a population growing according to the logistic model of population growth (Chapter 3) with growth parameters $r_{max} = 0.2$ and $K = 500$. This population will grow according to the model

$$N(t) = N(t) + N(t)r_{max}\left[1 - \frac{N(t)}{K}\right] - H(t)$$

If we harvest from this population at the per-capita rate $h(t) = H(t)/N(t)$, we know from Chapter 4 that the rate that will lead to MSY is $h(t) = r_{max}/2$ or 0.10. Harvesting at a rate higher than 0.10, or even above 0.2, can provide high short-term yield, but is not the maximum yield, is not sustainable, or both.

To see this, we display per-year and cumulative harvest yields from harvesting at five rates: 0, 0.05, 0.1, 0.2, and 0.3. Obviously, harvesting at 0 produces no yield, but does result in the population growing to 500. Harvesting at 0.05 allows the population to grow to 375 and produces a cumulative 100-year yield of 1842. Harvesting at 0.1 maintains the population at 250 and produces a yield of 2525, and harvesting at 0.2 or 0.3 produces declining populations and lower cumulative yields (1191 and 507 respectively), with the population harvested at 0.3 depleted by year 100. However, in both the last two cases (0.2 and 0.3) yield is higher (2–3 times higher initially) in the first few years. This result forcefully demonstrates that (i) over-exploitation, while providing short-term gains, is not sustainable long term, and thus (ii) setting the objective in terms of long-term, cumulative yield leads to both sustainable harvest and maximum long-term benefit. The spreadsheet for this example is available in the electronic companion of the book (see enclosed CD and website address on p. ii).

Year	0		0.05		0.1		0.2		0.3	
	N	Yield	*N*	Yield	*N*	Yield	*N*	Yield	*N*	Yield
0	250	0	250	0	250	25	250	50	250	75
1	275	0	263	0	250	25	225	45	200	60
2	300	0	274	0	250	25	204.75	40.95	164	49.2
⋮										
100	500	0	375	18.75	250	25	22.22827	4.445655	0	0
Cumulative		0		1842.354		2525		1190.811		507.1131

or populations today create resilience and augment future opportunities; conversely, degradation or loss of habitats or populations reduce resilience, and reduce or eliminate future opportunities. The conceptual model here simply formalizes this already commonsensical notion (Figure 15.5). We will revisit these ideas in the chapters that follow, when we deal with the role of uncertainty and introduce adaptive resource management.

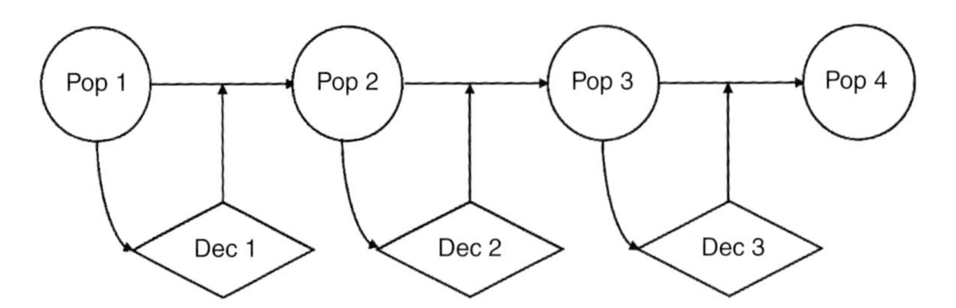

Fig. 15.5 **Generic dynamic decision model for natural resource conservation. Sequential decisions (Dec 1–Dec *n*) are made through time (or space) in response to observed conditions of the natural resource system (Pop 1–Pop *n*). Earlier decisions potentially affect later system conditions, and thereby the value that can be gained from later decisions.**

Summary

In this chapter we have introduced a structured approach to decision making, in which the context for the decision is described, decision alternatives are listed, and a model is constructed that can be used to predict the consequences of any decision in terms of achieving the resource objective. This approach can then be used to select among alternative candidate decisions, or to rank decisions in terms of their desirability. We considered simple decisions involving a single resource objective, decisions involving tradeoffs between two or more resource values, and finally decisions that are linked sequentially, in which options available to future decision makers are influenced by current decisions.

The methods and examples in this chapter have not accounted for uncertainty in the decision process, but instead have assumed that our decision model perfectly describes how our resource system will respond to decision making. In the next chapter we relax these assumptions, and more realistically allow for environmental, statistical, and other sources of uncertainty in the decision process.

16
Accounting for uncertainty in conservation decisions

In Chapter 15, we introduced models for decision making and outlined a generic approach for building conservation models. This approach allows decision alternatives to be compared to one another and ranked, leading to the selection of the decision(s) that best led to the desired objective. However, so far we have not accounted for uncertainty in the decision process, but instead have assumed that our decision model perfectly describes how our resource system will respond to decision making.

Sources of uncertainty

Uncertainty arises from a number of sources, and these fall into four principal categories. **Environmental uncertainty** includes chance events, such as weather or other factors beyond the control of management. Uncertainty due to change in demographic processes such as birth and death, although somewhat different, can be considered as part of environmental uncertainty for our purposes. In either case, we have a model (mental, graphical, or mathematical) of how the system (populations, habitats, etc.) is thought likely to respond to our decision (Figure 16.1A). Even if our model is essentially correct, the real response, because it is influenced by other factors beyond our control, will differ a bit (or maybe a lot) from our predictions (Figure 16.1B). On average, our predictions may be good, but any single outcome will differ by a chance degree.

A somewhat different source of uncertainty arises because our conservation actions are often imperfectly applied; this is referred to as **partial controllability**. For example, suppose an area of 100 ha is slated to be treated by prescribed fire. Because of weather conditions or other factors beyond our control, the actual area burned could be less than 100 ha (e.g., some areas are too moist to be burned, the wind shifts, air quality standards are in effect), or more than 100 ha (the fire escapes controls and burns too large an area). Similar situations arise with respect to hunting and angling regulations, which are intended to regulate harvest rates. Weather conditions, animal movements, and/or economics may influence the numbers of animals available, the numbers of hunters and anglers afield, or both, thus changing the resulting actual (vs. intended) harvest (Figure 16.1B).

Conservation biologists also have to deal with the fact that ordinarily our view of natural resources is imperfect, because it is based on sample data that contain statistical errors (Parts I and II). This results in an essentially "fuzzy" view of the system's response

Quantitative Conservation of Vertebrates, 1st edition. By M.J. Conroy and J.P. Carroll. Published 2009 by Blackwell Publishing, ISBN 978-1-4051-8228-7 (pb) and 978-1-4051-9098-5 (hb).

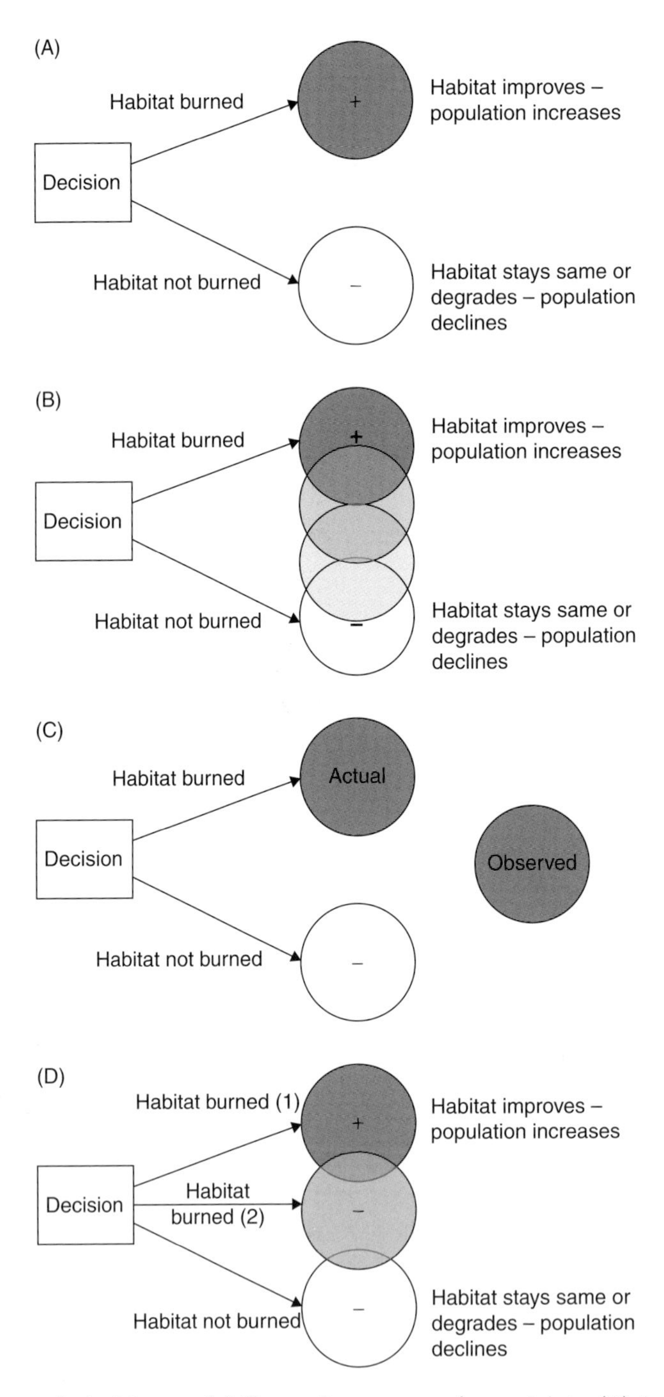

Fig. 16.1 **Example decision model illustrating sources of uncertainty. (A) Assumed model of habitat and population response to prescribed burning. (B) Influence of environmental uncertainty or partial controllability on response. (C) Influence of partial observability on observed response. (D) Influence of structural uncertainty on response.**

to conservation efforts, somewhat reducing our ability to see whether or not there has been an impact. This form of uncertainty is referred to as statistical uncertainty or **partial observability** (Figure 16.1C), and can be reduced by improved monitoring efforts and proper estimation (Part II), but never completely eliminated.

Conservation biologists are generally aware of the above forms of uncertainty, although they may or may not deal with them adequately in decision making. There remains a fourth and very important type of uncertainty that affects conservation, which we refer to as **structural uncertainty**. By structural uncertainty we mean (i) there is more than one tenable explanation or prediction for how the system may respond to conservation actions, and (ii) there exists uncertainty as to which (if any) explanation is "correct." Thus, in the case of prescribed fire, one hypothesis (perhaps favored by "conventional wisdom") is that burning will increase habitat quality for species that live in ecosystems shaped by fire and, by implication, carrying capacity for our desired species. However, it is prudent to entertain the plausible alternative viewpoint, namely that management will have little or no effect (Figure 16.1D).

Below, we approach the issue of uncertainty by expressing uncertainty as probabilities, and then using an uncertainty weighting approach for decision making. In Chapter 17 we will consider how to use monitoring information to improve decision making, under adaptive management.

Probability as a measure of uncertainty

Although there are many ways to express uncertainty, we prefer to use the well-understood and accepted approach of describing uncertainty in terms of probabilities. We have already dealt with **probability** in our discussion of statistical models and stochastic population models (Parts I and II). Here we focus on the issue of outcomes following a conservation decision. Briefly, we can describe an event-based (versus frequency-based) notion of probability on a zero to one scale, as follows: if we are 100% certain that an outcome will occur, it has probability 1; if we are 100% certain that it will *not* occur, it has probability 0; and if we are equally uncertain as to whether it will occur or not, it has probability 0.5. In some cases, we will have data-(frequency-) based measures of probability. For example, if in 100 previous studies of prescribed burning under conditions identical to ours, 75 resulted in habitat improvement and 25 did not, we may take (at least provisionally) the probability of that outcome as 0.75. Of course, in many cases we will not have the luxury of 100 previous studies, and may instead have to rely on estimates based on a few or even a single study, or in some cases on subjective, expert opinion. In Chapter 17 we deal more formally with how to incorporate new information from field studies and monitoring programs into decision making.

Expected values of outcomes

In decision making, we are concerned about the probability that a particular outcome will occur following decision making, but, more particularly, we are interested in how

Box 16.1 Calculation of expected value.

Expected values are calculated as the weighted sum over outcome values, with the weights being the probability of each outcome. The general formula for discrete events is

$$E(v) = \sum_x v(x)p(x)$$

where x is the event outcome, $v(x)$ is the value (utility) of x, and $p(x)$ is the probability of outcome x. For continuous distributions, integral calculus is required to evaluate expectation:

$$E(v) = \int_x v(x)p(x)\mathrm{d}x$$

All of the examples in this book are based on discrete probability distributions. For example, if on the roll of a fair die ($p(x) = 1/6$) one were paid \$2 for a '1' or '3' and \$3 for any other roll, the expected payoff would be

$$E(v) = v(1)p(1) + v(2)p(2) + v(3)p(3) + v(4)p(4) + v(5)p(5) + v(6)p(6)$$

$$(\$2)(1/3) + (\$3)(2/3) = 2.67$$

These calculations are also performed in the electronic companion (see enclosed CD and website address on p. ii), in which the reader can show, for example, that if $p(5) = 0$ and $p(x) = 1/5$ for all other throws (the p's must add to 1!), the expected value changes to 2.6.

uncertainty will affect the *value* of our decision and, thus, potentially which decision is optimal. As suggested above, one way to do this is by an uncertainty-weighted measure of value or utility, called an **expected value** (see Box 16.1). This is illustrated by the example of a bet on the flip of a fair coin. Suppose we are offered a bet such that we will win \$10 if the coin turns up heads, but lose \$12 if the coin turns up tails. Our model of the coin flip dictates $p = 0.5$ that the coin will turn up heads and $1 - p = 0.5$ that it will be tails. However, what we care about is how much money we stand to win or lose. The average (or expected) result to us will be the value resulting from each outcome, weighted by the probability that the outcome occurs. That is:

$$E(value) = v_{heads}p_{heads} + v_{tails}p_{tails} = (\$10)(0.5) + (-\$12)0.5 = -\$2$$

In this example, we stand to lose \$2 on average by making this bet; unless we know in advance that the coin will be heads, we would be foolish to take the bet. Of course, the bet might be different if we were dealing with a "loaded" (unfair) coin, or if the payoff for winning was much greater than a \$2 differential (as in a government lottery). In the case of the lottery, we would be betting on an unlikely but very rewarding outcome. For example, the odds of winning many lotteries is in the range of 17 million to 1. If a ticket is $1 the payoff needs to be more than $17 million. If you play long enough, the "law of averages" says that the state (dealer, house, etc.) will always come out ahead. Familiarity with this principle should dampen enthusiasm for gambling as a money-making strategy, even if we find it enjoyable for purely recreational reasons.

Using probability and expected value in decision making

To illustrate how these concepts can be applied to conservation decision making, we will return to the simple reserve decision problem introduced in Chapter 15. We reproduce here the scenario in which the species either persists or does not following management (Figure 16.2A). Each decision-outcome has a specified value (utility), the rationale for which was also discussed in Chapter 15 (Figure 16.2B and Box 16.2).

Now instead of assuming that each decision is associated with a particular outcome with certainty, we assign probabilities to each outcome under each decision. Under an initial model, we assume that extinction and persistence are equally likely, and that the action of constructing the reserve has no impact on persistence (Figure 16.2C). Under this scenario, the expected value of each decision is calculated by the uncertainty-weighted outcome values. Thus, the value of constructing the reserve is

$$\begin{aligned} E(reserve) &= v_{persistence,reserve}p_{persistence} + v_{extinction,reserve}p_{extinction} \\ &= (70)(0.5) + (20)0.5 = 45 \end{aligned}$$

while the value of *not* constructing the reserve is

$$\begin{aligned} E(nothing) &= v_{persistence,nothing}p_{persistence} + v_{persistence,nothing}p_{extinction} \\ &= (100)(0.5) + (0)0.5 = 50 \end{aligned}$$

Thus, in this example, if we define "optimal" as that decision which on average yields the highest value to the decision maker, the optimal decision is to not build the reserve (Figure 16.2D). Notice that, although the decision outcomes themselves are essentially a coin flip, which decision is optimal is clear.

Of course, this result could change if either the decision-outcome values changed or the model probabilities are different from 50:50. Because our focus here is on uncertainty, we consider the latter case, in which there is a second model that predicts that if the reserve is built, persistence probability increases to 0.65 (with the complementary event, extinction, dropping to 0.35; Figure 16.2E). Under this model, the expected value of building the reserve is now

$$\begin{aligned} E(reserve) &= v_{persistence,reserve}p_{persistence} + v_{extinction,reserve}p_{extinction} \\ &= (70)(0.65) + (20)0.5 = 52.5 \end{aligned}$$

while the value of *not* constructing the reserve remains unchanged at 50. This now results in the optimal decision switching from "not build" to "build" (Figure 16.2F).

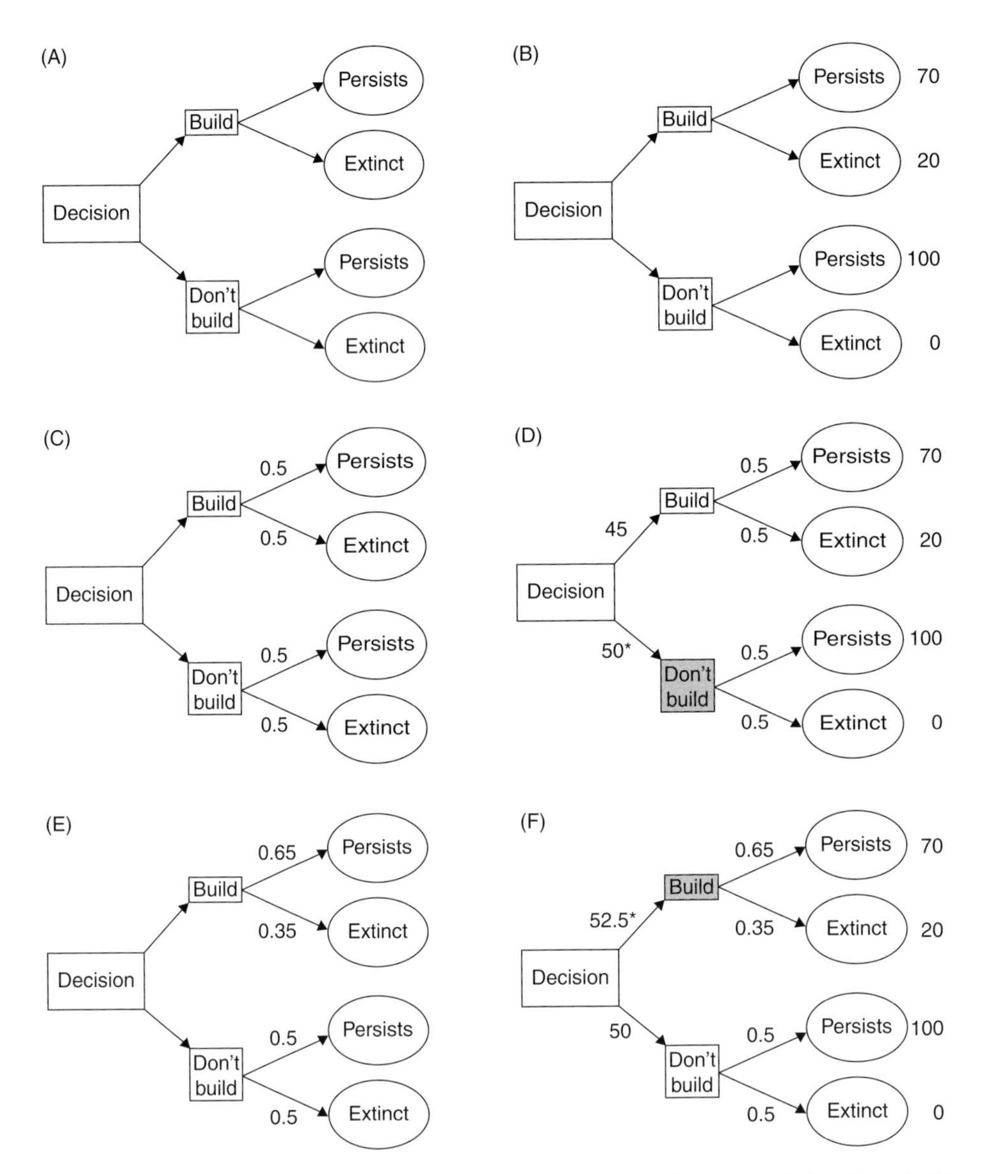

Fig. 16.2 **Reserve design example. (A) Decision-outcome combinations. (B) Values (utilities) of decision-outcome combinations. (C) Outcome probabilities for each decision under model 1. (D) Expected decision values, model 1. (E) Outcome probabilities for each decision under model 2. (F) Expected decision values, model 2.**

If we knew for certain which model was true, we would take this into account when we formulated our decisions: model 1 dictates "no reserve," but model 2 says it is optimal to build the reserve. Likewise, if we could discover which model was true, we would do so – considering what is at stake in decision making. Generally, we do not *know* which model is true, any more than we know whether it will rain tomorrow, or that any other uncertain event will occur. However, we may have a notion – again based on probability – of how likely it is that each model is true. Initially, we might assign

Box 16.2 Expected values for decisions.

The expected value of alternative decisions is calculated the same way as expected values in general, by computing the uncertainty-weighted values over the uncertain outcomes following the decision. That is, the expected value $E(v_i)$ of decision i is

$$E(v_i) = \sum_x v_i(x)p_i(x)$$

where $v_i(x)$ and $p_i(x)$ are, respectively, the values and probabilities of outcome x given decision i. For the outcome values and probabilities in Figure 16.2D we obtain

$$E(v_{build}) = \sum_x v_{build}(x)p_{build}(x) = 0.5(70) + 0.5(20) = 45$$

and

$$E(v_{nothing}) = \sum_x v_{nothing}(x)p_{nothing}(x) = 0.5(100) + 0.5(0) = 50$$

Thus, the optimal decision is not to build the reserve.

These calculations are also performed in the electronic companion (see enclosed CD and website address on p. ii), in which the reader can see that the optimal decision changes to "build" when $p_{build}(persist) = 0.7$.

each model equal probability weight, unless we have some empirical or other *a priori* reason to favor one model over the other. We can then determine which decision is optimal by "double averaging" – first over the uncertain outcomes for each model and then across models, thus:

$$E(reserve) = \bar{v}_{1,1}\pi_1 + \bar{v}_{1,2}\pi_2 = (45)(0.5) + (52.5)0.5 = 48.75$$

and

$$E(nothing) = \bar{v}_{2,1}\pi_1 + \bar{v}_{2,2}\pi_2 = (50)(0.5) + (50)0.5 = 50$$

where the values are averaged over the uncertain outcomes of each decision for each model. Under equal (0.5) weights for the two models, the optimum decision now reverts to "no reserve" (Figure 16.3A). Given higher weight on the second versus first model, the scenario changes:

$$E(reserve) = \bar{v}_{1,1}\pi_1 + \bar{v}_{1,2}\pi_2 = (45)(0.30) + (52.5)0.7 = 50.25$$

and

$$E(nothing) = \bar{v}_{2,1}\pi_1 + \bar{v}_{2,2}\pi_2 = (50)(0.3) + (50)0.7 = 50$$

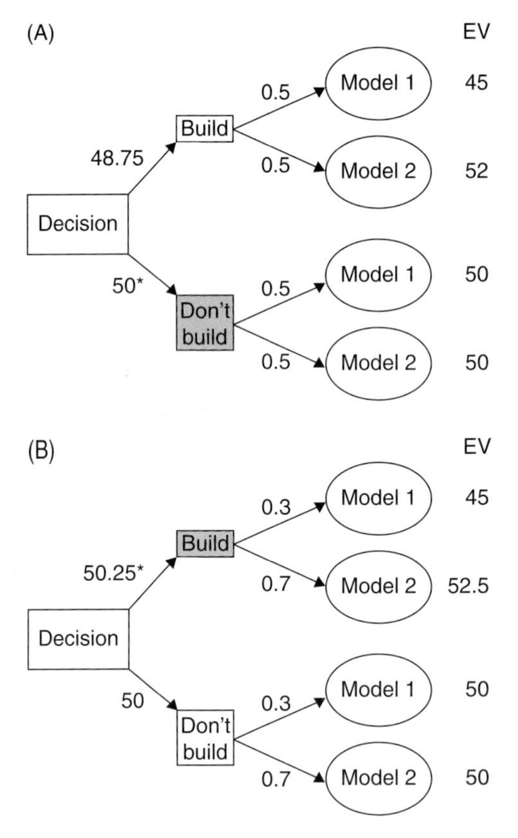

Fig. 16.3 **Reserve design example with structural uncertainty. (A) Equal model weights for models 1 and 2. (B) 0.3 weight for model 1, 0.7 weight for model 2.**

resulting in a shift to the "reserve" decision (Figure 16.3B and Box 16.3). This example forcefully illustrates that new information – such as evidence favoring one model over the other – can profoundly affect decision making. We will return to this in Chapter 17, when we consider how to incorporate new information from monitoring programs into our decision-making process.

Many in the conservation community might find the above example trivial, because we have placed a seemingly low value on something as serious as whether a species goes extinct. However, the point of this exercise is to illustrate that *all* conservation decisions have consequences, and that we *always* operate under uncertainty. Thus, "building the reserve" when the species nevertheless goes extinct has consequences, because it means that we have essentially wasted resources that could have been used elsewhere. Unless we *know* that the reserve will succeed in meeting our objective – and we cannot know – then our decision requires us to "bet hedge." We believe that these sorts of calculated tradeoffs will be increasingly important to conservation, as humans continue to encroach on wild lands, the numbers of species of concern increase, and other human needs conflict with the already limited resources devoted to conservation.

Box 16.3 Expected values averaged over models.

To take into account structural or model uncertainty, we need to average the expected values of each alternative decision across both the uncertain events, given each model, and across the uncertain models (weighted by model uncertainty). That is, for each model the expected value of each decision is

$$\bar{v}_{i,j} = E(v_i|j) = \sum_x v_i(x) p_{i,j}(x)$$

where $p_{i,j}(x)$ is the model-specific probability of outcome x given decision i. Then, averaging across models for each decision we have.

$$E(d_i) = \sum_j \pi_j \bar{v}_{i,j}$$

where π_j are the probability weights for each model j. For the example in Figure 16.3B, we have

$$E(reserve) = \bar{v}_{1,1}\pi_1 + \bar{v}_{1,2}\pi_2 = (45)(0.30) + (52.5)0.7 = 50.25$$

and

$$E(nothing) = \bar{v}_{2,1}\pi_1 + \bar{v}_{2,2}\pi_2 = (50)(0.3) + (50)0.7 = 50$$

These calculations are also performed in the electronic companion (see enclosed CD and website address on p. ii), in which the reader can see that whereas $\pi_2 = 0.7$ in favor of model 2 supports building the reserve, $\pi_2 = 0.5$ does not.

Summary

In this chapter, we more realistically assumed that resource decision making involves several sources of uncertainty, including variation due to environmental and other intrinsic sources, statistical uncertainty, partial controllability of management actions, and inherent structural uncertainty. We have seen how uncertainty can be described by probability measures. These in turn may be used to compute uncertainty-weighted estimates of the value of decision outcomes, which can then be used to select among decision alternatives. In many cases, incorporation of uncertainty can profoundly affect the decisions that are made, making its consideration critical to decision making (for a recent example in the realm of endangered species conservation, see Conroy *et al.* 2008).

In Chapter 17 we will see how monitoring information can be integrated into decision making, to provide information feedback for reducing uncertainty and improving decision making.

17
Learning and adaptive management

In Chapters 15 and 16, we introduced a formalized approach for conservation decision making, and showed how various sources of uncertainty can influence decision making. In particular, in Chapter 16 we showed how uncertainty about how our conservation system will respond to management – sometimes referred to as "structural uncertainty" – can profoundly affect the types of conservation decisions that appear to be optimal. Thus, it is critical that we account for this type of uncertainty in decision making and, if possible, reduce it. In this chapter we show how data that are collected in the course of monitoring programs can be "fed back" into the decision-making loop, reducing uncertainty and thereby improving resource decisions.

Prediction and monitoring

Using models as alternative hypotheses

When we make a conservation decision, we are really implementing a statement about how we view reality. That is, we are hypothesizing that our resource system will respond a certain way when we take particular actions, and then we are (hopefully) selecting the action that we think will best achieve our objective. Stated this way, our decision model can be thought of as a hypothesis. As we discussed in Chapter 16, there is usually more than one feasible model that describes how our system may respond to management, and we can think of these as alternative **hypotheses** (Chapter 5).

This last view of reality, and the models that approximate it, summarize how we will later apply models to decision making.

We will illustrate some of these points with an example from the development of **adaptive harvest management** (AHM) models for American black ducks (*Anas rubripes*; Conroy *et al.* 2002a; http://coopunit.forestry.uga.edu/blackduck/), but the lessons should be generally applicable to many systems. Please note that in the specific examples below, we have taken some liberties with the actual data results (parameter estimates, model weights, etc.). We have done this both to simplify the problem and to make specific points that would have been confusing if the actual analyses were used.

In North America the black duck is a fairly widespread and popular game animal. There is a long history of legal hunting in both Canada and the USA. Although still common over the last 50 years there has been a gradual and long-term decline in populations. The main controversial points for black duck management can be summarized

Quantitative Conservation of Vertebrates, 1st edition. By M.J. Conroy and J.P. Carroll. Published 2009 by Blackwell Publishing, ISBN 978-1-4051-8228-7 (pb) and 978-1-4051-9098-5 (hb).

as follows (Conroy *et al.* 2002a). First, essentially two competing factors have been "blamed" for declines in black duck populations: (i) harvest and (ii) encroachment by mallards (*Anas platyrhynchos*). The first point is actually legal hunting and not poaching, and the second point relates to range expansion and hybridization by mallards which is a closely related species. Second, there is at least some empirical support for the contribution of both factors. Third, the degree of belief in "harvest" vs. a "mallard" vs. "both" vs. "neither" models greatly affects what appears to be optimal for black duck management. Finally and not surprisingly, different stakeholder groups, and (since this is an international resource) people in different countries, view the "facts" surrounding black ducks differently.

Before we delve into the details of the black duck problem, we would like to make some additional points about the role of modeling in conservation (and science, for that matter).

Faith in models vs. models as tools

People who build and use models sometimes develop a paternal (maternal) fondness for their models. Even worse, they begin to believe that their models are real. They have forgotten (if they ever knew) the admonition of George Box (1979): "All models are wrong, some models are useful." The problem is that model builders and users who act this way often cause biologists (who know better) to disdain models altogether – even when they may be useful. It might be useful to distinguish two terms we use to describe these phenomena. Belief in a model is when a person weighs the empirical evidence and makes a decision that the model represents real processes. Faith on the other hand is when we believe in a model in the absence of empirical evidence. We believe faith should be left to other fields of endeavor.

For the black duck problem, the "useful" aspects of models include:

- succinctly describing the four major competing hypotheses about black duck dynamics *as they relate to management*;
- potentially being 'testable' (or at least comparable) by data;
- allowing for the generation of predictions about management alternatives.

Plausible vs. implausible models

For a model to be useful, it has to be plausible. That means that the model must have at least *some* theoretical basis and, ideally, also has support from previous studies. All of the major hypotheses we considered for black duck AHM have theoretical support (from basic population ecology) and at least some degree of evidence supporting them, as reviewed in Conroy *et al.* (2002a).

By contrast, we could deliberately insert a model into our model set that is implausible, i.e., that we *know* is false. What would be the purpose of such an effort? If we do not have any belief in the biology behind the model, then we surely cannot believe any of its predictions (especially about management). If we collected data under an experiment or observational study, we would surely expect to falsify the model, and if we did not, we would probably conclude that something was wrong with our experiment.

Please do not confuse "plausible" with "correct"! We *could* proceed as if there is one and only one model of reality (see "faith" vs. "belief" above), and claim that there is only one plausible model. Besides being unscientific, this is risky, since we have now conveniently ignored the consequences if we are wrong in our assertion. An honest examination of nearly every question in ecology will reveal at least one, and several, plausible alternative hypotheses.

Hypothesis tests vs. weight of evidence

Although hypothesis testing is an important component of science, it may not always be the most efficient way to convert scientific knowledge into management decisions. Often, what we really want is (i) an estimate of some "effect size" (essentially, a prediction about what to expect in a similar manipulation), and (ii) a measure of the strength of evidence in favor of alternative hypotheses. There are several standard ways of getting effect size and a useful approach for examining relative evidence based on information theory (Chapter 5). We will use these twin ideas of prediction and information weighting in the discussion below, as illustrated by the black duck AHM problem.

Constructing the models

In the black duck problem, we first had to develop models that expressed our alternative views about what makes black duck populations tick. We were particularly interested in the views that say different things about the impacts of management on black duck populations. This boils down to two sub-models of black duck dynamics: (i) a production sub-model and (ii) a survival sub-model. The production sub-model describes the relationships between black duck abundance (density-dependence) and mallard numbers (competition) on autumn age ratios for black ducks. The general form of this model is

$$\log(A_t) = \beta_0 + \beta_1 N_t + \beta_2 M_t + \beta_3 X_t$$

where N_t and M_t are the numbers (in hundreds of thousands) of black ducks and mallards in the breeding population in year t, A_t is the predicted age ratio for black ducks in the autumn populations, and X_t is a time index (describing a downward trend in productivity through time). The above model assumes both density and competition; by setting $\beta_2 = 0$ we obtain the alternative reproduction model, which does not include competition:

$$\log(A_t) = \beta_0 + \beta_1 N_t + \beta_3 X_t$$

We fit historical abundance survey data to both models and obtained parameter estimates and AIC values. The AIC values can be used for two purposes. First, they can be used to compute model-averaged parameter estimates. For example, the weighted estimate and unconditional standard error for β_1 (which appears in both models) is -0.14563 (SE $= 0.04683$). Second, the AIC weights give a measure of the current (past on data to this point) belief in each model. Based on our analyses, we give the "no competition" model weight of 0.41 and the "competition" model weight of 0.59, thereby suggesting at least initially that we have stronger evidence for competition than lack of competition.

On the survival side, the key issue of contention is the impact of harvest on survival. This can be summarized by the sub-model

$$S_t = S_0 - \alpha K_t$$

which assumes an additive impact of harvest mortality; that is, starting at S_0, each additional increment of harvest morality K_t is assumed to decrease annual survival by α. The extreme forms of this specify $\alpha = 1$ (completely additive mortality, AMH) and $\alpha = 0$ [completely compensatory, CMH, at least up to a threshold (we will assume that harvest rates never exceed this threshold)]. For a number of technical reasons, the empirical estimates of α and S_0 are unsatisfactory, and here we use values for these that are (i) based on life history characteristics of black ducks, and (ii) assume either complete compensation or additivity. These assumptions result in

$$S_t = 0.6 - K_t \text{ (AMH)}$$

$$S_t = 0.6 \text{ (CMH)}$$

Further, because of the technical issues alluded to, we do not have reliable, empirical weights for these two models (Conroy *et al.* 2002a came up with some weights, which put almost all weight on AMH, but we will not use these here). Given the contentious nature of harvest, and depending on the data used to "test" AMH vs. CMH, one could derive weights over nearly the entire range of 0 (no evidence for AMH, perfect for CMH) to 1 (the reverse). Given this circumstance, we chose weights that spread uncertainty evenly among the models; so 0.5 for each model in this case.

Under the assumption that the evidence in favor of competition/no competition is independent of that in favor of AMH/CMH, we can simple multiply the corresponding model weights: e.g., "no competition-AMH" $= 0.41 \times 0.5$, etc. We can now summarize the four competing hypotheses (Box 17.1). Notice that instead of trying to "reject" any of these alternative models, we are keeping all four of them, but applying weights of belief/evidence to each. In this way, we can take the next step: predicting under each model, and comparing these predictions to new data.

Prediction

Now we can take the above models and apply them to predicting next year's population size of black ducks, given observed current levels of black ducks and mallards, habitat

Box 17.1 Estimates and AIC weights under four alternative black duck models.

We use an example from American black duck (*Anas rubripes*; Conroy *et al.* 2002a) to illustrate the computation and use of AIC weights in predictive modeling. Decision modeling for black ducks is based on considering four alternative models, which represent combinations of assumptions about reproductive rates (affected or not by competition with mallards) and survival rates (compensatory versus additive mortality), together with AIC-based model weights under each model. Historical data were fit to two alternative reproduction models, the first not including the effects of mallard abundance on black duck age ratios, and the second including the mallard effect:

$$\text{Model 1:} \quad \log(A_t) = \beta_0 + \beta_1 N_t + \beta_3 X_t$$
$$\text{Model 2:} \quad \log(A_t) = \beta_0 + \beta_1 N_t + \beta_2 M_t + \beta_3 X_t$$

where A_t is the autumn age ratios for black ducks (representing recruitment rates), N_t and M_t are numbers of black ducks and mallards (hundreds of thousands) in surveys conducted the previous January, and X_t is a year index, representing declining habitat trends.

The historical analysis produced estimates of the coefficients under each model, as follows:

Model	AIC	Delta AIC	wt.	β_0	β_1	β_2	β_3
m1	2.82	0.7	0.413382	0.97578	−0.1627		−0.01095
m2	2.12	0	0.586618	1.23519	−0.1336	−0.0959	−0.0144

Historical analyses were less helpful at providing empirical AIC weights for the alternative compensatory versus additive models of survival; we therefore assume, for illustration, that these weights are equal (0.5 on each model). The composite models and weights are formed by combining the respective production and survival submodels and (assuming independence between production and survival hypotheses) multiplying the respective model weights:

Combined models

Model	Mallards	Harvest	Model wt.	Production	Survival
1	No_compet.	CMH	0.206691	$\log(A_t) = \beta_0 + \beta_1 N_t + \beta_3 X_t$	$S_t = 0.6$
2	No_compet.	AMH	0.206691	$\log(A_t) = \beta_0 + \beta_1 N_t + \beta_3 X_t$	$S_t = 0.6 - K_t$
3	Compet.	CMH	0.293309	$\log(A_t) = \beta_0 + \beta_1 N_t + \beta_2 M_t + \beta_3 X_t$	$S_t = 0.6$
4	Compet.	AMH	0.293309	$\log(A_t) = \beta_0 + \beta_1 N_t + \beta_2 M_t + \beta_3 X_t$	$S_t = 0.6 - K_t$

These estimates and weights are used in Boxes 17.2–17.5 for prediction and updating. The computations for model weights are provided in the spreadsheet example in the electronic companion of the book (see enclosed CD and website address on p. ii).

conditions, and harvest rates. Whereas earlier we fit data to an estimation model, now we are going to take estimated parameters and apply them to predicting age ratios, survival rates, and population size from current conditions. This will involve three steps. First, a prediction equation for

$$\log(\tilde{A}_t) = \hat{\beta}_0 + \hat{\beta}_1 N_t + \hat{\beta}_2 M_t + \hat{\beta}_3 X_t$$

which predicts natural log of age ratio, with coefficient estimates $\hat{\beta}_j$ and predictors N_t, M_t, X_t; note that this prediction will be different under each model! Once we get $\log(\tilde{A}_t)$ we easily get predicted age ratio by the exponential function $\tilde{A}_t = e^{\log(\tilde{A}_t)}$. Finally, note that we are using "$\sim$" to stand for prediction, to distinguish this from estimation "$\wedge$": under estimation, we fit the equation to data, while under prediction we apply the estimated equation to predicting the response, based on specific values of the predictor values.

For the survival portion we have simply

$$\tilde{S}_t = 0.6 - \alpha K_t$$

where $\alpha = 1$ under AMH and $\alpha = 0$ under CMH. Finally, we put the production and survival predictions together to predict population size next year as

$$\tilde{N}_{t+1} = N_t \tilde{S}_t (1 + \tilde{A}_t)$$

under each of the four models (combinations of production and survival assumptions). These calculations are illustrated in Box 17.2.

Note that because the predictions are based on statistical estimates, they have standard errors. Also, other forms of uncertainty (including environmental uncertainty) will add to statistical uncertainty. The methods for incorporating all these sources of uncertainty are complex; here we will assume that prediction error is proportional to the size of the prediction, by a constant coefficient of variation, which is initially 0.2 (20%).

Finally, we can, if we wish, obtain a single prediction, which averages over the alternative models. This is done in much the same way as model averaging. In this case, the model-averaged prediction (Box 17.2) provides a model-averaged prediction of about 392,000 (SE = 302,000). Note that this SE is quite large – reflecting the fact that there is a lot of uncertainty (due to both model and statistical uncertainty).

Comparing predictions to observations – prediction likelihood

As we have seen in Chapter 16, predicting outcomes under alternative assumptions can be used to obtain uncertainty-weighted estimates of the value of alternative outcomes. In the next section we will see more formally how these values can be used to influence decision making, but here we assume that we have already made an **optimal** decision, have made predictions under alternative models, and now wish to incorporate new survey information. That is, once we have made some predictions, we are (hopefully)

Box 17.2 Prediction

We illustrate prediction under the black duck model from current conditions of 400,000 black ducks, 300,000 mallards, and a time index of 32 (this essentially assumes late 1990s habitat conditions, and is effectively treated as in intercept term). In terms of the black duck model, $N_t = 4, M_t = 3, X_t = 32$. We will also assume a harvest mortality rate of 0.2 ($K_t = 0.2$).

These values are used as input in each of the alternative production models to predict age ratios of 0.9749 under the "no competition" model and 0.9534 under the "competition" model. Likewise, the harvest mortality rates are input into each of the alternative survival models, resulting in predictions: 0.6 under CMH and 0.4 under AMH. Finally, these predictions are input into the combined models to predict abundance next year as follows:

Model	Production	Survival	Predicted_abundance (N)
1	No compet.	CMH	4.73976088
2	No compet.	AMH	3.15984059
3	Compet.	CMH	4.68818457
4	Compet.	AMH	3.12545638

A model-averages prediction of black duck abundance is obtained by weighting each of the individual model predictions by their respective AIC weights (Box 17.1). The example is coded in the electronic companion of the book (see enclosed CD and website address on p. ii) and users can vary the inputs by changing the number of black ducks, mallard, and harvest rates to see how these changes affect predictions.

going to continue to monitor the system to see how well our predictions match up with observations we obtain via our monitoring programs. To see how this might work, consider the example that we just set up, in which we observed 400,000 black ducks, 300,000 mallards, and harvest rates were 0.2. We then made predictions under each of our four models, which ranged from about 313,000 (competition, AMH) to 474,000 (no competition, CMH). In Box 17.3 we show how these data can be used to compute a measure of agreement of each of our models to the data called a statistical **likelihood** (Chapter 5).

Updating belief: Bayes' Theorem

The likelihood measures we calculated (Box 17.3) are useful, but do not actually give us what we need, namely, an updated measure of belief in our models. There are two reasons for this. First, the likelihood is not on a probability scale (notice that the likelihood weights do not sum to one). More importantly, the likelihood does not take into account prior information about model – our prior relative beliefs, which may (or may not) be informed by data.

Box 17.3 Calculation of likelihood values under alternative models.

Continuing the black duck example (Boxes 17.1–17.2), suppose that next year we observe 370,000 black ducks in the surveys. Notice that models 2 and 4 seem to predict closer to this observed value than models 1 and 3 (Box 17.2). However, none of the models exactly agrees.

We need a formal way of measuring this agreement of observations with predictions that take into account prediction error. That is, we are not going to necessarily get too excited if a model is off a bit on its predictions, if there was a lot of prediction error. We can do this formally by means of a *likelihood*, which now has a very similar meaning to the likelihoods we refer to in maximum likelihood estimation (Chapter 5), except now we are talking about the likelihood of an observation (the survey value) giving the prediction of a particular model. Here we will use a likelihood form that is based on the normal distribution and is nice because it is very easy to see how it works. The general expression for the likelihood of the observation under model i is

$$L_i(N_{t+1}) = \exp\left(-\frac{(N_{t+1} - \tilde{N}_{i,t+1})^2}{\sigma^2}\right)$$

where N_{t+1} is the observed value, $\tilde{N}_{t+1,i}$ is the prediction under model i, and σ is the prediction error referred to earlier.

Note that if the observed value exactly matches the prediction, the likelihood will be 1; in all other cases the values will be highest for the models that come closest to predicting the observed value, and vice versa. In our case the observed value is 3.7, and the likelihood under model 1 (no competition, CMH) is

$$L_i(N_{t+1}) = \exp\left(-\frac{(3.7 - 4.74)^2}{0.948^2}\right) = 0.3003$$

A similar procedure is used to obtain the likelihoods under the other three models, so that

Model	Likelihood
1	0.30026831
2	0.48164109
3	0.32931995
4	0.4296389

From this, we can see that in this example, the observation $N_{t+1} = 370{,}000$ is most likely under model 2 (no competition, AMH) and least likely under model 1 (no competition, AMH). However, all the models have decent likelihood weights and so need to be considered in management.

The example is coded in the electronic companion of the book (see enclosed CD and website address on p. ii) and users can vary the inputs by changing the number of black ducks, mallard, harvest rates, and observed number of black ducks next year to see how these changes affect predictions and likelihoods.

We can solve both problems by invoking one of the most famous – yet simple – theorems from probability, **Bayes' Theorem** (BT). In our case, BT says that the new weight of a model is obtained by the likelihood of that model (see above), weighted by the prior (previous) model weight, and divided by the sum of this quantity over all the models:

$$wt_i(t+1) = \frac{wt_i(t)L_i(N_{t+1})}{\sum_m^M wt_m(t)L_m(N_{t+1})}$$

The $wt_i(t)$ is just the current weight for each model; initially this will be the model weights we obtained when we developed the models. The likelihoods are obtained by the procedure we just went through, comparing model predictions to observed values and computing a likelihood. For example, the computations for the new model weight for model 3 are provided in Box 17.4.

Box 17.4 Bayes' Theorem and Bayes' updating using the prior model weights and likelihood.

Bayes' Theorem (BT) provides a general way of incorporating new information into models. Quite simply, BT says that "new information is proportional to old information times the likelihood." In the context of our prediction problem, this is "the new model weight is proportional to the old model weight, times the likelihood of observing N_{t+1} under the model," or in equation form:

$$wt_i(t+1) \propto wt_i(t)L_i(N_{t+1})$$

To express this in terms of probabilities (which add to 1 across models) we simply normalize by the sum of the right-hand-side across models, obtaining

$$wt_i(t+1) = \frac{wt_i(t)L_i(N_{t+1})}{\sum_m^M wt_m(t)L_m(N_{t+1})}$$

To see how BT works for our example, let us take the predictions and likelihoods for each model (from Box 17.4) and compute the new model weight for model 3 (the old weight was 0.293). We obtain

$$\begin{aligned} wt_3(t+1) &= \frac{wt_3(t)L_3(N_{t+1})}{\sum_m^4 wt_m(t)L_m(N_{t+1})} \\ &= \frac{(0.293)(0.329)}{(0.206)(0.300)+(0.206)(0.482)+(0.293)(0.329)+(0.293)(0.429)} \\ &= 0.251 \end{aligned}$$

Box 17.4 Continued.

The table below summarizes the inputs and results for the four models.

Model wt.	Likelihood	Updated_wt.
0.206691	0.30026831	0.16152808
0.206691	0.48164109	0.25909681
0.293309	0.32931995	0.25139674
0.293309	0.4296389	0.32797837

We can see that now model 4 (competition, AMH) receives the most weight, based (i) on our prior belief (partially informed by data) which has been (ii) modified by data (the likelihood). The example is coded in the electronic companion of the book (see enclosed CD and website address on p. ii), in which users can vary the inputs, illustrating how stronger or weaker likelihoods affect the rate at which model weights are updated.

Adaptive management

In this section, we combine the two major themes covered in this part of the book: (i) using models to make optimal resource decisions, and (ii) reducing uncertainty via monitoring and feedback of information into model predictions. As before, we are trying to make an optimal management decision, but we are faced with two or more alternative models about how the system works. When we do this, and *also* conduct monitoring to follow up on the response of our system to management *and then feed back this information into future decision making*, we are engaging in **Adaptive Resource Management (ARM)**.

ARM has these key features:

- an explicit objective;
- model-based predictions under two or more alternative models and weights of evidence for each;
- a means of obtaining an optimal decision considering the objective and the model predictions and weights;
- a monitoring program to compare future system states to model predictions and update model weights;
- incorporation of new model weights into future decision actions.

ARM thus ordinarily requires some type of sequential decision-making process. That is, if a decision will be made once, and then never again, there is no possibility of adaptation. However, this is not a particularly restrictive assumption, and in fact most natural resource decision problems can be viewed sequentially, and thus ARM is appropriate. However, if the decision problem is truly one time, we can (and should) still use the first four features:

- an explicit objective;
- model-based predictions under two or more alternative models and weights of evidence for each;
- a means of obtaining an optimal decision considering the objective and the model predictions and weights;
- a monitoring program to assess how well objectives of resources are being achieved.

These are the features common to any natural resource (or other) decision problem, where uncertainty exists. So, even if your problem is not one of the 99% of problems that are appropriate for ARM, it certainly falls into the broader class of problems.

The black duck harvest problem considered in the last section is certainly a good candidate for ARM, since (i) decisions are made sequentially, (ii) there are several alternative models of how the population might respond to management, and (iii) monitoring data are acquired annually and so can be used to periodically update model weights and influence decision making. However, a full description of the harvest ARM problem requires mathematical tools beyond the scope of this book. We instead return to a slight expansion of the reserve design problem considered in Chapters 15 and 16, where the question is whether to build or not to build reserves to protect a particular species from local extinction. Now, however, the decision, which is made sequentially through time, is whether to build each of two reserves. As before, the species currently exists at each site, and we have alternative models that make different predictions about whether or not the species will persist following each decision (one basically says it makes no difference, the other says building the reserve increases the probability of persistence). Following each decision, we monitor the population and observe whether it persists or goes locally extinct. Finally, each of these outcomes has a value to the decision maker (see Box 17.5 for more details).

Box 17.5 Adaptive updating – sequential decisions on two candidate reserves.

This example, taken from Chapter 16, is an elaboration on the "reserve design" problem. Now there are two candidate reserves, each of which potentially can arrest the local extinction of a species (we assume for the purposes of this problem that the reserves act independently). The first decision is whether to build a reserve on the first site, followed by a decision as to whether to build a reserve on the second site. As in Chapter 16, there are two alternative models: model 1 (predicting no enhancement of persistence by the reserve) and model 2 (probability of persistence following the reserve increases from 0.5 to 0.65). Let us suppose that at the first decision, we have (perhaps based on previous empirical work) greater (70%) belief in model 2 than in model 1.

Box 17.5 Continued.

Depending on the results following the first decision, we may change our model weights. Given the outcome utilities and probabilities (from Chapter 16) and these weights, the expected values under each decision are

$$E(reserve) = \bar{v}_{1,1}\pi_1 + \bar{v}_{1,2}\pi_2 = (45)(0.30) + (52.5)0.7 = 50.25$$

and

$$E(nothing) = \bar{v}_{2,1}\pi_1 + \bar{v}_{2,2}\pi_2 = (50)(0.3) + (50)0.7 = 50$$

so we build the reserve.

Suppose we then observe that the species persists following reserve construction. For each of our models, we have a likelihood of the events "persist" and "extinct". These can now be used with Bayes' Theorem to update model weights.

Model	Model wt.	Likelihood
1	0.3	0.5
2	0.7	0.65

The new weight for model 2 is

$$\begin{aligned} wt_2(t+1) &= \frac{wt_2(t)L_2(persist)}{wt_1(t)L_1(persist) + wt_2(t)L_2(persist)} \\ &= \frac{(0.7)(0.65)}{(0.3)(0.5) + (0.7)(0.65)} = 0.752 \end{aligned}$$

The new weight for model 1 can be found by replacing the numerator with the product of the prior weight and likelihood for model 1, or (since there are only two models) simply by subtraction from 1 to obtain 0.248.

This now changes the expected value of the alternative decisions at the second reserve, because we now use the new model weights. Using the new model weights we would have

$$E(reserve) = \bar{v}_{1,1}\pi_1 + \bar{v}_{1,2}\pi_2 = (45)(0.248) + (52.5)(0.752) = 50.64$$

and

$$E(nothing) = \bar{v}_{2,1}\pi_1 + \bar{v}_{2,2}\pi_2 = (50)(0.3) + (50)0.7 = 50$$

which again leads to reserve construction as the optimal decision. The reader can use the spreadsheet on the enclosed CD and website on page ii containing these calculations to explore other scenarios.

Notice that when the decision is to not build the reserve ("nothing"), the likelihoods for the persist/extinct event are the same under the two models. Thus, decision making in this direction can never lead to model updating. This will be generally true when two or more models make the same prediction, or when the optimum decision is the same no matter which model is true. One consequence is that management actions sometimes have value not because they necessarily produce desirable outcomes in the short term, but because they produce learning, which itself has value. This idea is explored in Box 17.6.

The value of information

As suggested in Box 17.5, **information** (which we define here as reducing uncertainty about which alternative model is true) can have value. The value of information depends on (i) the relative values of the decision-outcomes, (ii) the decision-outcome probabilities, and (iii) how much structural (model) uncertainty exists. Taking probability as our basic measure of uncertainty (Chapter 16), and the simple case of just two alternative models, the "most certain" case is when all of the weight is on a single model (and none on the other). Conversely, the "most uncertain" case is when we have 0.5 weight on each model. All other cases are intermediate. A natural question is then: "assuming that it is possible to completely eliminate uncertainty, how much value would that have to our decision making?" This is the essence of what is known as the **expected value of perfect information (EVPI)**. In words, EVPI is the expected gain from having perfect information, or

Expected value of the best decision given perfect information
minus
The maximum of the expected utilities given incomplete information.

Box 17.6 illustrates the calculation of EVPI for the reserve decision problem introduced in Chapter 16.

Box 17.6 The value of information.

To illustrate, take the single reserve decision problem introduced in Chapter 16 and assume that we have uncertainty expressed by model weights 0.3 and 0.7 for models 1 and 2, respectively:

$$E(reserve) = \bar{v}_{1,1}\pi_1 + \bar{v}_{1,2}\pi_2 = (45)(0.30) + (52.5)0.7 = 50.25$$

and

$$E(nothing) = \bar{v}_{2,1}\pi_1 + \bar{v}_{2,2}\pi_2 = (50)(0.3) + (50)0.7 = 50$$

The optimal decision for this degree of uncertainty is "build the reserve" and its expected value is 50.25; this forms the basis for determining the net gain in information possible.

If we had perfect information, we would know which model was true, and we would pick the decision corresponding to that model. For model 1, the expected decision values are

$$E(v_{build}) = \sum_x v_{build}(x)p_{build}(x) = 0.5(70) + 0.5(20) = 45$$

$$E(v_{nothing}) = \sum_x v_{nothing}(x)p_{nothing}(x) = 0.5(100) + 0.5(0) = 50$$

Box 17.6 Continued.

so the optimal decision is "nothing," with an expected value of 50. For model 2 the decision values are

$$E(v_{build}) = \sum_x v_{build}(x)p_{build}(x) = 0.65(70) + 0.35(20) = 52.5$$

$$E(v_{nothing}) = \sum_x v_{nothing}(x)p_{nothing}(x) = 0.5(100) + 0.5(0) = 50$$

so the optimal decision is "build." If we average these (since we do not know which of these models *really* is true) we obtain $(50 + 52.5)/2 = 51.25$. Finally, the net gain (EVPI) is

$$51.25 - 50.25 = 1.00$$

The example is coded in the electronic companion of the book (see enclosed CD and website address on p. ii). Users are encouraged to modify this code for their own particular applications.

Note that EVPI is always at least 0 and is generally positive, so information generally has value. How much value depends, again, on the utilities, degree of uncertainty under each model, and current model weights. Readers can use the spreadsheet in Box 17.6 containing these calculations to confirm, for instance, that if the model weights are 0.5 in this case, EVPI more than doubles, to 2.5. These may not seem like large quantities for EVPI, but keep in mind that conservation decisions are typically sequential (see Box 17.5), and therefore that gains in utility will also accumulate through time: such differences can be very large when time horizons are long (as in many conservation problems). Nonetheless, in some cases EVPI may be close to zero – or, the expenses of monitoring programs may outweigh possible information gains. In these situations, monitoring may be difficult to justify, at least in terms of its potential for reducing uncertainty conservation decision making. However, monitoring may still be justified as a means for assessing whether our management decisions seem to be leading us toward or away from our resource goals.

Summary

In the previous chapter, we have seen that uncertainty affects decision making, and thus that reducing uncertainty (via, for example, monitoring) can have value. In this chapter, we more formally showed how monitoring information can be fed back into our decision models and (using Bayes' Theorem) used to update model weights, thereby reducing uncertainty and improving decision making. Because decision making in conservation is typically sequential, this has important implications for long-term improvement in management. We also introduced the idea of "value of information" and the measure EVPI, which can be used to calculate the maximum gain (in terms of resource value) that can be gained from reducing uncertainty. In most cases EVPI will be significant, because uncertainty is great, but in all cases information measures provide metrics for comparing the relative utility of monitoring programs, something that is increasingly demanded by administrators and the public.

18

Case study: decision modeling and adaptive management for declining grassland birds in the southeastern USA

Now we outline a natural resources problem highlighting much of what we discuss throughout the book. In this example, we cannot touch upon all components of estimation and modeling, but rather hope to illustrate how several important principles from these areas can be integrated into a real-world decision-making problem. We have also deliberately avoided repeating an example that we are very familiar with, that of adaptive harvest management for North American waterfowl. We have done so for two reasons. First, this example is very well covered elsewhere (e.g., Williams *et al.* 2002, Chapter 25). Second, and more relevant, this example sets a very high standard, in terms of *in situ* monitoring programs, completed research, and technical sophistication that would be extremely difficult, if not impossible, to duplicate, especially in the developing world. We have instead chosen an example that, while familiar to us, admittedly falls short in several key areas. Nevertheless, with this example we hope to demonstrate how existing data and properly designed monitoring programs can be brought to bear on a conservation decision problem. Along the way, we identify weaknesses that might prevent such a program from fully succeeding at this time, and make recommendations to remediate those weaknesses. Finally, although this example reflects the authors' experience in North American game bird management, we think that the principles illustrated – and shortfalls identified – will be useful for problem solving in other taxa and in other parts of the world.

The southeastern USA has undergone dramatic changes in ecosystems and land use over the last several hundred years. Prior to European settlement, starting in the 16th century, these ecosystems were primarily forested, but were strongly influenced by both natural and anthropogenic disturbance, principally fire. Whether fire was mainly of anthropogenic or natural origins is largely unknown and hotly (!) debated (Frost 1993, 1998), but what is certain is that after European arrival a dramatic shift in the state of ecosystems occurred. The primarily fire-maintained forest and forest/savanna was replaced by European- (and then American-) style small farms. By the nineteenth century much of the region was farmed and by the early twentieth century farming reached its maximum, resulting in removal of much of the forest. For example, in Georgia

Quantitative Conservation of Vertebrates, 1st edition. By M.J. Conroy and J.P. Carroll. Published 2009 by Blackwell Publishing, ISBN 978-1-4051-8228-7 (pb) and 978-1-4051-9098-5 (hb).

the maximum land area devoted to crop production occurred just before 1950. Since that peak there has been a general trend downward in land area devoted to crops throughout the Southeast, as production agriculture shifted to other parts of the USA (Figure 18.1).

This background sets the stage for our conservation problem. Avian species associated with grassland and shrub/scrub ecosystems in the southeastern USA have been in long-term and dramatic decline (Sauer *et al.* 2007). Indices of abundance based on the Breeding Bird Survey (BBS) (Sauer *et al.* 2007) of several of these species, including the northern bobwhite (*Colinus virginianus*), grasshopper sparrow (*Ammodramus savannarum*), eastern meadowlark (*Sturnella magna*), have declined by as much as 70% since the survey began in 1966 (Table 18.1). Although we might question whether assumptions about homogeneous detection (Chapters 6 and 8) are met by BBS data to allow

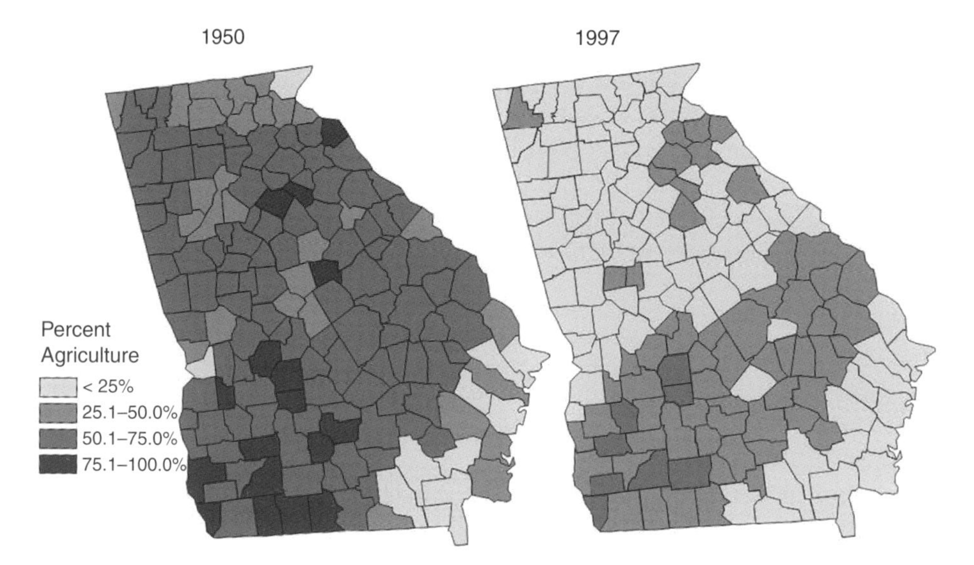

Fig. 18.1 **Land devoted to agricultural production in Georgia has been in long-term decline since 1950. The number of counties with more than 25% land area devoted to agriculture decreased from almost all of them in 1950 to only about a quarter by 1997.**

Table 18.1 Declines in some grassland and shrub/crub birds based on the Breeding Bird Survey in Georgia during 1966–2006 (from Sauer *et al.* 2007)

Species	Habitat affiliation	PAverage annual decline (%)	Total decline during 40 years (%)
Northern bobwhite	Shrub/scrub	−4.17	−81.80
Eastern meadowlark	Grassland	−4.21	−82.10
Grasshopper sparrow	Grassland	−5.76	−90.68
Mourning dove	Shrub/scrub	−1.47	−44.70
Loggerhead shrike	Shrub/scrub	−1.78	−51.25
Indigo bunting	Shrub/scrub	−0.12	−4.69
Eastern kingbird	Shrub/scrub	−2.29	−60.41

their valid use as indices of abundance, the trends are of sufficient magnitude to be unlikely due to changes in detection rates alone over this time span. In short, sufficient information exists to conclude that real and alarming degradation has occurred in these ecosystems over a fairly short period of time, motivating the question: what, if anything, can conservation efforts do to stop or reverse the decline?

In Georgia, as well as other parts of the southeastern USA, efforts to halt or reverse these declines have centered on the northern bobwhite. This species was chosen to be a model species representing guilds of grassland birds largely because of a long tradition of quail hunting in the region (the bobwhite is officially the state gamebird of Georgia). For this reason, much is known about the species, and there exist a large number of published research studies, as well as extensive efforts to monitor populations and estimate vital rates (DeMaso *et al.* 2002; Brennan 2007; Cederbaum *et al.* 2008); however, as noted below, some of these efforts may have produced information of questionable reliability.

As suggested above, declines in grassland birds in general, and bobwhite in particular, are thought to be principally related to large-scale ecosystem and land use changes, namely shifts from a mosaic of savannah and fire-dominated forest to an intensively cultivated landscape, with fire suppressed in the remaining forest patches. In effect, much of the remaining habitat for the bobwhite and other grassland birds is on privately owned land, and for most of this land the predominant land use is production agriculture. Under Georgia and US laws, landowners have broad rights to decide land use in their own interest, and ordinarily cannot be coerced into accepting land use practices that might benefit wildlife. Conversely, there exist a number of modifications to agricultural practices that could significantly improve habitat for bobwhites and other grassland species, with neutral or even beneficial impacts on agriculture. This has given rise to the creative idea of using financial incentives to encourage landowners to modify management of their land in such a way that would benefit the target guild of avian species.

The State of Georgia has created an incentive program along these lines, called the Bobwhite Quail Initiative (BQI). Previous research (Thackston and Whitney 2001) suggests that a range of management options potentially could improve habitat conditions for bobwhites and other grassland species. These options would operate, and have their impact, at different landscape scales. For instance, at the scale of an agricultural field, field margins, strips, or odd parts of fields (such as those not reached by center-pivot irrigation, where circular patterns of irrigation are used in what are generally square or rectangular fields) could be maintained in early succession habitat. Likewise, conservation tillage and winter cover crops could produce important winter cover habitats in this moderate temperate ecosystem. In the surrounding landscape, loblolly pine (*Pinus taeda*) has commonly invaded or has been planted in old (abandoned agricultural) fields during much of the 20th century. However, if these stands are thinned to allow sufficient sunlight on the ground, they potentially mimic the once widespread native pine savanna ecosystems. Landowners who are enrolled in the program receive a financial payment to undertake approved activities, but otherwise conduct production agriculture as usual.

Most of the land ownership patterns in Georgia mean that any particular landowner will control less than 100 ha. Thus, the scale for which management can be done for

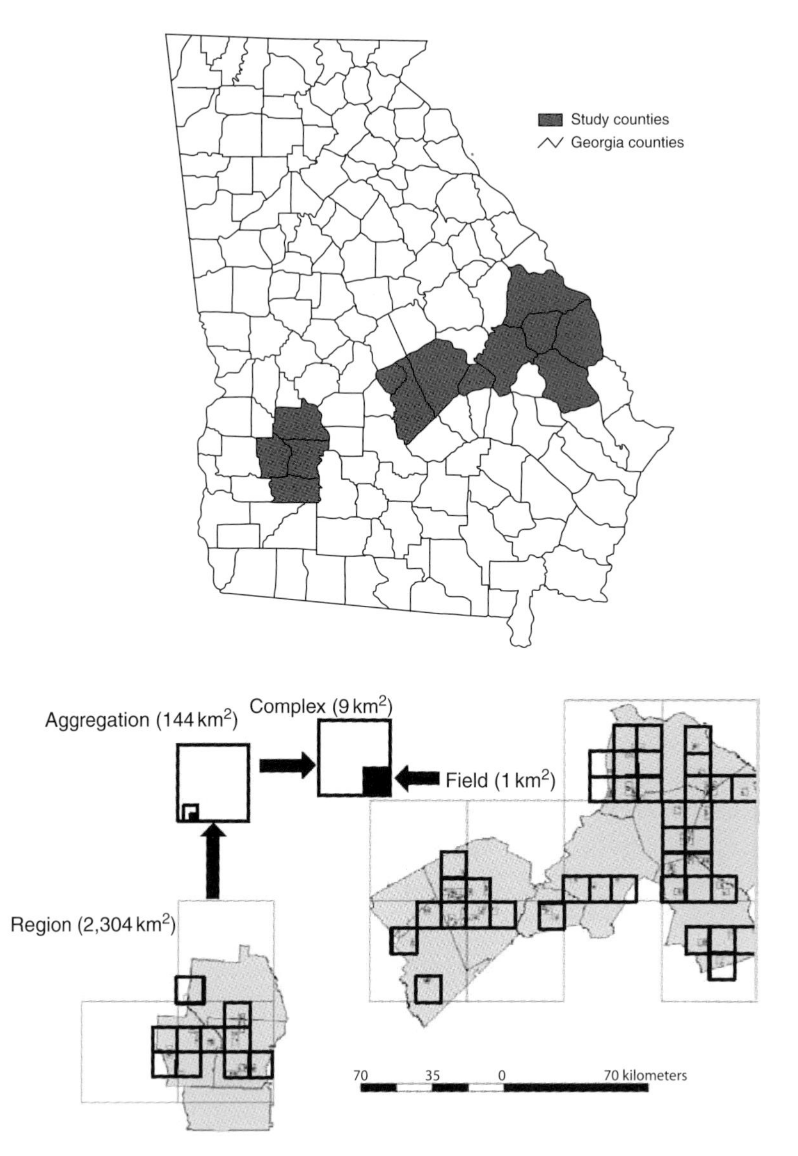

Fig. 18.2 **State of Georgia showing the part of the state where BQI management is being undertaken. Within those counties the area is divided, showing the scales for which habitat, habitat management, and bobwhite abundance were assessed (from Howell *et al.* 2006).**

any particular incentive plan will be quite small. However, clusters of landowners in the program might mean greater impact, by influencing a greater amount of land than can be done in isolation (see Figure 18.2 for four scales used in the modeling approach).

To summarize, the goal of BQI is to use financial incentives to encourage practices that will affect habitat conditions in the landscape, so as to slow or reverse the negative population trend for bobwhites and other grassland birds. However, as one would expect, the program has limited financial support, thus limiting the amount of area and landowners that can be enrolled in the program at any given time. Thus, an additional goal is to maximize the efficiency in which incentive payments are made to landowners over a broad landscape scale, so as to have the greatest positive impact on grassland birds for the given financial resources.

We now proceed with a more formal and complete development of the BQI decision model.

Elements of a BQI decision model

Objectives

As we see it, the **fundamental objective** (Chapter 15) of the BQI program is to increase populations of northern bobwhite and associated early-succession-habitat songbirds. The principal **means objective** (Chapter 15) to achieve this goal is via increases in suitable habitat for these guilds of birds. Immediately we can see that implicit assumptions are being made. First, we are assuming that bobwhites will respond to habitat modifications, and that populations will not be limited by other factors. Second, we assume that habitat modifications beneficial to northern bobwhite populations are also beneficial to sympatric species; that is, the northern bobwhite serves as a suitable "umbrella" species for a suite of grassland and shrub/scrub birds. For this case study, we will take the latter assumption as a given, and focus on the first assumption. This will be key to guiding our thinking about model development, consideration of uncertainty, and the reduction of uncertainty through adaptive management. We take this approach not because we are dismissive of the importance of testing the applicability of the "umbrella hypothesis," but rather because we think that the first set of questions (i) stands a better chance of being addressed with foreseeable monitoring efforts, and (ii) is in a sense the limiting question: if a habitat–bird population response cannot be established for bobwhite, it is unlikely to be established for other species.

Decision alternatives

Ideally, managers of a program such as BQI would be able to select from a range of options regarding on-the-ground management practices that might affect bobwhites and other birds. In practice there are many constraints, including the total amount of funds available (determined by the state legislature and sales of a special vehicle license plate), existing land management practices, and political considerations. Given these constraints, the essential decision regarding BQI can be summarized as: "select the list of parcels to include in BQI that will produce the maximum number of birds on the landscape, given available resources and existing land practices."

Basic decision model

As discussed in Chapter 15, a decision model includes a statement (perhaps mathematical) about the predicted relationship between a candidate decision and a predicted outcome given that decision, often dependent on the present state of the system under management. For the BQI problem, this idea is captured very simply by a flow or "**influence diagram**," in which the system state (habitat quality, bird numbers) is presumed to be altered to a new state via some management intervention, in this case the decision to enroll a particular list of land units in BQI (Figure 18.3), with an associated value (utility), in this case, numbers of birds produced, under each candidate decision. Below we will expand this schematic to develop an actual predictive model relating our candidate decisions to objective outcomes, but, for the moment, assume that this model exists. Then, in principle, the task is to use the model to discriminate among the competing decision alternatives, and to pick the one (d^*) that appears to best achieve the objective (V^*) (Figure 18.4).

At this point we must acknowledge that there is fundamental uncertainty about how much response to expect, even on average, in the face of a particular decision (which parcels to include on the incentive list). Even assuming that the decision to

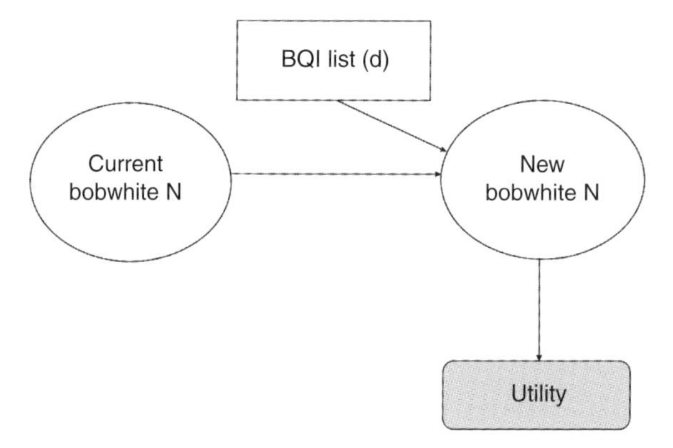

Fig. 18.3 **Influence diagram indicating the relationship between selection of a particular list of parcels for inclusion in BQI, predicted number of bobwhite resulting, and utility of that result.**

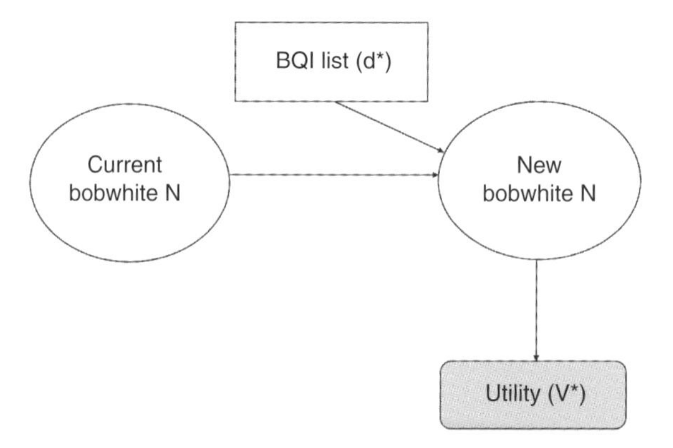

Fig. 18.4 **Optimal decision (d^*) leading to highest expected utility under current assumptions about the relationship between land use practices, habitat response, and population response.**

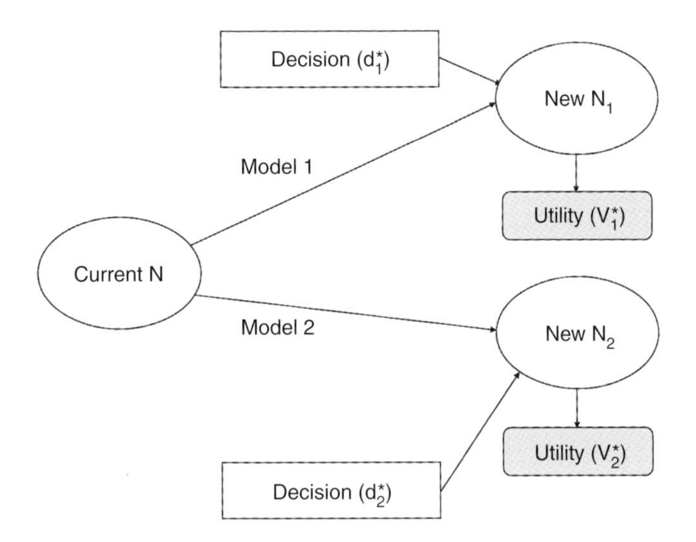

Fig. 18.5 **Incorporation of model (structural) uncertainty into BQI decision model.**

proceed with a particular list of parcels in BQI leads to a desired habitat outcome (see "Partial controllability", Chapter 16), it is possible that some other factor, and not habitat, is actually limiting bobwhites. This potentially sets up scenarios where under two hypotheses we expect different responses, potentially leading to different optimal decisions (Figure 18.5). Below we will see how this kind of uncertainty ("Structural or process uncertainty", Chapter 16) can be reduced through adaptive management.

Construction of a predictive model for decision making

The above expresses in the broadest terms a possible connection between BQI program decisions and response/objective values, but provides no quantitative predictions that could be used to discriminate either among alternatives or against which to judge eventual success via monitoring. Howell *et al.* (in press) constructed predictive models using two types of data: (i) counts of quail coveys using accepted techniques for monitoring abundance during mid-October to mid-December, 1999–2001, on a sample of fields including those enrolled in the BQI program, adjusted for detection rates as described below; and (ii) landcover and management practices as assessed by a combination of remote sensing/GIS and field surveys. The former produced estimates of quail abundance for approximately 1 km^2 units of land; the latter produced local and landscape-level attributes for habitat and land use. These two data sources were used to fit a series of hierarchical linear models using MCMC methods. These models describe the relationship between landscape-level random effects, management variables (number of fields, field borders, hedgerows, years enrolled, and acres enrolled), and habitat variables (acreage in agriculture and broad cover types) at several scales of resolution: Field (1 km^2), Complexes of nine fields (9 km^2), Aggregation of 16 complexes (144 km^2), and Region: 16 aggregations (2304 km^2). Fits of alternative models to these data produced four top-ranked (by AIC) predictive models (Table 18.2). These models

Table 18.2 Comparison of models examining the impact of scale and habitat factors on numbers of northern bobwhite coveys (Howell *et al.*, in press)

Model	Landscape effects	Management effects	Habitat effects	ΔAIC	Weight
4	Field and complex	Field	Absent	0	0.52
2	Complex	Field	Absent	1.59	0.24
3	Complex	Absent	Present	2.08	0.18
1	Complex	Field	Present	4.32	0.06

were then used to rank, via stochastic simulation, combinations of two fields selected from 36 possible fields, taking into account complex- and site-level predictors, model uncertainty, and stochastic uncertainty in responses (Table 18.3).

Results are provided separately for predictions under each of the four top-ranked models and for model-averaged predictions across the four models. These results illustrate two points relevant to decision making. First, for this simple example, it is possible to use these models to rank candidate fields for selection. However, we note that the mean objective values among the alternative choices under each model are similar, so that decisions between candidate sets of fields could easily "flip" given slightly different information. Second, these rankings appear to be highly sensitive to the choice of the underlying model. For example, the combination (19, 24) ranked third or fourth under two models, but not in the top 20 under the other two. Thus, uncertainty in this system may strongly influence decision making. We will consider below how uncertainty may be reduced through improved monitoring and adaptive management, thereby improving management over time. A key point is that reduction of this uncertainty through improved monitoring and adaptive management has the potential to improve decision making and therefore has conservation value. We emphasize this point, below.

Dealing with uncertainty

Like all models integrating management, monitoring, and research, the integration of uncertainty is crucial in maximizing efficiency of the program. Environmental uncertainty is comprised of a number of factors for which we have no control, but which could reduce the effectiveness of management. For example, weather, bobwhite predators, fire ants (*Solenopis invicta*), disease, and/or climate change might all influence our models, yet we have no control over these. However, many of these things can be monitored or measured in some way and possibly incorporated in the model predictions if necessary.

Monitoring of response following management

As we have previously emphasized throughout the book, we believe that monitoring is a critical component of any management program. It not only will tell us if the

Table 18.3 Results of simulations to rank combinations of fields included in the BQI incentive program,[a] taking into account complex- and site-level predictors, model uncertainty, and stochastic uncertainty in responses (Howell *et al.*, in press.)

Rank	Model (see Table 18.2)									
	Average		1		2		3		4	
	Pair	Mean[b]	Pair	Mean	Pair	Mean	Pair	Mean	Pair	Mean
1	(06, 19)	18.60	(00, 08)	26.48	(08, 25)	21.77	(01, 07)	9.97	(01, 26)	19.08
2	(03, 05)	18.49	(01, 08)	26.45	(19, 21)	21.76	(00, 07)	9.92	(06, 07)	19.02
3	(01, 03)	18.29	(06, 08)	25.71	(01, 08)	21.65	(03, 05)	9.87	(19, 24)	18.99
4	(01, 21)	18.19	(05, 08)	25.58	(19, 24)	21.59	(09, 11)	9.82	(01, 24)	18.96
5	(00, 01)	18.05	(01, 06)	25.46	(02, 06)	21.58	(01, 09)	9.82	(04, 22)	18.91
6	(05, 06)	18.03	(02, 08)	25.41	(22, 23)	21.50	(01, 08)	9.82	(20, 25)	18.91
7	(02, 05)	18.01	(01, 03)	25.36	(01, 23)	21.41	(15, 16)	9.81	(03, 06)	18.87
8	(00, 06)	18.01	(01, 07)	25.35	(02, 18)	21.41	(01, 02)	9.80	(24, 25)	18.86
9	(03, 21)	18.00	(03, 06)	25.17	(00, 20)	21.39	(05, 15)	9.77	(06, 24)	18.86
10	(00, 03)	17.95	(06, 07)	25.13	(08, 19)	21.38	(04, 10)	9.76	(20, 24)	18.84
11	(07, 08)	17.94	(02, 03)	25.11	(00, 24)	21.31	(01, 16)	9.75	(24, 26)	18.82
12	(01, 06)	17.88	(03, 08)	25.04	(05, 23)	21.27	(11, 17)	9.72	(06, 08)	18.76
13	(01, 07)	17.88	(05, 06)	25.02	(04, 21)	21.26	(10, 17)	9.71	(08, 19)	18.75
14	(04, 24)	17.88	(01, 02)	25.01	(00, 19)	21.26	(02, 07)	9.71	(01, 23)	18.75
15	(04, 21)	17.83	(00, 01)	24.97	(04, 25)	21.24	(07, 11)	9.71	(06, 21)	18.67
16	(18, 24)	17.78	(03, 05)	24.97	(00, 08)	21.23	(06, 13)	9.70	(01, 06)	18.65
17	(05, 08)	17.78	(01, 04)	24.89	(02, 24)	21.20	(09, 14)	9.68	(04, 26)	18.64
18	(01, 23)	17.75	(04, 07)	24.86	(02, 26)	21.20	(06, 09)	9.68	(06, 26)	18.62
19	(02, 19)	17.74	(02, 04)	24.82	(21, 26)	21.19	(01, 14)	9.67	(07, 20)	18.60
20	(05, 24)	17.65	(00, 04)	24.80	(20, 24)	21.19	(14, 16)	9.66	(01, 21)	18.60

[a] Cluster characteristics: better habitat/more management (fields 0–8), better habitat/less management (fields 9–17), poorer habitat/more management (fields 18–26), poorer habitat/less management (fields 27–35).
[b] Coveys per square kilometer.

program is having any effect at all, but also can allow us to feed back to our models to determine what components of the management program are having a greater impact and what components might be having no effect. Using as our guiding principles ideas that we have previously discussed in this book (Part II), we sought to incorporate appropriate metrics from monitoring into an adaptive management program for northern bobwhites. To summarize these principles, we sought monitoring programs that would:

- allow us to monitor bobwhite abundance in an efficient manner with sufficient resolution over the landscape scale that was the target of the habitat management;
- be statistically repeatable and comparable among areas and over time;
- take into account the issue of incomplete and possible heterogeneous detection rates; and
- make efficient use of available resources (and be achievable, given limitations on these resources).

We immediately faced several challenges in this project. There have been many attempts to estimate abundance of the northern bobwhite using a wide variety of approaches. Although some intensive techniques such as mark–recapture (Palmer and Wellendorf 2007; Terhune *et al.* 2007) and distance sampling (Guthery 1988) have been used in intensive studies on small areas, the scale of BQI covers tens of thousands of hectares, thus precluding use of these techniques. Therefore we adapted some techniques for more broad-scale application to determine which might be applied most cost effectively and these are summarized in Hamrick (2002). We adopted the multi-observer described by Hamrick (2002) to quadrat counts of bobwhite in order to estimate detection rates and test for homogeneity of detection (Figure 18.6).

This technique was originally developed at Tall Timbers Research Station and Land Conservancy, Inc. in Florida to provide an effective means of estimating bobwhite abundance on managed pine savanna ecosystems in southern Georgia and northern Florida (Wellendorf *et al.* 2001, 2004). It uses multiple observers to monitor a defined quadrat while accounting for detectability of bobwhites during autumn counts. Observers are placed out in the landscape at four predefined points that represent the mid-points of the four sides of a 0.25 km^2 square. They arrive before sunrise with synchronized watches and compasses. As bobwhite coveys move out from their night-time roost about sunrise they begin with a distinct group call. The observers note the exact time and direction. There are two issues related to detection. The first is whether the covey calls in the first place – which sometimes happens and is related to covey density. Wellendorf *et al.* (2001) developed models for that detection rate. The second is the observer's ability to detect the call if made. This is handled using the four multiple observers covering a small area where we can have the covey heard by up to four observers. As it turns out in these small areas with four observers, if a covey calls within the quadrat it is detected usually by more than two observers. The system works because coveys almost always call in the morning and even at fairly high densities observers are usually only trying to detect from 0 to 5 coveys (S. Wellendorf, personal communication).

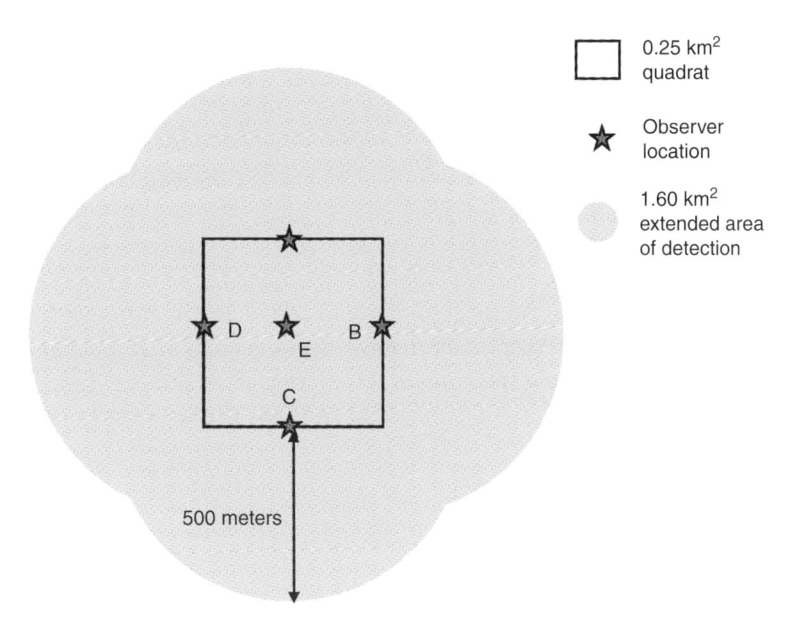

Fig. 18.6 **Multiple observer estimation of bobwhite covey abundance developed in Hamrick (2002).**

However, when this technique was applied to much larger landscapes with far lower and more heterogeneous bobwhite densities, we found that it was not very efficient for estimating bobwhite abundance (Hamrick 2002). We found that most quadrats returned zeros, but we often detected coveys outside of the quadrat. Hamrick (2002) modified the original technique to make it more effective over a much larger area while maintaining similar levels of detection (Figure 18.6). Our effective coverage was 1.60 km^2 which allowed us to increase our per quadrat detection rate without increasing manpower efforts. Eventually for application to monitoring programs we created several other modification of the technique to reduce the number of observers to as few as two (Hamrick 2002). For this example, we used the four-observer models described in Hamrick (2002). The data for these models are detection histories similar to the capture histories used to estimate abundance via capture–recapture models (Chapter 10). For a given visit to a quadrat, the observers are treated as "capture occasions" with 1 indicating that a covey was detected by an observer and 0 indicating no detection. For example, the history "1010" would indicate that observers 1 and 3 detected a covey but observers 2 and 4 did not. These data were then used in the program MARK to fit a number of models allowing for variation in detection probabilities (the analog to capture probability for these data) by observer, over sites, or across time occasions. Although there was some evidence of detection heterogeneity, overall the analysis supported a constant detection rate (Hamrick 2002), which is what we have used in the modeling exercise below.

For our modeling exercise here we linked the detection-adjusted monitoring (described above) at local scales with habitat management conducted under the BQI program and the Georgia landcover map (Kramer *et al.* 2003). We note that sites containing BQI management are not randomly assigned, which potentially creates a problem in drawing conclusions about the impact of BQI management on our responses of interest (Chapter 5). Therefore, our recommended monitoring protocol calls for the pairing of BQI sites with non-BQI sites serving as controls. As discussed later, our recommendations have not yet been implemented, but for the purposes of this illustration we proceed as if such monitoring program were in place. We now consider how monitoring data of this type could, in turn, be useful, in a program to reduce uncertainty and improve decision making through adaptive management.

Adaptive management

Under adaptive management, we take management actions that appear to be optimal (i.e., have the best chance of achieving our objective), given our current knowledge (Chapter 17). In our very simplified BQI example, our decision is "which two fields should we select, in order to have the highest expected number of coveys?" Taking into account our statistical, structural, and environmental sources of uncertainty, we have the result that the pair (06, 19) produces this result. Note that we use the "average" column of this table because that column, in addition to statistical and environmental uncertainty, averages over our four alternative models, weighting the predictions under each model by our current relative belief in each model (the AIC weights from Table 18.2).

Once we have made that decision, we are in a position to use monitoring data to readjust our model weights through time. Suppose that we implement the (06, 19) decision, and subsequently (say after 5 years) observe that the number of coveys on these fields has increased from 10 to 18/km^{-2}. Because our models make different predictions about bird response to management, the result "$X = 18$" is more likely under some models than others. We used our simulation approach to evaluate a statistical likelihood for this result under each model, which also takes into account the fact that the covey surveys are subject to statistical error for this exercise we assume that this error was a constant coefficient of variation [(mean/SE) of 0.2]. This results in a likelihood under each of the four models of 2.75×10^{-6}, 5.73×10^{-7}, 3.82×10^{-13}, and 6.87×10^{-8} for models 1, 2, 3, and 4, respectively. We then use these values with Bayes' Theorem (Chapter 17) to compute new, posterior probabilities for each model. For example, the new probability for model 2 is computed as:

$$
\begin{aligned}
wt_2(t+1) &= \frac{wt_2(t)L_2(X_{t+1})}{\sum_m^M wt_m(t)L_m(X_{t+1})} \\
&= [0.2352(5.73 \times 10^{-7})]/[0.0601(2.75 \times 10^{-6}) + 0.2352(5.73 \times 10^{-7}) \\
&\quad + 0.1841(3.82 \times 10^{-13}) + 0.5207(6.87 \times 10^{-8})]^{-1} = 0.4013
\end{aligned}
$$

In a similar manner, we can calculate new model probabilities under the other models as 0.4922, 0.00, and 0.1064 for models 1, 3, and 4, respectively (note that the probabilities across all the models need to sum to 1!). These calculations are summarized

Table 18.4 Likelihoods and posterior model probabilities for three possible monitoring outcomes following a decision to implement optimal management decision for BQI (rank 1, Table 18.3)

Model	Prior weights	Observed outcome (X = estimated number of coveys per square kilometer)					
		$X = 10$		$X = 18$		$X = 25$	
		Likelihood	Posterior	Likelihood	Posterior	Likelihood	Posterior
1	0.0601	1.25E−11	0.0000	2.75E−06	0.4922	1.99E−08	0.6553
2	0.2352	4.06E−08	0.1583	5.73E−07	0.4013	2.13E−09	0.2746
3	0.1841	3.64E−08	0.1110	3.82E−13	0.0000	2.16E−15	0.0000
4	0.5207	8.46E−08	0.7306	6.87E−08	0.1064	2.46E−10	0.0701

in Table 18.4, along with the results for two other possible outcomes, $X = 10$ (no change) and $X = 25$ (a much greater change). Notice how these contrasting results would provide different relative support to the alternative model.

How do we use our new information? Under adaptive management, the idea is that we now apply our information gains to improve decision making at our next opportunity to make a management decision. In this example, when we are next faced with a list of potential BQI sites from which to select candidate fields, we will be operating from a new knowledge base. This could also mean we make different decisions relative to the 3-year life of each BQI contract. We could decide that if a landowner puts in a proposal for a second 3 years after the first period we might then reject it. In this example, if we had just obtained the result $X = 18$ following management, our new model probabilities will be 0.49, 0.40, 0.00, and 0.11 under the four models (note that the third model is not actually "zero" but that we have rounded this very small number to two places). When we now run our simulation to see which pairing of fields will be optimal [taking into account that we have already included (06, 19)], our new result is (10, 33). In reality, of course, we would have a much longer list of fields to include in our program, but the principle is exactly the same: we are always using our best, current information to select the list of fields that best achieves our objectives, given our available resources.

Unfortunately, we have not yet been able to implement an adaptive program to BQI, because of reductions in funding to support research and monitoring. Failure to maintain a robust research and monitoring program can be self-defeating: we are in effect in the position of making decisions about how to spend money (the BQI program itself has continued), with no feedback as to success and no opportunity to learn. We suggest that a well-designed adaptive monitoring program in fact more than pays for itself; that assertion can, of course, be evaluated by computing EVPI (see Chapter 17).

Summary

Here we have illustrated several principles discussed in this book by way of a real conservation example. In this example, we have shown how monitoring data and predictive modeling can be used together to evaluate optimal management practices, taking into account all relevant sources of uncertainty. We suggest that many if not most conservation problems worldwide can be approached using these basic principles, although the exact methods for monitoring and modeling will differ. We encourage readers to look at their local conservation problems in this light and to freely adapt these approaches to their specific needs.

19
Summary and recommendations

Throughout this book, we have tried to provide readers with a mixture of basic approaches and advanced methods that potentially are suitable for a wide range of conservation studies. These approaches, while often relatively simple, still require a basic understanding of scientific and statistical principals, and some use of mathematical notation. We continually struggled with the need to maintain rigor – tending to pull us toward more quantitative and complex descriptions – and the need to keep this material accessible to and readable by conservation biologists. We hope that our liberal use of real-world examples, augmented by our Glossary, website and other materials freely available on the internet (see Appendices A and B), will provide readers with a sufficient context to apply these ideas to their own work.

In the process of keeping this book relatively short, readable, and accessible, we have made many decisions on what to include or exclude. We have also in many cases (particularly in statistical modeling) taken an informal (but still, we hope, essentially accurate) approach to description. Readers who desire a more complete and mathematically rigorous treatment of these topics are encouraged to seek it in texts such as Williams *et al.* (2002), MacKenzie *et al.* (2006), or references therein.

Here we make no attempt at a comprehensive summary of the book, but rather seek to emphasize some of the book's major themes, and provide some insights as to how conservation studies can benefit from these themes.

Use of models

Obviously, models form a central theme of this book. We are aware that many conservation biologists avoid using models through fear, or because they think them irrelevant to their work, or both. For the former, we hope we have provided a sufficiently "gentle" coverage to enable them to overcome some of their trepidation.

For the latter, we emphasize that models are *not* meant to replace observational approaches, natural history, or other traditional bastions of field biology. Rather, these methods – and they are just methods – *can* help field biologists put their work, and the resulting data, into a broader context. Thus, for example, population models can be very useful in considering the ecological and evolutionary meaning of temporal, spatial, and individual pattern of abundance, survival, and reproduction. Indeed, these patterns often *only* make sense if considered in some broader theoretical and predictive context – for which models are ideally suited.

Quantitative Conservation of Vertebrates, 1st edition. By M.J. Conroy and J.P. Carroll. Published 2009 by Blackwell Publishing, ISBN 978-1-4051-8228-7 (pb) and 978-1-4051-9098-5 (hb).

In addition to models as tools for explanation and synthesis, they are also very powerful tools for *prediction* and *testing*. In conservation biology we are usually not just interested in what is happening at a particular site or at a particular time: we are also interested in what this might mean for other sites under similar or different conditions. This is particularly the case when some of the model inputs relate to factors that are directly or indirectly under human control, such as harvest, habitat manipulation (or destruction), introductions, and others. In these cases, biologists often wish (or need) to make "what if" predictions: what will happen to the abundance (age composition, distribution, habitat occupancy) of species X if I do Y (or Z, which I cannot control, happens)? At the least, models are a way of formalizing the biologist's belief about what *may* happen, and – particularly if they involve data collected under a range of conditions, including experimental controls – the models may have some at least provisional empirical support. Of course, the models are just that – only models – and they may be at least partially wrong (as may the biologist's own intuition). This raises the very important need to consider alternative models (explanations), to thoroughly question (and, if possible, test) underlying assumptions, and, where possible, to validate model predictions with independent data.

Proper design of field studies

Having mentioned "data" now several times, it is important to remember that the quality of data depends upon the underlying sampling or experimental design under which the data were collected (Chapter 5). This in turn, of course, depends upon the objectives of the study, which may range from purely descriptive statements (estimates of abundance and vital rates), to mechanistic or predictive modeling. In all of these cases, it is critical to keep in mind the objectives of the study, which will dictate the nature of the sampling design. An appropriate sampling design will result in data that can be used to make inferences about the **target population** of interest, and, conversely, an inappropriate design will result in invalid or inappropriate inferences. Too frequently, biologists gather observations according to proximity, convenience, or serendipity – all considerations that may reduce the costs of a survey, but seldom will result in data that can be generalized to a system of interest.

The above general statements are applicable to *any* sampling situation, but sampling for vertebrate conservation involves some additional and somewhat unique issues. An important feature of most sampling for vertebrates is that the selection of a particular sample of time or space where animals may occur – or even do occur with certainty – is no guarantee that all, or even any, of the animals present will be detected. Failure to incorporate detection into the sampling design has been repeatedly and convincingly (to us) shown to result in data that provide biased estimates of parameters, and that cannot be used to make even relative statements about occupancy, abundance, vital rates, or other parameters without assumptions that are untestable and unsupportable. Nevertheless, we still often see data collected in which the investigators seem sublimely oblivious to these principles. There is, unfortunately, little that can be done with such data. By contrast, studies that involve the collection of ancillary detection data typically at least allow the testing of critical assumptions, and ideally allow the direct estimation of rates of detection and, thus, unbiased estimates and comparisons.

Proper analysis of data

Assuming that data have been collected according to an appropriate design, and with proper consideration of incomplete detection rates, there remains the task of appropriately analyzing these data to obtain parameter estimates and make comparisons. These approaches are the subject of Part II, in which we emphasize methods based on identifiable and testable assumptions that make the most efficient use of the data. These methods involve both specific types of data (and sampling design) and accompanying models, and so are really more appropriately termed "sampling schemes" than either designs or analyses alone. The methods cover a wide range of types of sample data, including occupancy or "presence–absence" sampling (Chapter 7), sample counts (Chapter 8), distance sampling (Chapter 9), and methods involving tagging and recapture, monitoring, or recovery of marked animals (Chapters 10–12). The methods overlap with respect to parameters estimated, with, for instance, abundance estimation covered in Chapters 8–12. Obviously not all approaches will be appropriate for a given problem, so that, for instance, capture–recapture obviously can only be used for animals that can practicably (or safely) be captured or otherwise marked, and distance sampling only for animals that can be detected visually or by other means and distances recorded. In Appendix D we provide a "key" to parameter estimation that may be useful to readers in sorting through the many, overlapping methods covered. In Part II we also discuss sampling designs and analysis appropriate for addressing questions of resource selection (Chapter 13) and community estimation (Chapter 14).

Systematic approaches to decision making

This book has emphasized applications of models and data to conservation problems. We think that it is absolutely critical that conservation biologists keep the end applications of data and modeling in mind as they design studies and develop models. It is very frustrating (to all parties) when a conservation study is completed, only to find that the data collected and models developed cannot address the conservation decision problem at hand.

Much of this frustration can be avoided if conservation decision problems are approached in a systematic, organized way. Just as building a population model can help us organize thinking about how a population behaves, so too can a model help in systematically approaching a conservation problem. In a **decision model**, we formally describe – ideally in mathematical terms – the relationships between the objectives of the decision maker and the available decision alternatives. Usually, this requires some type of a model of the biological system, which captures our belief in how the system is likely to respond to management. The decision model should also capture key sources of uncertainty, including uncertainty in our model of the biological system. With the decision model in hand, it is now possible to objectively search for the decision alternative that best seems to meet the conservation objective (the **optimal** decision), taking into account what we know about the system. We consider these topics in Chapters 15 and 16.

Organized in this way, it begins to be clearer how and where monitoring data and research enter into the decision-making picture. Monitoring data can tell us not only how well we are doing at meeting our objectives, but also how good of a job our models are doing at predicting the impacts of conservation. Of course, as we have stressed, it is also important to consider **alternative models** in decision making. That is, although we might have a model that we think describes the most likely outcome of our decision, there are no doubt plausible alternatives that would predict different outcomes. Prudent decision making takes into account this type of uncertainty, but seeks to reduce it. In Chapter 17 we show how this can be done via the feedback of monitoring information, leading to **adaptive resource management**.

We attempt to bring all of these themes together in our Case Study (Chapter 18), in which we have deliberately chosen a rather difficult and messy conservation problem. In that chapter, we start by building up the decision-making context (Part III), which then motivates the development of some simple predictive models relating conservation decisions to outcomes. These models, of course, have parameters that must be estimated with data, and their predictions have to be validated against real world observations, the focus of Parts I and II. We return to Part III to show how a monitoring program can potentially improve decision making through time, under adaptive management.

Finally, this book is definitely intended as a "hands-on" tool. We strongly encourage readers to work through all the examples; see p. ii for spreadsheets or computer input/output for all the major examples in this book. We of course encourage readers to move beyond these examples, and apply the concepts and tools in this book to the design, analysis, and decision making in their own applications. We have provided many examples, from which readers may find examples that nearly fit their own problem. However, we cannot have anticipated (or if we did, could not include) all possible problems that can arise in conservation studies. We hope, though, that the concepts and examples herein provided will sufficiently inform and motivate readers so that they can seek solutions in other sources. We have provided many additional sources in Appendices A and B, and encourage readers to seek out these resources, which are generally free of cost. Finally, we welcome comments, questions, and suggestions from readers, and have established a list serve (see p. ii) that we hope will be of value to readers (and us) as we try to advance scientific conservation.

Literature cited

Aebischer, N.J., R.A. Robertson, and R.E. Kenward. 1993. Compositional analysis of habitat use from animal radio-tracking data. *Ecology* 74:1313–1325.

Akçakaya, H.R., M.A. Burgman, and L.R. Ginzburg. 1999. *Applied Population Ecology: Principles and Computer Exercises using RAMAS EcoLab 2.0.* Sinauer Associates, Sunderland, MA.

Allee, W.C., A.E. Emerson, O. Park, T. Park, and K.P. Schmidt. 1949. *Principles of Animal Ecology.* W.B. Saunders Co., Philadelphia, PA, USA.

Anderson, D.R., K.P. Burnham, G.C. White, and D.L. Otis. 1983. Density estimation of small-mammal populations using a trapping web and distance sampling methods. *Ecology* 64:674–680.

Augustin, N.H., M.A. Mugglestone, and S.T. Buckland. 1996. An autologistic model for spatial distribution of wildlife. *Journal of Applied Ecology* 33:339–347.

Bailey, L.L., J.E. Hines, J.D. Nichols, and D.I. MacKenzie. 2007. Sampling design trade-offs in occupancy studies with imperfect detection: examples and software. *Ecological Applications* 17:281–290.

Bart, J. and D.S. Robson. 1982. Estimating survivorship when the subjects are visited periodically. *Ecology* 63:1078–1090.

Beier, P.H. Quigley, M.R. Vaughan, M.J. Conroy, and H. Quigley. 2006. Evaluating scientific inferences about the Florida Panther. *Journal of Wildlife Management* 70:236–245.

Beverton, R.J.H. and S.J. Holt. 1957. *On the Dynamics of Exploited Fish Populations.* Her Majesty's Stationery Office, London.

Boer, A.H. 1988. Mortality rates of moose in New Brunswick: a life table analysis. *Journal of Wildlife Management* 52:21–25.

Box, G.E.P. 1979. Robustness in the strategy of scientific model building. In *Robustness in Statistics*, R.L. Launer and G.N. Wilkinson, Editors. Academic Press, New York.

Brennan, L.A. 2007. *Texas Quails: Ecology and Management.* Texas A&M Press, College Station, TX, USA.

Brownie, C., D.R. Anderson, K.P. Burnham, and D.R. Robson. 1985. *Statistical Inference from Band-recovery Data: A Handbook.* Second edition. U.S. Fish and Wildlife Service Resource Publication 156.

Buckland, S.T., D.R. Anderson, K.P. Burnham, and J.L. Laake. 1993. *Distance Sampling: Estimation of Biological Populations.* Chapman & Hall, New York, USA.

Buckland, S.T., K.P. Burnham, and N.H. Augustin. 1997. Model selection: an integral part of inference. *Biometrics* 38:469–477.

Buckland, S.T., D.R. Anderson, K.P. Burnham, J.L. Laake, D.L. Borchers, and L. Thomas. 2001. *Introduction to Distance Sampling: Estimating Abundance of Biological Populations.* Oxford University Press, Oxford, UK.

Burnham, K.P. 1993. A theory for combined analysis of ring recovery and recapture data. In *The Study of Bird Population Dynamics Using Marked Individuals*, J.D. Lebreton and P.M. North, Editors, pp. 199–213. Birkhauser-Verlag, Berlin, Germany.

Burnham, K.P. and D.R. Anderson. 2002. *Model Selection and Multimodel Inference: A Practical, Information-Theoretic Approach.* Springer-Verlag, New York, USA.

Burnham, K.P. and W.S. Overton. 1979. Robust estimation of population size when capture probabilities vary among animals. *Ecology* 62:927–936.

Byers, C.R., R.K. Steinhorst, and P.R. Krausman. 1984. Clarification of a technique for utilization-availability. *Journal of Wildlife Management* 48:1050–1053.

Carroll, J.P., R.D. Crawford, and J.W. Schulz. 1995. Gray partridge winter home range and use of habitat in North Dakota. *Journal of Wildlife Management* 59:98–103.

Caswell, H. 2001. *Matrix Population Models. Construction, Analysis, and Interpretation.* Second edition. Sinauer Associates, Sunderland, MA, USA.

Cederbaum, S., B. Faircloth, T. Terhune, J. Thompson, and J. Carroll, Editors. 2008. *Gamebird 2006: Quail VI and Perdix XII.* Warnell School of Forestry and Natural Resources, University of Georgia, Athens, GA, USA.

Clemen, R.T. 1996. *Making Hard Decisions: An Introduction to Decision Analysis.* Second edition. Duxbury Press, Belmont, CA, USA.

Cochran, W. 1977. *Sampling Techniques.* Wiley, New York, USA.

Conroy, M.J. 1992. RAMAS/Space. Spatially-structured population models for conservation biology. *Quarterly Review of Biology* 67:252–253 [Software review].

Conroy, M.J., R.J. Barker, P.W. Dillingham, D. Fletcher, A.M. Gormley, and I.M. West Brooke. 2008. Applications of decision theory to conservation management: recovery of Hector's dolphin. *Wildlife Research* 35:93–102.

Conroy, M.J., G.R. Constanzo, and D.B. Stotts. 1989. Winter survival of female American black ducks on the Atlantic coast. *Journal of Wildlife Management* 53:99–109.

Conroy, M.J., M.W. Miller, and J.E. Hines. 2002a. Identification and synthetic modeling of factors affecting American black duck populations. *Wildlife Monographs* 150.

Conroy, M.J., J.C. Senar, and J. Domènech. 2002b. Analysis of individual and time-specific covariate effects on survival of *Serinus serinus* in north-eastern Spain. *Journal of Applied Statistics* 29(1–3):125–142.

Conroy, M.J., C.J. Fonnesbeck, and N.L. Zimpfer. 2004. Development of an integrated, adaptive management protocol for American black ducks. Final Report. Cooperative Agreement 1434-hq-97-RU-0155 Research Work Order No. 50, Georgia Cooperative Fish and Wildlife Research Unit, University of Georgia, Athens, 268pp.

Conroy, M.J., P. Beier, H. Quigley, and M.R. Vaughan. 2006. Improving the use of science in conservation: lessons from the Florida Panther. *Journal of Wildlife Management* 70:1–7.

Conroy, M.J., J.P. Carroll, K.L. Cook, C.J. Fonnesbeck, and J.T. Peterson. In prep. Hierarchical modeling of resource utilizations using Markov chain Monte Carlo.

Cook, R.D. and J.O. Jacobson. 1979. A design for estimating visibility bias in aerial surveys. *Biometrics* 35:735–742.

Cooper, A.B. and J.J. Millspaugh. 1999. The application of discrete choice models to wildlife resource selection studies. *Ecology* 80:566–575.

Cooper, A.B., and J.J. Millspaugh. 2001. Accounting for variation in resource availability and animal behavior in resource selection studies. In *Radio Tracking and Animal Populations,* J.J. Millspaugh, and J.M. Marzluff, Editors, pp. 243–274. Academic Press, San Diego, CA, USA.

Cox, D.R. and D. Oakes. 1984. *Analysis of Survival Data.* Chapman & Hall, London.

DeMaso, S.J., M.J. Peterson, J.R. Purvis, N.J. Silvy, and J.L. Cooke, Editors. 2002. *Quail V: Proceedings of the Fifth National Quail Symposium.* Texas Parks and Wildlife Department, Austin, TX, USA.

Drummer, T.D., and L.L. McDonald. 1987. Size bias in line transect sampling. *Biometrics* 43:13–22.

Efford, M. 2004. Density estimation in live-trapping studies. *Oikos* 106:598–610.

Erickson, W.P., T.L. McDonald, K.G. Gerow, S. Howlin, and J.W. Kern. 2001. Statistical issues in resources selection studies with radio-marked animals. In *Radio Tracking and Animal Populations*, J.J. Millspaugh, and J.M. Marzluff, Editors, pp. 211–245. Academic Press, San Diego, CA, USA.

Folk, T.H., J.B. Grand, W.E. Palmer, J.P. Carroll, H.L. Stribling, D.C. Sisson, T.M. Terhune, and S.D. Wellendorf. 2007. Estimates of survival from radio-telemetry: a response to Guthery and Lusk. *Journal of Wildlife Management* 70:1027–1033.

Freidman, M. 1937. The use of ranks to avoid the assumption of normality implicit in the analysis of variance. *Journal of the American Statistical Association* 32:671–701.

Frost, C.C. 1993. Four centuries of changing landscape patterns in the longleaf pine ecosystem. *Proceedings of the Tall Timbers Fire Ecology Conference* 18:17–43.

Frost, C.C. 1998. Presettlement fire frequency regimes of the United States: a first approximation. *Proceedings of the Tall Timbers Fire Ecology Conference* 20:70–81.

Guthery, F.S. 1988. Line transect sampling of bobwhite density on rangeland: valuation and recommendations. *Wildlife Society Bulletin* 16:193–203.

Guthery, F.S. and J.J. Lusk. 2004. Radiotelemetry studies: are we radio-handicapping northern bobwhites. *Wildlife Society Bulletin* 32:194–201.

Hamrick, R.G. 2002. Evaluation of northern bobwhite (*Colinus virginianus*) population monitoring methods and population trends in agricultural systems in the Upper Coastal Plain of Georgia. M.S. Thesis, University of Georgia, Athens, 144pp.

Hardin, G. 1968. Tragedy of the commons. *Science* 162:12443–12448.

Henny, C.J. and D.R. Anderson. 1979. Osprey distribution, abundance, and status in western North America. III. The Baja California and Gulf of California population. *Bulletin of the South California Academy of Science* 78:89–106.

Hensler, G.L. and J.D. Nichols. 1981. The Mayfield methods of estimating nesting success: a model, estimators, and simulation results. *Wilson Bulletin* 3:42–53.

Hines, J.E., T. Boulinier, J.D. Nichols, J.R. Sauer, and K.H. Pollock. 1999. COMDYN: software to study the dynamics of animal communities using a capture–recapture approach. *Bird Study* 46(Suppl):S209–S217.

Howell, J.E., C.T. Moore, M.J. Conroy, J.P. Carroll, R. Hamrick, and R.J. Cooper. Conservation of northern bobwhite on private lands under uncertainty about landscape-level habitat effects. *Landscape Ecology* (Accepted).

Hutchinson, G.E. 1957. Concluding remarks. *Cold Spring Harbor Symposia on Quantitative Biology* 22:415–427. Reprinted in 1991: Classics in theoretical biology. *Bulletin of Mathematical Biology* 53:193–213.

Jolly, G.M. 1965. Explicit estimates from capture–recapture data with both death and immigration-stochastic model. *Biometrika* 52:225–247.

Johnson, D.H. 1979. Estimating nest success: The Mayfield method and an alternative. *Auk* 96:651–661.

Johnson, D.H. 1980. The comparison of usage and availability measurements for evaluating resource preference. *Ecology* 61:65–71.

Karanth, K.U. and J.D. Nichols. 1998. Estimation of tiger densities in India using photographic captures and recaptures. *Ecology* 79:2852–2862.

Kenward, R.E. 2001. *A Manual for Wildlife Radio Tagging*. Academic Press, London, UK, and San Diego, USA.

Kramer, E.A., M.J. Conroy, M.J. Elliott, W. Bumback, and E. Anderson. 2003. *The Georgia Gap Analysis Project: Final Report.* University of Georgia, Athens.

Laake, J.L., S.T. Buckland, D.R. Anderson, and K.P. Burnham. 1993. *DISTANCE User's Guide.* Colorado State University, Fort Collins, CO, USA.

Lacy, R.C. and T. Kreeger. 1992. *VORTEX Users Manual. A Stochastic Simulation of the Extinction Process.* IUCN SSC Captive Breeding Specialist Group, Apple Valley, MN, USA.

Laplace, M. 1786. Sur les naissances, les marriages et les morts. *History of the Royal Academy of Science, for the year 1783.* 693–702.

Larkin, P.A. 1977. An epitaph for the concept of maximum sustainable yield. *Transactions of the American Fisheries Society* 106:1–11.

Lebreton, J.-D., K.P. Burnham, J. Clobert, and D.R. Anderson. 1992. Modelling survival and testing biological hypotheses using marked animals: a unified approach with case studies. *Ecological Monographs* 62:67–118.

Lenth, R.V. 1981. On finding the source of a signal. *Technometrics* 23:149–154.

Lindley, D.V. 1986. *Making Decisions.* Wiley, New York, USA.

Link, W.A. and R.J. Barker. 1994. Density estimation using the trapping-web design: a geometric analysis. *Biometrics* 50:733–745.

Link, W.L., E. Cam, J.D. Nichols, and E. Cooch. 2002. Of bugs and birds: Markov chain Monte Carlo for hierarchical modeling in wildlife research. *Journal of Wildlife Management* 66:277–291.

Lukacs, P.M. 2001. Estimating density of animal populations using trapping webs: evaluation of web design and data analysis. M.S. Thesis, Colorado State University, Ft. Collins, CO, USA.

Lukacs, P.M., and K.P. Burnham. 2005. Estimating population size from DNA-based closed capture–recapture data incorporating genotyping error. *Journal of Wildlife Management* 69:396–403.

Lukacs, P.M., A.B. Franklin, and D.R. Anderson. 2004. Passive approaches to detection in distance sampling. In *Advanced Distance Sampling: Estimating Abundance of Biological Populations,* S.T. Buckland, D.R. Anderson, K.P. Burnham, J.L. Laake, D.L. Borchers, and L. Thomas, Editors, pp. 260–280. Oxford University Press, Oxford, UK.

MacKenzie, D.I. J.D. Nichols, J.E. Hines, M.G. Knutson, and A.B. Franklin. 2003. Estimating site occupancy, colonization, and local extinction when a species is detected imperfectly. *Ecology* 84:2200–2207.

MacKenzie, D.I., J.D. Nichols, G.B. Lachman, S. Droege, J.A. Royle, and C.A. Langtimm, 2002. Estimating site occupancy when detection probabilities are less than one. *Ecology* 83:2248–2255.

MacKenzie, D.I., J.D. Nichols, J.A. Royle, K.H. Pollock, L.L. Bailey, and J.E. Hines. 2006. *Occupancy Estimation and Modeling: Inferring Patterns and Dynamics of Species Occurence.* Elsevier, Inc., Oxford, UK.

MacKenzie, D.I. and J.A. Royle 2005. Designing occupancy studies: general advice and allocating survey effort. *Journal of Applied Ecology* 42:1105–1114.

Manly B., L. McDonald, and D. Thomas. 1993. *Resource Selection by Animals: Statistical Design and Analysis for Field Studies.* Chapman & Hall, London, UK.

Marques, F.F. and S.T. Buckland. 2004. Covariate models for the detection function. In *Advanced Distance Sampling,* S.T. Buckland, D.R. Anderson, K.P. Burnham, J.L. Laake, D.L. Borchers, and L. Thomas, Editors, pp. 31–47. Oxford University Press, Oxford, UK.

Mayfield, H. 1961. Nesting success calculated from exposure. *Wilson Bulletin* 73:255–261.

McCullough, D.R., D.S. Pine, D.L. Whitmore, T.M. Mansfield, and R.H. Decker. 1990. Linked sex harvest strategy for white-tailed deer. *Wildlife Monographs* 112:1–41.

Miller, H.W. and D.H. Johnson. 1978. Interpreting the results of nesting studies. *Journal of Wildlife Management* 42:471–476.

Millspaugh, J.J., and J.M. Marzluff, Editors. 2001. *Radio Tracking and Animal Populations.* Academic Press, San Diego, CA, USA.

Moore, C.T. and M.J. Conroy. 2006. Optimal regeneration planning for old-growth forest: addressing scientific uncertainty in endangered species recovery through adaptive management. *Forest Science* 52:155–172.

Mordecai, R.S. 2007. Ecological patterns of occupancy and use: new methods for analysis and applications to species and communities. Ph.D. Dissertation, University of Georgia, Athens, GA, USA.

Navarro, A.G., A.T. Peterson, and A. Gordillo-Martínez. 2003. Museums working together: the atlas of the birds of Mexico. *Bulletin of the British Ornithological Club,* 123A:207–225.

Neu, C.W., C.R. Byers, and J.M. Peek. 1974. A technique for analysis of utilization-availability data. *Journal of Wildlife Management* 43:760–765.

Nichols, J.D. and M.J. Conroy. 1996. Estimation of species richness. In: *Measuring and Monitoring Biological Diversity. Standard Methods for Mammals,* D.E. Wilson, F.R. Cole, J.D. Nichols, R. Rudran, and M. Foster, Editors, pp. 226–234. Smithsonian Press, Washington, DC, USA.

Nichols, J.D., J.E. Hines, J.-D. Lebreton, and R. Pradel. 2000. The relative contribution of demographic components to population growth: a direct approach based on reverse-time capture–recapture. *Ecology* 81:3362–3376.

Nichols, J.D., J.E. Hines, D.I. MacKenzie, and M.E. Seamans, and R.J. Gutiérrez. 2007. Occupancy estimation and modeling with multiple states and state uncertainty. *Ecology* 88:1395–1400.

Nichols, J.D., J.E. Hines, J.D. Sauer, F.W. Fallon, J.E. Fallon, and P.J. Heglund. 2000. A double-observer approach for estimating detection probability and abundance from point counts. *Auk* 117:393–408.

Nichols, J.D., K.H. Pollock, and J.E. Hines. 1984. The use of a robust capture–recapture design in small mammal population studies: a field example with *Microtus pennsylvanicus. Acta Theriologica* 29:357–365.

Otis, D.L., K.P. Burnhmam, G.C. White, and D.R. Anderson. 1978. Statistical inference from capture data on closed animal populations. *Wildlife Monographs* 62:1–135.

Pace, R.M. III. 1988. Measurement error models for common wildlife radio-tracking systems. *Minnesota Wildlife Reports* 5:1–19.

Palmer, W.E. and S.D. Wellendorf. 2007. The effects of radiotransmitters on bobwhite survival and recovery rates. *Journal of Wildlife Management* 70:1281–1287.

Pearson, O.P. 1960. A mechanical model for the study of population dynamics. *Ecology* 41:494–508.

Peterson, J.T., R.F. Thurow, and J.W. Guzevich. 2004. An evaluation of multi-pass electrofishing for estimating the abundance of stream-dwelling salmonids. *Transactions of the American Fisheries Society* 133:462–475.

Pollock, K.H. 1982. A capture–recapture design robust to unequal probability of capture. *Journal of Wildlife Management* 46:757–760.

Pollock, K.H. and W.L. Kendall. 1987. Visibility bias in aerial surveys. A review of estimation procedures. *Journal of Wildlife Management* 51: 502–510.

Pollock, K.H., J.D. Nichols, C. Brownie, and J.E. Hines. 1990. Statistical inference for capture–recapture experiments. *Wildlife Monographs* 107.

Pollock, K.H. and M.C. Otto. 1983. Robust estimation of population size in closed animal populations from capture–recapture experiments. *Biometrics* 39:1035–1049.

Pollock, K.H., S.R. Winterstein, C.M. Bunck, and P.D. Curtis. 1989. Survival analysis in telemetry studies: the staggered entry design. *Journal of Wildlife Management* 53:7–15.
Possingham, H.P. and Davies, I. 1995. ALEX: a population viability analysis model for spatially structured populations. *Biological Conservation* 73:143–150.
Pradel, R. 1996. Utilization of capture–mark–recapture for the study of recruitment and population growth rate. *Biometrics* 52:703–709.
Pulliam, H.R. 1988. Sources, sinks, and population regulation. *American Naturalist* 132:652–661.
Robinson, J.G. and K.H. Redford. 1991. Sustainable harvest of neotropical forest mammals. In *Neotropical Wildlife Use and Conservation*, J.G. Robinson and K.H. Redford, Editors, pp. 415–429. University of Chicago Press, Chicago, IL, USA.
Royle, J.A. 2004. N-mixture models for estimating population size from spatially replicated counts. *Biometrics* 60:108–115.
Royle, J.A. and J.D. Nichols. 2003. Estimating abundance from repeated presence/absence data or point counts. *Ecology* 84:777–790.
Sargeant, G.A., M.A. Sovada, C.C. Slivinski, and D.H. Johnson. 2005. Markov chain Monte Carlo estimation of species distributions: a case study of the swift fox in western Kansas. *Journal of Wildlife Management* 69:483–497.
Sauer, J.R., J.E. Hines, and J. Fallon. 2007. *The North American Breeding Bird Survey, Results and Analysis 1966–2006. Version 10.13.2007.* USGS Patuxent Wildlife Research Center, Laurel, MD, USA.
Seber, G.A.F. 1965. A note on the multiple-recapture census. *Biometrika* 52:249–259.
Seber, G.A.F. 1970. Estimating time-specific survival and reporting rates for adult bids from band returns. *Biometrika* 57:313–318.
Schwarz, C.J. and A.N. Arnason. 1996. A general methodology for the analysis of capture–recapture experiments in open populations. *Biometrics* 52:860–873.
Skalski, J.R., D.S. Robson, and M.A. Simmons. 1983. Comparative census procedures using single mark–recapture methods. *Ecology* 65:1006–1015.
Springer, J.T. 1979. Some sources of bias and sampling error in radio triangulation. *Journal of Wildlife Management* 43:926–935.
Terhune, T.M., J.B. Grand, D.C. Sisson, and H.L. Stribling. 2007. Factors influencing survival of radiotagged and banded northern bobwhites in Georgia. *Journal of Wildlife Management* 70:1288–1297.
Thackston, R. and M. Whitney. 2001 *The Bobwhite quail in Georgia: History, Biology, and Management.* Georgia Department of Natural Resources, Social Circle, GA, USA.
Thomas, D.L., and E.J. Taylor. 2006. Study designs and tests for comparing resource use and availability II. *Journal of Wildlife Management* 70:324–336.
Tyre, A.J., B. Tenhumberg, S.A. Field, D. Neijalke, K. Parris, and H.P. Possingham. 2003. Improving precision and reducing bias in biological surveys: estimating false-negative error rates. *Ecological Applications* 13:1790–1801.
Udevitz, M.S. and B.E. Ballachey. 1998. Estimating survival rates with age-structure data. *Journal of Wildlife Management* 62:779–792.
Wellendorf, S.D., W.E. Palmer, and P.T. Bromley. 2001. Effect of call stimulation on rates of covey calling by northern bobwhite. *Proceedings of the International Galliformes Symposium* 2:191–195.
Wellendorf, S.D., W.E. Palmer, and P.T. Bromley. 2004. Estimating calling rates of northern bobwhite coveys and censusing populations. *Journal of Wildlife Management* 68:672–682.
White, G.C. 2008. *Program MARK v.5.0.* Colorado State University, Fort Collins, CO, USA.

White, G.C. and R.A. Garrott. 1990. *Analysis of Wildlife Radio Tracking Data.* Academic Press, San Diego, CA, USA.

White, G.C. and K.P. Burnham. 1999. Program MARK: survival rate estimation from both live and dead encounters. *Bird Study* 46(Suppl.):S120–S139.

Williams, B.K., J.D. Nichols, and M.J. Conroy. 2002. *Analysis and Management of Animal Populations.* Academic Press, New York, USA.

Winarni, N.L. 2002. The abundance and distribution patterns of great argus pheasant (*Argusianus argus*) in Bukit Barisan Selatan National Park, Sumatra, Indonesia. M.S. Thesis, University of Georgia, Athens.

Winarni, N.L., J.P. Carroll, and T.G. O'Brien. 2005. The application of camera traps to the study of *Galliformes* in Southern Sumatra, Indonesia, R.A. Fuller, and S.J. Browne, *Galliformes 2004. Proceedings of the Third International Galliformes Symposium.* Editors, pp. 133–144. World Pheasant Association, Fordingbridge, UK.

Wintle, B.A., M.A. McCarthy, K.M. Parris, and M.A. Burgman. 2004. Precision and bias of methods for estimating point survey detection probabilities. *Ecological Applications* 14:703–712.

Withey, J.C., T.D. Bloxton, and J.M. Marzluff. 2001. Effects of tagging and location error in wildlife radiotelemetry studies. In *Radio Tracking and Animal Populations*, J.J. Millspaugh and J.M. Marzluff, Editors, pp. 43–75. Academic Press, San Diego, CA, USA.

Zimpfer, N.L. and M.J. Conroy. 2006. Models of production rates in American black duck populations. *Journal of Wildlife Management* 70:947–954.

Glossary

Absence, absent Non-occurrence of an individual or species at a sampled location. Distinguished from **non-detection**, in which it is unknown whether the animal is truly absent or present but not detected.

Abstraction An approximation of reality. See **model**.

[Abundance or Population] estimate Sample-based value for abundance. See **estimate**.

Abundance [population size] True, total numbers of animals in population at a specified time and over a defined geographic area.

Accurate Having low bias and variance. Estimates tend to be repeatable and close to true value.

Adaptive harvest management Application of **adaptive resource management** to the objective of **sustainable harvest**.

Adaptive [resource] management (ARM) Management involving an explicit objective, model-based predictions under two or more alternative models, a method for making an optimal decision considering the objective and model predictions and weights, and a monitoring program to update model weights for inclusion in future decision making.

Age distribution Relative numbers of animals in each age class of a population.

Age frequency data Sample data on the relative numbers of animals in a population at various ages or age classes. Potentially useful for estimation of **reproduction** and **survival rates**.

Age-specific reproduction Per-capita rate of reproduction as a function of age.

Age-specific survival Per-capita rate of survival as a function of age.

Akaike Information Criterion (AIC) Statistic for comparing the information content of competing models. Used for **model selection** and **model averaging**.

Allee effect Population growth slows at low densities, often because of difficulty of animals finding mates. See **density-dependent**.

Alternative hypothes(is/es) Alternative structural forms of a statistical or predictive model that express differing biological, physical, or other assumptions.

Analytical model Model that is written algebraically and that may be analyzed mathematically.

Applied ecology The science of ecosystems, communities, and populations applied to **decision making**.

Batch marking Marking in which groups of animals (e.g., cohorts) rather than individuals are assigned a common mark.

Bayesian estimation Approach for obtaining inference on parameter values via **Bayes' Theorem**, in which inference is a mixture of prior information and data via a **likelihood**.

Bayes' Theorem Formula for updating information about a system using prior knowledge/model weights and **likelihoods** under alternative models.

Bernoulli trials Random trials in which the outcome is a success or failure.

Bias Difference between long-term average of sample estimates from true parameter value. See **unbiased**.

Binomial [distribution, model] Distribution describing the number of successes in n independent **Bernoulli trials**. Commonly used to model survival in known fates studies.

Bootstrap sampling Generation of samples via repeated computer-drawn samples, either from a larger sample or from an assumed distribution.

Capture–mark–recapture (CMR) Sampling design and models for abundance estimation in which animals are captured or otherwise marked and subsequently recaptured or their marks otherwise detected.

Capture probability (*p*) Probability that an animal that is alive at a particular sampling occasion in a **CMR** study is captured.

Carrying capacity Upper limit to population growth, usually due to resource limitation.

Catch-per-unit-effort (CPUE) Estimation of abundance based on relationship between numbers of animals caught and known capture effort.

Censoring Removal of subjects from a sample following some event; for example, following radio failure in a radiotelemetry study.

Census A complete, exact count of abundance for a population. Generally not achievable in free-ranging populations.

Change-in-ratio Abundance estimation based on change in proportion of animals in each of two or more types (e.g., antlered or not) following known removals classed by type.

Closed [population, model] Population remains at constant level over study interval, with no births, deaths, emigration, or immigration.

Cluster [sampling] Observations in which groups of animals or other objects appear together as a group (and thus are not independent of one another).

Coefficient of variation Ratio of the **standard deviation** to the **mean**. Measure of estimate precision.

Cohort Group of animals all entering the population at the same time, for example, all born in the same year.

Cohort life table See **vertical life table**.

Competition Interference by one animal with the activities (resource use, mate selection, etc.) of another, usually involving a gain to one animal and concomitant loss to another, especially with respect to birth, death, or growth rates. May be **intraspecific** (between animals of the same species) or **interspecific** (between animals of different species).

Conceptual models Abstractions of reality that are envisaged by a biologist or other investigator but not necessarily formalized graphically, physically, or mathematically.

Consequences Outcomes that follow from decision making (may be influenced by other, random factors as well).

Conservation biology Applied ecology, especially to problems involving small populations or sustainable harvest in developing countries.

Continuous-time Models where time is treated continuously and rates of growth are instantaneous.

Control Experimental group in which the factor under investigation is excluded or otherwise accounted for.

Cormack–Jolly–Seber (CJS) Multiple sample CMR models applied to estimation of survival rates.

Decision alternatives Actions that the decision maker has at his or her disposal in trying to reach the objective.

Decision context The setting in which the decision occurs.

Decision making Examination of alternatives in order to meet an objective. May involve a formal **decision model.**

Decision model A model representing the relationship between **decision alternatives, objectives**, and a model of a population or other system.

Demographic stochasticity Uncertainty in population persistence due to chance birth and death events. Relatively more important in small populations.

Density Number of animals per unit area in a population at a particular time.

Density-dependent Population growth rates are affected (usually negatively, but sometimes positively) by the abundance or density of the population. See **logistic model, Allee effect.**

Density-independent Population growth rates are not affected by the abundance or density of the population. See **exponential model.**

Detected, detection Animal is both **present** at a site and detected in a sample.

Detection probability Probability that an animal that is present at a site is detected in a sample.

Deterministic Completely predictable, not involving any random components. See **stochastic.**

Difference equations Systems of equations that treat time in discrete intervals.

Discrete-time Models where time is treated as discrete intervals and rates of growth are finite.

Distance sample Count-based sampling where auxiliary information from distances to detected objects is used to model incomplete detection. See **line transect, point sampling.**

Diversity Measure of community structure, typically involving both the number of species present and the **frequency distribution** of animals among species.

Double sampling Design in which two samples are taken, one involving measurements of X and Y on all units, and the other involving only X. Typically employed when Y is expensive or difficult to measure compared to X and may be predicted from X.

Dynamics Changes in a state variable (e.g., abundance, age structure, spatial structure) over time.

Effective grid [trap] area Area of influence of trapping grid or array, used to obtain a valid estimate of density from closed CMR studies.

Empirical models Models in which data are used to estimate parameters or test predictions.

Environmental resistance Physical or biotic factors that slow or limit population growth. See **carrying capacity**, **density-dependent**.

Environmental uncertainty Chance events, such as weather or other factors beyond the control of a decision maker.

Equilibrium Population is unchanging over time.

Equilibrium analysis Investigation of the behavior of a population or other system with respect to equilibria.

Estimate A sample-based value for a parameter; by definition, subject to random, statistical variation.

Estimation The process of obtaining statistical estimates of parameters from data.

Estimator A formula or computer algorithm for computing the value of an estimate. When sample data are used with an estimator, the numerical result is an **estimate**.

Expected value Uncertainty-weighted measure of outcome value. Also describes the large-sample average or mean of an attribute.

Expected value of perfect information (EVPI) The expected gain to decision making from having perfect information.

Exponential [geometric] model Model of population growth in which population grows at a constant (exponential) rate. See **density-independent**.

Finite rate of increase [growth] (λ) Multiplier for population growth, usually for discrete-time growth models. $\lambda = 1.0$ means population is at equilibrium, $\lambda > 1.0$ means it is increasing, $\lambda < 1.0$ means it is decreasing. See **instantaneous growth rate**.

Fisheries management Applied ecology for the objective of maintaining and enhancing populations of fish, often for recreational or commercial harvest.

Fitness Relative contribution of an individual to succeeding generations. Determined by **age-specific survival** and **reproduction** rates.

Frequency distribution Relative numbers of animals or other sample units that take on particular values in a sample.

Fundamental objectives What the decision maker wants to accomplish. See **means objectives**.

Game management Applied ecology for the objective of producing harvestable populations of wildlife.

Goodness of fit Measure of agreement between a statistical model and sample data.

Graphical model Model in which a **conceptual model** of a system is converted to graphical form. May or may not involve a formal, mathematical model.

Horizontal life table Distribution of ages at specific points in time. Each **age distribution** is comprised of multiple **cohorts**.

Hypothesis Specific statement about reality, often testable via comparison of predictions under two or more hypotheses to data. See **likelihood, AIC**.

Inbreeding Tendency of animals to interbreed with genetically similar (related) animals. May occur with high frequency in small populations.

Inbreeding depression Negative impact on **fitness** through inbreeding.

Independ(ent)(ence) Animals, samples, units, or other objects can be modeled by statistical distributions one at a time, without dependence on the values of the other animals/samples/units/objects. Two outcomes are statistically independent if their joint probability is the product of their separate (marginal) probabilities.

Index Any measure or count of a species based on direct observation or observation of a sign of the species that provides some numerical scale of observation without a measure of detection rate (β).

Influence diagram Graphical representation of the relationship between actions and outcomes in a **decision model.**

Information Knowledge that we have about a system, generally from data. See **likelihood, AIC.**

Initial conditions Set of conditions specified at the beginning of the time frame or other dimension over which the **state variables** of a **model** change.

Instantaneous growth rate (r) Rate of population growth for continuous-time population models. $r = 0$ means population is at equilibrium, $r > 0$ means it is increasing, $r < 0$ means it is decreasing. See **Finite rate of increase.**

Island biogeography Theory of population colonization, persistence, and extinction that emphasizes the role of spatial isolation and connectivity in population dynamics. See **Metapopulation.**

Jackknife Procedure for variance estimation based on excluding observations one at a time and predicting the excluded observations from the remaining data.

Jolly–Seber (JS) Multiple sample CMR models applied to estimation of survival rates, abundance, and recruitment.

Kaplan–Meier Generalization of the **binomial** model that allows for staggered entry and censoring in survival estimation from known fates studies.

Key function Basic shape for the detection data in **line** or **point transect sampling** that describes the way that detection changes as a function of increasing distance from the observer.

Lambda (λ) See **finite rate of increase.**

Likelihood Statistical model describing probability of data outcome under an assumed model. Used to estimate model parameters, compare predictions to observations, and test hypotheses.

Lincoln–Petersen ["Index"] **CMR** design for closed abundance estimation, in which animals are captured or otherwise marked at one occasion and the numbers of unmarked and marked animals are recorded at a second occasion. Not actually an **index** but rather a design for obtaining data that may then be used to estimate abundance via the Lincoln–Petersen estimator.

Line transect [sampling] Distance sampling for abundance or density in which sample units are randomly or systematically placed lines from which observers detect animals and record perpendicular distances.

Logistic model Model of population growth in which population initially grows at an exponential rate, with growth slowing as density increases. See **density-dependent.**

Lotka–Volterra Models of simultaneous population growth for two species. See **competition** and **predator–prey.**

Markov chain Monte Carlo (MCMC) A computer-intensive approach for simulating values from the posterior distribution of parameters. See **Bayesian estimation.**

Maximum likelihood Method for obtaining estimates of parameters of a statistical model. See **likelihood**.

Maximum sustainable yield (MSY) Maximum size or rate of harvest that can be taken while maintaining a population in the long term. See **sustainable harvest**.

Mayfield method Approach for estimating **nesting success** using an extension of the **binomial** model that accounts for nests being found at different points over the nesting interval.

Mean [sample] Average across a population or sample.

Means objectives Intermediate objective that must be accomplished along the way to **fundamental objectives**.

Median Middle value of a list of ordered values; 50th **percentile**.

Metapopulation Network of two or more populations in which each population potentially received individuals from or exports individuals to the alternate populations. See **island biogeography**.

Minimum viable population Smallest population size capable of maintaining extinction risk below a desired threshold probability over a desired time horizon.

Mode Most frequent or likely value in population or sample.

Model Abstraction of the real world. May be conceptual, physical, graphical, algebraic, or numerical (computer).

Modeling The casting of biological, physical, or other relationships in abstract form.

Model selection Choice of optimal model for estimation. See **AIC**.

Multimodel inference (MMR) Statistical inference based on consideration of multiple plausible models, each weighted by **AIC**.

Multinomial distribution Distribution describing the number of successes in n independent trials in which the outcome is one of k mutually exclusive types. Commonly used to model tag-recovery and mark–recapture data.

Multiple sample CMR CMR design for closed abundance estimation, in which animals are captured or otherwise marked at $k>2$ occasions and all marked animals are recorded and unmarked animals are marked and released [see **Schnabel "Census"**].

Multi-state (multistate) models Open population or other system models that allow for animals or other subjects to occur in two or more states (e.g., location, breeding propensity, disease) with stochastic transition between states.

Nest success Probability that a nest survives from initiation (for birds, often when the first egg is laid) until at least one young is fledged or reaches some other defined stage of maturity.

Normal distribution Statistical distribution describing frequency of continuous outcomes and described by two parameters: a mean and the variance.

Not detected Animal is not detected in a sample, due to actual non-occurrence (**absence**) or it is present but not seen in the sample.

Not surveyed Animal's presence is not detected at a local or time because of the absence of a survey. Animal may be present or absent.

Numerical models Models that report quantitative outcomes, often via a computer algorithm.

Objective(s) Statements of what the decision maker would like to achieve. Incorporates the decision maker's values.

Occupancy Condition or probability that a site is **occupied**. See **Site occupancy**.

Occupied At least one animal is present at a site (but may or may not be detected).

Open [population, model] Abundance is allowed to vary over time, subject to losses from death and emigration and gains from birth and immigration.

Optimal Best, most desirable. In decision making, decision outcome with the highest objective value.

Optimal allocation Method for determining stratum sample sizes in **stratified random sampling**, which considers costs or variances as well as sizes of the strata [see **proportional allocation**].

Parameter Constant in a model. In dynamic models, constants that control the rate of change of state variables. In a **statistical model**, unknown constant that is estimated using sample data.

Partial controllability Inability of decision maker to completely determine the management controls applied to a conservation system.

Partial observability Inability of decision maker to observe system under management with certainty, due to sampling and other statistical errors.

Per capita rate Number (of animals alive, birth, deaths, etc.) divided by number alive at beginning of interval of interest.

Percentile Values of random variable associated with specific cumulative probabilities, e.g., 0.025 (2.5%), 0.5 (50%). The **median** is the 50th percentile.

Physical model Model in which a **conceptual model** of the system is converted to physical form, as in an analog or scale model. May or may not involve a formal, mathematical model.

Point [transect] sampling Distance sampling for abundance or density in which sample units are randomly or systematically placed points from which observers detect animals and record radial distances.

Poisson distribution Discrete statistical distribution describing outcomes that are nonnegative integers (e.g., counts).

Population reconstruction Calculation of cohort abundance fat some initial time based on known ages at death.

Population viability analysis (PVA) Analysis to investigate extinction risk for small populations. See **minimum viable population**.

Precision Repeatability of sample values or estimates; low dispersion about mean. See **variance**.

Predator–prey Models of the interaction of predator and prey populations. See **Lotka–Volterra**.

Presence, present Actual occurrence of an animal at a site. Animals may be present but not detected.

Probability Measure of uncertainty between 1 (complete certainty in an outcome) and 0 (complete certainty in the complement of an outcome).

Proportional allocation Method for determining stratum sample sizes in **stratified random sampling**, based only on the relative sizes of the strata. See **optimal allocation**.

Randomization Assignment or selection of experimental or sampling units at random.

Recoveries Marked animals that are re-encountered a single time, usually as dead recoveries (e.g., in a harvest).

Recovery [rate, probability] (*f*) Fraction of marked animals alive at one sample occasion that are recovered the subsequent recovery period; probability that an animal alive at one sample occasion is recovered in the next recovery period.

Recruitment rate Number of young produced over a time interval per adult animals (sometimes, per adult female) alive at the beginning of a time interval that survive to the subsequent breeding period (i.e., become recruited as breeders). For game animals, often considered as recruitment into the harvestable population.

Relative species richness Relative numbers of species present in a community in comparison to numbers present in a different community, or at a different time.

Reliable [estimator, estimate] Evidence that is repeatable and defensible. An estimator is reliable if it provides **accurate** information about a parameter of interest.

Removal sampling Closed population estimation of abundance based on known removals of animals. Removal may be physical or by marking.

Replication Assignment or selection of multiple experimental units, usually by **randomization**.

Reproduction rate Number of young produced over a time interval per adult animals (sometimes, per adult female) alive at the beginning of a time interval.

Robust Estimate or other result is not sensitive to moderate violations of model assumptions.

Robust design (RD) Two-stage CMR design involving primary sampling periods between which the population is assumed to be demographically open, and secondary periods over which the population is assumed closed.

Sampled population Population from which samples are taken. See **target population.**

Sampling design Method for selection of sampling units from a **sampled population** so as to obtain reliable estimates.

Schnabel "Census" [design, estimator] CMR design for closed abundance estimation, in which animals are captured or otherwise marked at $k > 2$ occasions and all marked animals are recorded and unmarked animals are marked and released. Not actually a **census** but rather a design for obtaining data that may then be used in multiple-sample CMR models. See **multiple sample CMR.**

Sensitivity Measure of the influence of model output to changes in model input or parameter values.

Sensitivity analysis Identification of the relative importance of parameters or inputs in a particular model.

Series adjustments Terms added to the **key function** in **line** or **point transect sampling** that improved model fit to distance data.

Simple random sampling Selection of sampling units from **sampled population** by complete randomization, with no **stratification** or other restrictions.

Site occupancy Probability that a site is occupied by a species at a particular sample time; for a finite study area, proportion of sites that are occupied at any time.

SLOSS (**S**ingle **L**arge **O**r **S**everal **S**mall) Refers to the tradeoff between conservation of single large populations, which are numerically less likely to become extinct due to **demographic stochasticity**, versus smaller, separated populations, which may provide a **metapopulation** rescue effect.

Source–sink Metapopulation model in which source populations ($\lambda > 1$) export excess animals to sink populations ($\lambda < 1$), achieving overall equilibrium.

Species richness The total number of species present in a community at a given time.

Stability Tendency of a population to return to or oscillate about an equilibrium following a perturbation.

Stable age distribution Age distribution that does not change through time. Achieved when age-specific birth and survival rates remain constant.

Stable equilibrium Population level to which population tends to converge toward, with diminishing oscillations, over time.

Staggered entry Entry of subjects into a study over time, as in release of batches of radiotelemetered animals over several days or weeks.

Standard deviation (SD) Square root of the **variance** of a population or sample.

Standard error (SE) Standard deviation of repeated sample **estimates.** The standard error for the sample **mean** is $SE = SD/\sqrt{n}$, where n is sample size.

Standard normal distribution Normal distribution with mean 0 and variance 1. Given a specified mean and variance, all normal distributions can be obtained from the standard normal.

Static life table See **horizontal life table.**

State variable Features of a system such as abundance, age structure, or habitat conditions that tend to vary over time.

Statistic A function of sample data. Examples include **means**, **variance**, and **percentiles**, as well as parameter **estimates.**

Statistical model Models that use sample data to address population or other questions.

Stochastic Not completely predictable; random. See **deterministic.**

Stratified random sampling Selection of sampling units from **sampled population** by random selection from predefined strata. See **simple random sampling.**

Structural uncertainty Uncertainty about the model describing the system's response to **decision alternatives.**

Survival [rate, probability] Per capita numbers of animals alive at the beginning of a time interval that survive the interval; probability that an animal alive at the beginning of the interval survives the interval.

Sustainable Action that results in long-term production of yield or other benefit from a population or other system.

Sustainable harvest [yield] Harvest that can be taken while maintaining a population in the long term. See **maximum sustainable yield (MSY).**

Systematic sampling Selection of sampling units by non-random means (often following an initial randomization).

Target population Population for which inferences are desired. See **sampled population.**

Trap happy Tendency of marked animals in a **CMR** study to be recaptured at a higher rate than unmarked animals.

Trap shy Tendency of marked animals in a **CMR** study to be recaptured at a lower rate than unmarked animals.

Trapping web Geometrics configuration of traps used with **distance sampling** to estimate density.

Unbiased Long-term average of sample estimates equals parameter. See **bias**.

Uncertainty Inability to completely determine an outcome. Measured by **probability**.

Validation Comparison of model predictions to independent data not used to calibrate or estimate the model.

Values Outcomes that matter (have values) to a decision maker.

Variance Measure of dispersion of sample values or estimates about the mean. See **precision**.

Verification Assessment that model behaves according to general expectations and assumptions. For example, a population model must predict nonnegative numbers.

Vertical life table Data that track one or more **cohorts** through time until all members of the cohort have died.

Viable Likely to persist. See **minimum viable population**.

Wildlife management Applied science of the management of habitats and populations for human benefit and enjoyment.

Appendix A: Statistical and modeling programs available on the worldwide web

*Fee charged; free otherwise

Modeling software

RAMAS* – http://www.ramas.com/software.htm
VORTEX – http://www.vortex9.org/vortex.html
PYTHON – http://www.python.org/
MATLAB* – http://www.mathworks.com/products/matlab/
STELLA* – http://www.iseesystems.com/

Statistical analysis

Basic data analysis

R – http://www.r-project.org/
S+* – http://www.insightful.com/support/doc_splus_win.asp

Capture–recapture

MARK – http://welcome.warnercnr.colostate.edu/~gwhite/mark/mark.htm
CAPTURE – http://www.mbr-pwrc.usgs.gov/software.html
POPAN – http://www.cs.umanitoba.ca/~popan/
JOLLY – http://www.mbr-pwrc.usgs.gov/software.html#a

Distance estimation

DISTANCE – http://www.ruwpa.st-and.ac.uk/distance/

Presence–absence (occupancy) estimation

PRESENCE – http://www.mbr-pwrc.usgs.gov/software/presence.html

Community estimation

COMDYN – http://www.mbr-pwrc.usgs.gov/software.html
SPECRICH – http://www.mbr-pwrc.usgs.gov/software.html
SPECRICH2 – http://www.mbr-pwrc.usgs.gov/software.html

Links to these sources are also maintained (and occasionally updated) at http://coopunit.forestry.uga.edu/quant_cons_book/web_resources.

Appendix B: Other internet resources

Software for population estimation

Patuxent Software Archive – http://www.mbr-pwrc.usgs.gov/software.html
Colorado State software page – http://welcome.warnercnr.colostate.edu/~gwhite/software.html
Evan Cooch (Cornell University) software page – http://www.phidot.org/software/

Courses in population estimation, modeling, and decision theory

(University of Georgia)

Applied population dynamics – Undergraduate course (J.P. Carroll), http://coopunit.forestry.uga.edu/FORS5770
Estimation of parameters of fish and wildlife populations – Graduate course (M.J. Conroy), http://coopunit.forestry.uga.edu/FORS8390/
Open source computing seminar – Graduate seminar, http://coopunit.forestry.uga.edu/open_source
Quantitative approaches to conservation biology – Graduate course (J.T. Peterson), http://coopunit.forestry.uga.edu/unit_homepage/Peterson/fors8360/FORS8360_Class

Short courses/workshops

World Pheasant Association Scientific Training Workshop – http://coopunit.forestry.uga.edu/WPA_STW
GA Unit Cooperator Workshop – http://coopunit.forestry.uga.edu/Coop_Wkshop
Occupancy workshop – http://coopunit.forestry.uga.edu/occupancy_workshop

Adaptive management

Blackduck Adaptive Harvest Management – http://coopunit.forestry.uga.edu/blackduck
Concepts in Adaptive Harvest Management – http://www.ecologyandsociety.org/vol3/iss1/art8/

Links to these sources are also maintained (and occasionally updated) at http://coopunit.forestry.uga.edu/quant_cons_book/other_resources.

Appendix C: Modeling and statistical notation

Symbol	Definition(s)	Chapter references
A	Area of study for estimating density	Chapter 9
	Measure of habitat availability in resource selection study	Chapter 13
AIC	Aikaike Information Criteria	Chapter 5 and on
$AICc$	AIC corrected for small sample size	Chapter 5 and on
AMH	Additive mortality hypothesis of harvest impacts	Chapter 17
B	Number of births, usually over a specific time interval	Chapter 3
b	Per capita birth rate, usually over a specific time interval	Chapter 3
C	Count statistic describing number of animals, species, or other attribute detected in a sample	Chapter 6 and on
CI	Confidence interval usually reported with error, e.g. 95% CI	Chapter 5 and on
CMH	Compensatory mortality hypothesis of harvest impacts	Chapter 17
c	Probability of recapture	Chapter 10
c_x	Proportion of animals in age class x	Chapter 11
CV	Coefficient of variation	Chapter 5
D	Number of deaths, usually over a specific time interval	Chapter 3
	Also refers to number of animals per unit area (N/A)	Chapter 9
d	Per capita death rate, usually over a specific time interval	Chapter 3
	Sample number of animals dying in an interval during a known fates study	Chapter 11
	Probability of detection [in k Bernoulli trials (detection sample)]	Chapter 7
E	Number of emigrants, usually over a specific time interval	Chapter 3
	Expected value [as in $E(x)$ is the expected value of x]	Chapter 5 and on
$f(x)$	Frequency (probability) distribution	Chapter 5 and on
f	Recovery probability	Chapter 12
f_x	Frequency of animals observed in age class x	Chapter 11
$g(x)$	Detection (sighting) probability as function of distance	Chapter 9

Continued

Symbol	Definition(s)	Chapter references
H	Number of animals harvested, usually over a specific time interval	Chapter 4
h	Per capita harvest rate, usually over a specific time interval	Chapter 4
I	Number of immigrants, usually over a specific time interval	Chapter 3
K	Upper limit to population growth (e.g., under logistic model)	Chapters 3 and 4
L	Length or sampling effort of a line transect	Chapter 9
M	Number of elements in a finite sample (see also N)	Chapter 8
	Number of marked animals in the population in a CMR study	Chapter 12
MSY	Maximum sustain(ed, able) yield	Chapter 4
MVP	Minimum viable population (size)	Chapter 4
m	Number of sampled elements (see also n)	Chapter 8
m	Number of recaptured (marked) animals	Chapter 10
N	Abundance, population size	Chapter 2 and on
	Number of possible sample units in a finite sample	Chapter 5
n	Sample size	Chapter 5
	Number of animals detected per sample (distance sampling) or captured per session (capture–recapture studies)	Chapters 9, 10 and 12
P or p	Probability of an outcome	Chapter 5 and on
p	Probability of detection in a sample (e.g., a Bernoulli trial)	Chapter 6 and on
	Probability of capture on a sample occasion	Chapter 10 Chapter 12
p_0	Probability of extinction (usually over a specified duration of time)	Chapter 4
$QAIC$	AIC adjusted for quasi-likelihood	Chapter 5 and on
q	Probability of failure outcome in binomial, equal to $1 - p$	Chapter 5 and on
r	Instantaneous rate of population growth, see also λ	Chapters 2 and on
	Number of animals "at risk" in a radiotelemetry or other known fates study	Chapter 11
	Reporting rate of animals found dead in a tag recovery study	Chapter 12
r_{max}	Maximum instantaneous rate of population growth (e.g., under logistic model)	Chapter 3

(Continued)

Symbol	Definition(s)	Chapter references
S	Survival probability	Chapter 3 and on
	Species richness (total number of species of interest in a community)	Chapter 14
s^2	Sample variance	Chapter 5 and on
s	Number of species detected in a sample	Chapter 14
SD	Standard deviation	Chapters 3, 5 and on
SE	Standard error	Chapters 3, 5 and on
t	Index for time (e.g., years) in population growth models; may change continuously or discretely	Chapters 2 and on
T_E	Expected time to extinction	Chapter 4
$\bar{x}$	Sample mean	Chapter 5
X_ω	Frequency of animals with capture history ω	Chapter 10
U	Number of unmarked animals in the population in a CMR study	Chapter 12
	Measure of habitat used in resource selection study	Chapter 13
	Utility or value of a decision outcome	Chapter 15 and on
u	Number of unmarked animals in a sample of captured animals in a CMR study	Chapter 12
v	Value of an outcome following a decision or other action. See also U	Chapter 15 and on
wt	Model weight or probability	Chapter 17
β	Probability of detection for a count statistic [generic]. See p	Chapter 6 and on
Δ	Change in, e.g. Δt	Throughout
λ	Finite rate of population increase centered on 1.0. See also r	Chapter 3 and on
μ	Population mean	Chapter 5
σ^2	Population variance	Chapter 5 and on
ϕ	[apparent] Survival in a CMR study	Chapter 12
ψ	Probably of [site] occupancy	Chapter 7
	Probability of movement between states (e.g., geographic sites) in a multi-state CMR study	Chapter 12
$\wedge$	Estimate of a parameter, e.g. $\hat{S}$	Chapter 5 and on
$\prod$	Product of	Chapter 5 and on
$\sum$	Sum of	Chapter 5 and on

Appendix D: Key to abundance and parameter estimation

Answer 'Yes' to all that apply:

D-I. *Is the goal of the study to support conservation decisions?*
  a. Yes – see **Part III**; see below for methods to estimate specific model parameters.
  b. No – go to D-II.

D-II. *Is the goal of the study to estimate abundance or density?*
  a. Yes – see D.1 and below.
  b. No – go to D-III.

D-III. *Is the goal of the study to estimate occupancy (presence/absence)?*
  a. Yes – see D.2 and below.
  b. No – go to D-IV.

D-IV. *Is the goal of the study to estimate survival, reproduction, or other demographic parameters in order to assess population status (viability)?*
  a. Yes – see D.3 and below.
  b. No see D-I and D-II.

D-V. *Is the goal of the study to investigate habitat use and resource selection?*
  a. Yes – see **Chapter 13** and below.
  b. No – Go to D-VI.

D-VI. *Is the goal of the study to estimate species richness/community parameters?*
  a. Yes – see **Chapter 14**.

D.1. Abundance Estimation

I. Are the animals readily observable and countable?

A. Yes – see below and II.
  Situation: large or conspicuous, usually diurnal, visible from air or visible/audible from ground.
  Is it possible to count every individual in a sampling unit?
  1. Yes, all individuals in a sampling unit can be counted.
     Situation: Large, conspicuous, diurnal mammals occupying open habitats; groups easily counted without error (groups not too large).

Method: complete counts (censuses, often conducted from aircraft) – see **Chapter 8**.

2. No, some individuals are missed in counting.
   Situation: diurnal, relatively conspicuous, but some underestimation errors likely (e.g. due to habitat obstruction or counting errors).
   Is it possible to count every individual in a small subunit of the sampling unit?
   a. Yes – see below.
      Situation: underestimation errors likely during primary survey method (e.g., counts from aircraft), but alternative counting methods (e.g. intensive methods such as ground counts) can yield exact counts.
      Method: double sampling to estimate observability – see **Chapter 8**.
   b. No.
   Is a marked subsample of animals available or easily obtained?
   a. Yes – see below.
      Method: marked subsample – see **Chapter 8**.
   b. No – see below.
   Can distances between the investigator and each detected animal be readily determined?
   a. Yes – see below.
      Method: distance sampling – see **Chapter 9**.
   b. No – see below.
      Methods: multiple observers; sighting probability models – see **Chapter 8**.

B. No – go to II, III, IV or V.

II. Can animals be captured or otherwise marked?

A. Yes – see below and also I, III, IV, and V.
   Situation: animals can be readily captured, marked, released and later recaptured and examined for marks. Often not suitable for large animals that are difficult to handle or for predators or other sparsely distributed animals that are difficult to capture, unless such animals can be identified by natural markings and are readily photographed using camera traps (e.g., see Karanth 1995).
   Is the study short term (i.e., mortality, recruitment, and movement in and out of the study area negligible)?
   1. Yes – see below.
      Situation: trapping, marking, and recapturing/resighting can be accomplished over a short period (e.g., several days) over which population can be assumed closed. Often appropriate for very abundant, easily trapped mammals (e.g., microtines).
      Methods: Lincoln–Petersen estimates; multiple capture–recapture estimates (program CAPTURE); trap web estimates (do not require recaptures) – see **Chapter 10**.
   2. No – see below.
      Situation: trapping, marking, and recapturing/resighting occur over a time period (e.g., months or years) in which mortality and recruitment are not

negligible. Need to estimate mortality (and sometimes recruitment) rates in addition to population size at each sampling period.
Methods: Jolly–Seber and related open population models (programs POPAN, JOLLY, JOLLYAGE) – see **Chapter 12**.

B. No – see I, III, IV, and V.

III. Are animals harvested in known numbers?

A. Yes – see below and also I, II, and IV.
Situation: animals are removed from the population by sport or commercial harvest. Ordinarily, these methods require a substantial portion of the population to be removed and good documentation of the size of the harvest for reasonable performance. Examples: permit-controlled sport harvest of white-tailed deer; some situations in commercial fisheries.
Are there two or more identifiable classes of animals whose relative frequencies can be observed before and after harvest?
   1. Yes – see below, and 2.
   Situation: e.g., two distinguishable classes (e.g., sexes) that can be observed before and after harvest; known numbers of either or both removed.
   Method: Change-in-ratio (if harvest is large enough to change ratio – otherwise go to 2) – see **Chapter 10**.
   2. No – see below.

Is the effort expended in harvest quantified (quantifiable)?
   1. Yes – see below, and b.
   Situation: harvest effort measured in time (e.g., hunter-days, trap-nights), money (e.g., expenditures in commercial fisheries) or some other indicator.
   Method: catch-per-unit-effort estimators – see **Chapter 10**.
   2. No – see below.

Is removal effort constant over time?
   1. Yes – see below.
   Situation: "Harvest" usually involves controlled removal by experimenter.
   Method: removal models (e.g., models Mb and Mbh) – see **Chapter 10**.

B. No – see I, II, IV, and V.

IV. Occupancy-based models

Does the study involve replicated, presence–absence (detection/non-detection) surveys in which counts of number of animals detected per sampling unit are recorded?

A. Yes – see below.
Method: occupancy-abundance (Royle–Nichols) models – see **Chapter 7**.

V. Abundance indices

Is relative (e.g., over time, space, species) abundance of primary interest and is relationship of index to abundance known to be constant or to depend on known variables in a known way?

A. Yes – see below.
Situation (very rare): past experience or experiments have validated that the index is strictly proportional to population size or density or that the relationship between the index and abundance depends only on certain variables (that are known and can be measured) in a known manner.
Methods: collect indices/count statistics (e.g. using standardized routes). Desirable to include covariates likely to influence index variability (e.g. observer experience, weather, etc.) – see **Chapter 8.**

B. No – see below.
Situation (common): experience suggests that the index and population density are related, perhaps monotonically. Examples: track and pellet surveys for deer; coyote vocal responses to distress calls or sirens; scent station surveys of foxes and bobcats.
Is it possible to census or estimate abundance for use in index calibration?
   1. Yes – see below.
   Method: calibrate index with censuses of population or estimation methods having limited or known bias (e.g., mark–recapture), then use a double-sampling design to estimate population density from the index – see **Chapter 8.**
   2. No – see below.
   Method: use the index (with proper replication, stratification, and recording of nuisance variables as in A), recognizing that it may or may not be correlated with actual abundance. (OPTION OF LAST RESORT - RELIES ON UNTESTED ASSUMPTION!) – see **Chapter 8.**

D.2. Occupancy estimation

See **Chapter 7** if answer to either question is Yes.

I. *Is the goal to estimate number of sites occupied or probability of occupancy over a single season?*
II. *Is the goal to estimate site occupancy/probability of occupancy over multiple seasons, where sites may become unoccupied or newly occupied over time?*

D.3. Demographic parameter estimation

I. Is a goal of the study to estimate survival or mortality rates?

A. Yes – see below.
Does the study of survival/mortality involve relatively short time intervals (week to months) or interest in cause-specific mortality?
   1. Yes – see below.

Can animals be captured and equipped with radio transmitters, or otherwise monitored through time to determine individual fates?
Method: radiotelemetry/known fates – see **Chapter 11**.
2. No – see B and below.

B. No – see II, II and IV.
Can animals be captured or otherwise marked?
1. Yes – see below.
Can animals be recaptured or re-detected visually or by other means?
a. Yes – see below.
Method: capture–recapture – see **Chapter 12**.
b. No – see below.
Are tag recoveries available from hunters, anglers, or other sources?
a. Yes – see below.
Method: tag-recovery – see **Chapter 12**.
2. No – see below.
Can age frequencies be estimated from harvest or other data, properly adjusted for biases in age-specific detection probabilities?
a. Yes – see below.
Method: analysis of age frequencies – see **Chapter 11**.

Note: Strong assumptions (e.g., age stability) required. Data should be collected to test these assumptions before using method.

II. Is the goal of the study to estimate reproduction rates?

A. *Can nests, dens or other reproductive sites be periodically monitored to determine reproductive success?*
1. Yes – see below.
Method: nest success/known fates – see **Chapter 11**.
2. No – see below.

B. *Can animals be captured, marked, and recaptured over periods when the population is open to reproductive recruitment?*
1. Yes – see below.
Method: open-population capture–recapture, including the Robust Design and Pradel temporal symmetry model – see **Chapter 12**.
2. No – see below.

C. *Can population age ratios post-reproduction be estimated via population surveys, harvest surveys, or other methods?*
1. Yes – see below.
Method: estimation of reproduction rates via age ratios – see **Chapter 11**.

Note: Strong assumptions required (e.g., homogeneous detection rates). Data should be collected to allow testing of these assumptions or estimation of age-specific detection to remove bias.

III. Is the goal of the study to estimate population growth rates?

A. *Are unbiased estimates of abundance available via monitoring through time?*
   1. Yes – see below.
      Method: direct estimation of growth by ratio of abundances – see **Chapters 8, 9, 10 and 12** for methods to estimate abundance.
   2. No – see B, C and below.

B. *Can animals be captured, marked, and re-detected over periods of time when the population is potentially growing or declining?*
   1. Yes – see below.
      Method: open-population capture–recapture – see **Chapter 12** (Jolly–Seber, Robust design).
      No – see C.

C. *Are indices of population size available for which detection rates are homogeneous through time?*
   1. Yes – see below.
      Method: estimate population growth as the ratio of indices – see **Chapter 8**.

      Note: Strong assumptions required. If possible collect data to test/avoid assumption of homogeneous detection.

IV. Is the goal of the study to estimate movement rates?

A. *Can animals be captured, marked, and recaptured over periods when the population is open to movement?*
   1. Yes – see below.
      Can animals be recaptured or re-detected visually or by other means?
      a. Yes – see below.
         Method: multi-state capture–recapture models – see **Chapter 12** and below.
      b. No – see below.
      Are tag recoveries available from hunters, anglers, or by other means?
      a. Yes – see below.
         Method: tag-recovery movement models – see **Chapter 12**.
      b. No – see below.
   2. No – see B.

B. Use alternative methods (e.g., isotope tracers) or revise study objective.

Index